Near-Field Antenna Measurements

The Artech House Antenna Library

Helmut E. Schrank, *Series Editor*

Blake, L.V., *Antennas*

Corzine, Robert G., and Joseph A. Mosko, *Four-Armed Spiral Antennas*

Djordjevic, A.R., M.B. Bazdar, G.M. Bazdar, G.M. Vitosevic, T.K. Sarkar, and R.F. Harrington, *Analysis of Wire Antennas and Scatterers: Software and User's Manual*

Evans, Gary E., *Antenna Measurement Techniques*

Gupta, K.C., and A. Benalla, eds., *Microstrip Antenna Design*

Hansen, Robert C., ed., *Moment Methods in Antennas and Scattering*

Hirsch, Herbert L., and Douglas C. Grove, *Practical Simulation of Radar Antennas and Radomes*

Kitsuregawa, Takashi, *Advanced Technology in Satellite Communication Antennas: Electrical and Mechanical Design*

Kumar, A., and H.D. Hristov, *Microwave Cavity Antennas*

Law, Preston E., Jr., *Shipboard Antennas*

Li, S.T., J.C. Logan, J.W. Rockway, and D.W.S. Tam, *The MININEC System: Microcomputer Analysis of Wire Antennas*

Pozar, David M., *Antenna Design Using Personal Computers*

Scherer, James P., *LAARAN: Linear Antenna Array Analysis Software and User's Manual*

Scott, Craig, *Modern Methods of Reflector Antenna Analysis and Design*

Sletten, Carlye J., ed., *Reflector and Lens Antennas: Analysis and Design Using Personal Computers*

Sletten, Carlyle J., ed., *Reflector and Lens Antennas: Software User's Manual and Example Book*

Weiner, M.M., et al., *Monopole Elements on Circular Ground Planes*

Wolff, Edward A., *Antenna Analysis, Second Edition*

Yamashita, E., ed., *Analysis Methods for Electromagnetic Wave Problems*

Near-Field Antenna Measurements

Dan Slater

Artech House
Boston • London

Library of Congress Cataloging-in-Publication Data

Slater, Dan, 1950-
  Near-field antenna measurements / Dan Slater.
    p. cm.
  Includes bibliographical references and index.
  ISBN 0-89006-361-3
  1. Microwave antennas--Testing. I. Title.
TK7871.6.S555 1991   91-2133
621.382'4--dc20   CIP

British Library Cataloguing in Publication Data

Slater, Dan
  Near-field antenna measurements.
  1. Antennas (Radio) Measurement
  I. Title.
  621.3824

  ISBN 0-89006-361-3

© 1991 Artech House, Inc.
685 Canton Street
Norwood, MA 02062

International Standard Book Number: 0-89006-361-3
Library of Congress Catalog Card Number: 91-2133

10 9 8 7 6 5 4

CONTENTS

PREFACE

The need for sophisticated, high-performance antennas is increasing as spacecraft, aircraft, ship, and ground vehicle mission requirements become more sophisticated. Ultralow-sidelobe, low-RCS antennas are now the norm for many aircraft. Likewise, high-performance, low-sidelobe, multibeam antennas can significantly improve the communication performance of satellites.

One problem in the development and manufacture of sophisticated antennas is the measurement of antenna performance. Techniques used in the past are becoming less capable of determining the performance of advanced antennas. This is due to a variety of problems, including weather effects, multipath, antenna gravitational distortions, and security. Near-field measurement techniques often can solve many of these problems in a very cost-effective and efficient manner.

The primary audience for this book comprises engineers, physicists, and graduate students working with spacecraft and other high-performance microwave antennas. The emphasis in this book is on the practical aspects of planar near-field measurements. Additionally, this book tries to explore some new and emerging near-field measurement concepts.

The basic concepts used in near-field measurements are very closely related to those of other fields, such as radioastronomy, *synthetic aperture radar* (SAR), seismology, underwater acoustics, and optical holography. Some of these interrelationships are described in this book. In fact, several of the tables herein translate terminology among the various disciplines. Robotic engineers should find the chapters on highly precise robotic systems design and coordinate measurements of particular interest. This book should prove useful as well to workers in fields other than antenna measurements.

This book attempts to explain many aspects of near-field antenna measurements in a straightforward and consistent way. This book derives from experience with a variety of near-field measurement systems that the author designed as a consultant to the Antenna Systems Laboratory in the TRW Space Communications Division and later at Nearfield Systems, Inc. Over the years, the author has benefited from technical discussions with many friends and colleagues, too numerous to list. Special acknowledgments are due to Greg Hindman for his unwavering support of my work, Don Jones for his unusual ability to find the true problem, Dean Mensa for showing me that SAR radars need not be complicated, my brother, Mark Slater, for working on the hard problems that no one else could or would handle, and Ron Young, for his insights into the fundamentals of the near-field measurement process. The author also wishes to thank Pamela George, Lorraine Fujita, and the staff of Artech House for their work in turning this book into a reality.

DAN SLATER
LA HABRA HEIGHTS, CALIFORNIA
AUGUST 17, 1990

Chapter 1
INTRODUCTION

1.1 INTRODUCTION

This book provides a detailed technical overview of the theory and practice of antenna near-field measurements. Near-field measurements provide a fast and accurate method of determining the antenna gain, pattern, polarization purity, beam pointing, and other parameters of interest to an antenna engineer. Near-field ranges (see Figure 1.1) are often complemented by other measurement systems, including compact ranges, far-field ranges, and anechoic chambers [1].

The planar near-field technique is an effective method for measuring the performance of large, high-frequency spacecraft antennas [2] and other advanced low-sidelobe antennas. The advantages of near-field measurements include high accuracy, high throughput (or data rate), a complete characterization of the antenna performance, control of zero gravity effects, elimination of delay due to weather, minimal "real estate" requirements, and compatibility with special project security requirements [3].

Planar near-field measurements provide a convenient method for determining the performance of large, high frequency spacecraft antennas. Information available from near-field measurements includes:

1. Far-field pattern;
2. Antenna gain;
3. Antenna directivity;
4. Axial ratio;
5. Beamwidth;
6. Beam pointing;
7. Phase center position;
8. Defocusing;
9. Autotrack (monopulse) bias, scale factor, and linearity;
10. Phased array element excitation;
11. Reflector surface distortion measurements.

Figure 1.1 A typical near-field test facility.

Many techniques can be used to measure antenna patterns [1]. Some of the more important methods include the following.

Far-Field Methods

1. Far-field range:
   - Outside test range,
   - Anechoic chamber;
2. Extraterrestrial:
   - Radio star,
   - Satellite beacon.

Near-Field Methods (Real Aperture)

1. Compact range;
2. Defocused antenna.

Near-Field Methods (Synthetic Aperture)

1. Planar near field;
2. Cylindrical near field;
3. Spherical near field.

Other

1. Primary feed pattern and reflector surface model.

A brief comparison between some of these methods is in Table 1.1. This table, by necessity, is a generalization and will not be correct for some applications.

1.2 ORGANIZATION OF THE BOOK

This book examines planar near-field antenna measurements; however, many of the basic concepts apply to other antenna applications and other branches of science and engineering. A near-field antenna measurement system consists of a high-precision robot carrying a microwave interferometer as a payload. Other payloads related to antenna manufacturing operations also can be carried by the robot. As an example, the robot also can measure mechanical dimensions of antenna components and surfaces or be used to modify an antenna surface with a high-speed cutter. The near-field measurement robot can carry one or more of the following payloads:

1. Microwave interferometer;
2. Mechanical coordinate measurement probe;
3. Optical surface measurement unit;
4. High-speed cutter assembly;
5. Other application-specific payloads (television, markers, *et cetera*).

This book is organized into an introduction, three major sections (payload, robot, and operations), and five appendixes.

- Introduction

  1. Introduction.

- Payloads

  2. Near-field measurement concepts;
  3. Near-field measurements;
  4. Microwave interferometers;
  5. Coordinate measurements and machining.

- Robotic Systems

  6. Small near-field measurement systems;
  7. Robotic systems design.

- Operations

  8. Operations;
  9. Near-field measurement error analysis.

Table 1.1
Comparison of Antenna Measurement Techniques

	Near-Field Planar Range	Outdoor Range	Anechoic Chamber	Compact Range	Near-Field Spherical	Defocused	Radio Star or Satellite	Primary Pattern and Surface Model
High-gain antenna	excellent	adequate	poor	excellent	poor	good	excellent	excellent
Low-gain antenna	poor	adequate	good	excellent	good	poor	poor	poor
Gain measurement	excellent	excellent	good	excellent	good	excellent	adequate	excellent
Close sidelobes	excellent	good	poor	excellent	excellent	adequate	—	—
Far sidelobes	adequate	good	poor	good	excellent	good	—	adequate
Low sidelobes	−50 dB	−40 dB	poor	good	excellent	−35 dB	—	—
Axial ratio	excellent	good	poor	good	excellent	good	poor	good
Zero gravity effects	excellent	poor	poor	poor	good	poor	poor	excellent
Multipath	good	adequate	adequate	good	good	good	good	excellent
Weather	excellent	poor	excellent	excellent	excellent	poor	poor	excellent
Security	excellent	adequate	excellent	excellent	excellent	adequate	poor	excellent
Facility cost	moderate	high	moderate	high	moderate	moderate	variable	low
Operating cost	moderate	high	moderate	moderate	moderate	moderate	variable	low
Speed	excellent	fair	excellent	excellent	adequate	fair	fair	excellent
Complexity	high	moderate	low	low	high	variable	variable	high
Surface measure	excellent	RF only	RF only	RF only	poor	RF only	RF only	required
Monopulse	poor	excellent	poor	excellent	poor	poor	excellent	poor
Closed-loop test	poor	excellent	excellent	excellent	poor	excellent	excellent	poor

Several related subjects are also discussed in this book. Pulse compression and SAR radar concepts as related to near-field measurements are discussed in Chapter 4. On-orbit microwave holographic measurements are discussed in Chapter 5 because of the close relationship between this technique and near-field measurement. Five appendixes end the book, covering several specialized subjects related to the near-field measurement ranges. Of particular interest are appendixes describing common misconceptions relating to near-field measurements and definitions of near-field terminology.

REFERENCES

1. Evans, G., *Antenna Measurement Techniques,* Artech House, Norwood, MA, 1990. A well-written introduction to antenna and RCS measurements. Describes near-field, far-field, and compact range measurement systems.
2. Slater, D., "Near Field Facility Design," *AMTA Conference Proceedings,* 1985. An overview of a near-field measurement system.
3. IEEE, *Standard Test Procedures for Antennas,* IEEE STD149-1979. Definitions of basic antenna test methods including near-field techniques.
4. Baird, R., *et al.,* "A Brief History of Near-Field Measurements of Antennas at the National Bureau of Standards," *IEEE Transactions on Antenna and Propagation,* Vol. AP-36, No. 6, June 1988. A paper in the special issue on near-field scanning techniques provides a history of the pioneering near-field work at NBS.
5. Hansen, J., and F. Jensen, "Spherical Near-Field Scanning at the Technical University of Denmark," *IEEE Trans. on Antennas and Propagation,* Vol. AP-36, No. 6, June 1988. A paper in the special issue on near-field scanning techniques provides a history of the pioneering spherical near-field work in Denmark.
6. Hansen, J., *Spherical Near-Field Antenna Measurements,* Peter Peregrinus, Stevenage, 1988. Covers the theory and application of spherical near-field measurements.
7. Hollis, W. *et al.,* "Microwave Antenna Measurements," *Scientific Atlanta,* 1981. Discusses a variety of antenna measurement techniques.
8. Joy, E., "A Brief History of the Development of the Near-Field Measurement Techniques at the Georgia Institute of Technology," *IEEE Trans. on Antennas and Propagation,* Vol. AP-36, No. 6, June 1988. A paper in the special issue on near-field scanning techniques provides a history of the pioneering planar near-field work at Georgia Institute of Technology.

Chapter 2
NEAR-FIELD MEASUREMENT CONCEPTS

A near-field range consists of a microwave interferometer connected to a field probing antenna carried by a very precise robotic system as shown in Figure 2.1. The probe antenna typically is moved throughout a planar, cylindrical, or spherical surface near the *antenna under test* (AUT). All near-field ranges determine the equivalent far-field antenna performance through two basic steps:

1. Measure the phase front of the AUT using a microwave interferometer probe positioned by a robot.
2. Sort the phase front into the actual directions of energy propagation using Fourier transform techniques. The result is an angular spectrum (antenna pattern). The angular spectrum in the near field is the same as the angular spectrum in the far field because electromagnetic energy in free-space travels in a straight line.

This section will cover the basic concepts of how the far-field characteristics of an antenna are determined from near-field phase-front measurements. The latter sections will cover the robot and interferometer design and operation.

2.1 NEAR- AND FAR-FIELD REGIONS

An antenna is a structure or transducer that converts between guided electromagnetic waves and those propagating in free space. The electromagnetic field associated with an antenna has properties that change gradually with distance from the antenna. Three regions are of interest—the transitions between them are quite gradual and the boundaries are not distinct. The three regions, as a function of distance from the antenna, are as follows:

1. The region nearest to the antenna is the evanescent or reactive near-field region. The evanescent component of the electromagnetic energy decays very rapidly with distance. The evanescent region includes both nonpropagating

---

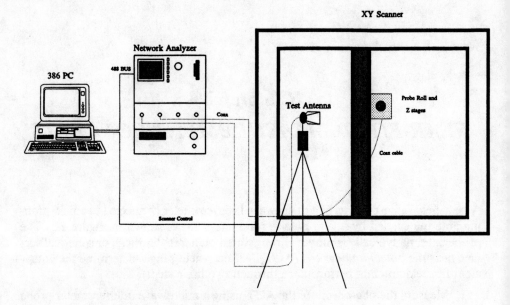

Figure 2.1 Near-field measurement system block diagram.

(reactive) and propagating energy. This region extends from any conductive surface for a distance of a few wavelengths away from that surface.

2. The second region is the radiating near-field or Fresnel region. The average energy densities remain relatively constant at different distances from the antenna although there are localized energy fluctuations. The near-field range measures the radiating near-field region of the AUT and converts those measurements by mathematical transform to the equivalent far-field measurements.

3. The region farthest from the antenna is the far-field or Fraunhofer region. The relative angular distribution does not vary with distance in the far-field region. The power radiated from an antenna in the far-field region decays according to the inverse square law as a function of distance. The far field extends from the near-field region to infinity.

Near- and far-field regions are compared in Table 2.1.

The near-field region normally is defined as extending from the evanescent region to an arbitrarily selected distance, where the path length difference to a point at that distance results in a phase curvature across the aperture of 22.5 degrees (1/16 wavelength). This distance, R, as derived from the geometry is

$$R = 2D^2/\lambda \tag{2.1}$$

Table 2.1
Comparison between Near- and Far-Field Regions

	Evanescent	Near Field	Far Field
Near limit	0	3λ	$2D^2/\lambda$
Far limit	3λ	$2D^2/\lambda$	∞
Power decay	R^{-n}	1	R^{-2}
E and H orthogonal	no	yes	yes
$Z_0 = 377\ \Omega$	no	yes	yes

Note: For power decay, n is a function of the particular antenna design and geometry. A typical value is 5.

where

D = antenna diameter,
λ = RF wavelength.

Typical far-field distances for high-gain spacecraft antennas are in the range of 50 ft to 3 mi. For low-sidelobe measurements, the phase curvature across the aperture should be much less than 22.5°, often in the vicinity of 0.01 wavelength or 3.6°. This would increase the far-field distance by a factor of 6. Most antennas are used at far-field distances, requiring that the antenna performance be known at those distances (see Table 2.2).

Table 2.2
Representative Near- and Far-Field Distances for Various Antennas

Antenna	Frequency (f) GHz	Diameter (D) ft	Gain (G) dB	Near-field Start (3λ) in.	Far-field Start $(2D^2/\lambda)$ ft
SGH	10.70	0.25	17	3.3	1.36
Landsat	15.00	6	47	2.4	1098
ACTS	29.75	9	57	1.2	4900
TDRSS SA	15.00	15	56	2.4	6863
STDN	2.30	210	61	15.4	39.1 mi
Arecibo	430.00 MHz	1000	59	82.4	165.6 mi

Evanescent energy is coupled to the near-field probe capacitively or inductively, but not by free-space propagation. Because of this, the E and H fields are not orthogonal nor related by the impedance of free space (377 Ω). Near-field measurements are generally made outside of the evanescent region. Otherwise, higher sampling densities and separate E and H field measurements are required.

The evanescent energy decays very rapidly with distance because the evanescent energy is nonpropagating but capacitively or inductively coupled. The evanescent energy normally has completely decayed at a distance of three wavelengths (3λ) from a conducting surface.

2.2 NEAR-FIELD MEASUREMENT CONCEPTS

All near-field measurement systems compute the various directions in which the electromagnetic field is propagating. These directions of propagation are completely independent of distance to the AUT, related rather to the Fourier transform of the phase front. This fundamental concept will be examined from three different but equivalent viewpoints:

1. The near-field measurement system operates by measuring the phase front of the AUT and then mathematically transforming the phase front into the equivalent far-field angular spectrum. For a planar near field, the phase front and angular spectrum are related by a two-dimensional Fourier transform. This is the Fourier optics approach.
2. The near-field measurement systems operate by processing the doppler signal from a moving probe. Energy approaching the probe antenna from the side will be shifted up in frequency due to the doppler principle, if the probe antenna is moving in that direction. A bandpass filter tuned to the doppler frequency will detect energy coming from that direction only. A two-dimensional Fourier transform will implement a set of bandpass filters that will separate the doppler frequencies corresponding to the different directions in the angular spectrum. This concept is called *doppler beam forming*.
3. The near-field measurement systems operate by forming a synthetic aperture phased array antenna with beams steered simultaneously to all angles of interest. In a planar near field, the phase shift and summing required for beam forming are conveniently done with a two-dimensional Fourier transform. This technique is called *aperture synthesis*.

The terminology used in these three types of measurement is compared in Table 2.3.

Other viewpoints include dechirping the doppler frequency shift and correlating with a reference planewave and a plane-wave-matched filter [1].

2.3 FOURIER OPTICS

The following are some basic concepts on which Fourier optics is based.

1. Phase angles can be measured in a variety of ways, for example, $1\lambda = 360°$ $= 2\pi$ radians $= 1$ cycle.

Table 2.3
Terminology Comparison

Near-field Term	Doppler Beam Forming	Aperture Synthesis
Spatial frequency	doppler frequency	phase tilt
Spatial filter	doppler filter	beam former
Far-field transform	doppler beam former	beam former
Aliasing, undersampling	ambiguity	grating lobes
Near field	focused	focused
Probe antenna	antenna	element
Probe pattern	antenna pattern	element factor
Probe correction	deconvolution	array factor
K space		UV plane

2. A phase front is defined as a surface of equal phase; for example, a horn antenna radiates a spherical phase front with a radius equal to the horn phase center to observer distance (see Figure 2.2).
3. A phase front with a flat surface of equal phase is called a *plane wave;* for example, a parabolic antenna normally radiates a planar phase front (see Figure 2.3).
4. The near-field system measures, on an arbitrary surface, the amplitude and phase angle of the electromagnetic field of the AUT.
5. The tangential component of the field (i.e., the field component in the direction of propagation) is always zero in free space.
6. Energy leaving an antenna always propagates in a straight line (at least, in our environment). Equivalently, the direction in which energy travels is the same at all distances from the AUT.
7. All near-field measurements can be used to compute the far-field pattern by determining the various directions in which the electromagnetic field is propagating. These measurements can be made at *any* distance from the AUT.
8. The near-field interferometer probe, positioned by a robotic system, is used to measure the phase front of the AUT.
9. A Fourier transform is used to sort the phase front energy into the actual directions of propagation.
10. A complete transformation of the near field to the far field does not add or delete data. The inverse transform will produce the original phase front.

The concept behind near-field measurements is best understood by studying a simple case. Assume that an ideal lens antenna is emitting energy traveling to the right, as shown in Figure 2.4. This energy is shown as a phase front by identifying the lines of equal phase angle at a given time. The vertical lines represent the lines of a zero phase angle relative to an arbitrary reference. The spacing between the

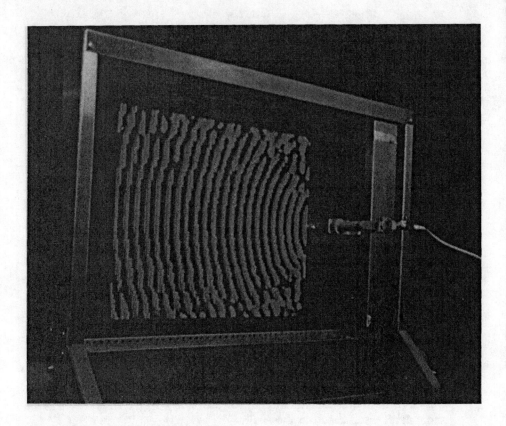

Figure 2.2 Energy leaving a horn antenna.

vertical lines in Figure 2.4 is at an interval of 360° in phase or 1 λ. Note that distances and dimensions are often measured in terms of wavelengths (λ) or degrees of phase (360° = 1 λ). Because we assume that the antenna is ideal we can say that all energy is traveling to the right in the form of a plane wave.

The lines of constant phase can be measured by probing the phase front of the antenna with a microwave probe. Figure 2.4 shows four probes providing the same phase measurement at all four positions. The phase measurement is 180° as the four probe antennas are equidistant between the 0° phase front lines. Note that either four separate probes or one probe moved sequentially to the four positions would provide the same information. The way in which the probe actually measures the phase will be covered in more detail below.

We will now examine what happens if the probe scan plane is tilted relative to the phase front shown in Figure 2.4. In this example (see Figure 2.5 and Table

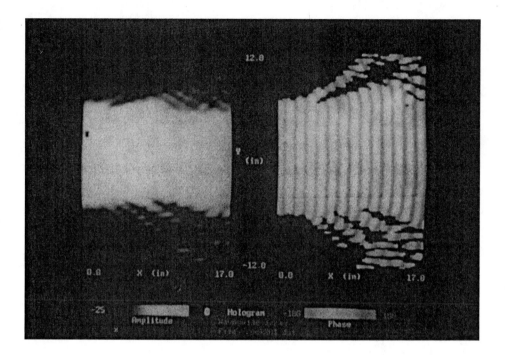

Figure 2.3 Energy leaving a parabolic antenna.

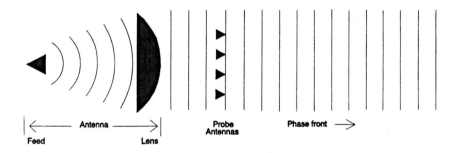

Figure 2.4 An idealized antenna with a planar phase front and four probe antennas.

2.4), the first probe antenna will measure 0°, the second −60°, the third −120°, and fourth −180°. The probe positions are separated vertically by one wavelength.

If the vertical spacing between the probes is 1λ, we can say that the measurement plane is tilted by phase slope of −60° per 360° of lateral travel (1 λ). This is

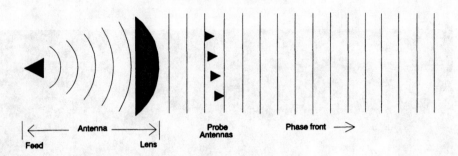

Figure 2.5 An idealized antenna with a planar phase front and four probe antennas tilted to an angle of 9.6°.

Table 2.4
Dimensions of the Probe Antenna of Figure 2.5

Probe #	y Position	Phase	Slope
1	0 λ	0°	−60°/λ
2	1 λ	−60°	−60°/λ
3	2 λ	−120°	−60°/λ
4	3 λ	−180°	−60°/λ

equal to a phase slope of −⅙. To convert the slope into an angle simply take the arcsine of −⅙, which equals −9.6°. The energy from the idealized antenna is traveling at an angle of −9.6° relative to the plane of the four probe antennas.

A slope of −60° of phase per 360° (1 λ) of lateral travel is equal to a phase slope of −⅙ wavelength per wavelength. Because a wavelength is equal to 360° of phase, it is equivalent to a cycle of rotation. For reasons that will become apparent, the slope will be specified as −⅙ cycle per wavelength. The arcsine of the slope is the actual angle of tilt between the probe scan plane and the propagation direction of the phase front from the ideal antenna.

The units of cycles per wavelength define a spatial frequency just as units of cycles per second define a temporal frequency (see Figure 2.6). Likewise, the spatial frequency is a measure of the period of a sine wave relative to a given distance interval. Spatial frequency is a frequency measured in units of distance. For example, the lines on a television monitor may repeat at 0.1-inch intervals. The lines would have a spatial frequency of 10 cycles per inch. Spatial frequency may be measured in a variety of units:

$$1 \text{ cycle/wavelength} = 2\pi \text{ rad/wavelength}$$

$$= 360°/\text{wavelength}$$

$$= c/f \text{ cycles/m}$$

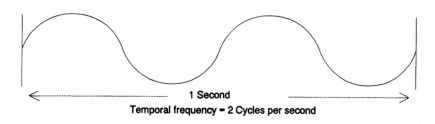

1 Second

Temporal frequency = 2 Cycles per second

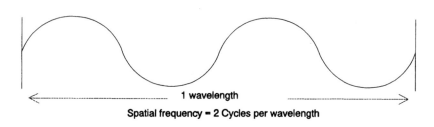

1 wavelength

Spatial frequency = 2 Cycles per wavelength

Figure 2.6 Similarity between spatial and temporal frequencies.

where

c = propagation velocity (m/s)
f = frequency (Hz)

Spatial frequency is a direct measure of beam tilt: Beam tilt (degree) = arcsine (spatial frequency). Note that spatial frequency is measured in cycles/wavelength.

2.3.1 Principle of Superposition

The principle of superposition states that, if a system is linear, then the response of that system to the sum of N components is equal to the sum of the responses of the N individual components. For example, the output of an electrical filter driven by a square wave is equal to the sum of the filter outputs to an equivalent Fourier series of sine waves.

In near-field antenna measurements, the principle of superposition can be used to show that a real antenna may be described equivalently as a set of imaginary antennas radiating planewaves. This results in the concept of a planewave spectrum.

2.3.2 The Phasor

The electric field at a given point and time can be described in terms of a phasor, which has a complex value:

$$E = I + Qi \qquad (2.2)$$

where

I = in-phase component,
Q = quadrature component,
i = square root of -1.

The magnitude of the phasor is equal to the magnitude of the electric field intensity:

$$|E| = \sqrt{I^2 + Q^2} \qquad (2.3)$$

The angular orientation of the phasor is equal to the phase angle of the electric field intensity relative to a reference phase angle:

$$\arg(E) = \arctan(Q/I) \qquad (2.4)$$

Phasors can be added and multiplied using the rules of complex arithmetic. Each amplitude-phase measurement made by the near-field microwave receiver can be represented as a phasor. A unit length phasor at an angle of θ can be defined by Euler's identity as described in Appendix B:

$$A = e^{i\theta} \qquad (2.5)$$

A two-element vector (E) with the components I, Q can be rotated through an angle θ by

$$I' = I\cos\theta + Q\sin\theta \qquad (2.6)$$
$$Q' = Q\cos\theta - I\sin\theta$$

If the vector (X) is defined in complex form (I, iQ), the rotation becomes

$$X' = I\cos\theta + Q\sin\theta + i(Q\cos\theta - I\sin\theta) \qquad (2.7)$$

The rotation of the vector X by θ can be rewritten using Euler's identity (see Appendix B) and a complex multiply or divide:

$$A = Xe^{i\theta} = X/e^{-i\theta} \tag{2.8}$$

These concepts can be used to explain the near- to far-field transformation process as follows. Assume you have a set of n numbers defining vector E. The average value of the set of numbers in vector E is the sum of the values divided by the number of values; that is,

$$A_{ave} = \frac{1}{n}\sum_{j=1}^{n} E(j) \tag{2.9}$$

Similarly, the average value of n phasors is the complex sum divided by n, which is also a phasor. If the n phasors corresponded to a set of uniformly sampled aperture phase-front voltage measurements, the magnitude squared of the average value phasor corresponds to the antenna power on boresight. Dividing the boresight antenna power by the equivalent isotropic power results in the boresight directive gain.

The determination of the directive gain in other directions can be accomplished by a simple modification of the preceding procedure. The modification is to "rotate" the phasors prior to the summation at a rate corresponding to the spatial frequency of interest. A given spatial frequency is equal to the sine of the angle of energy travel. The rotation is accomplished by a complex multiply with a complex exponential:

$$A(K_x) = \frac{1}{n}\sum_{j=1}^{n} E(j)\, e^{-iK2\pi x(j)K_x} \tag{2.10}$$

or equivalently;

$$A(az) = \frac{1}{n}\sum_{j=1}^{n} E(j)\, e^{-iK2\pi x(j)\sin(az)} \tag{2.11}$$

where

$E(j) = j$th complex voltage measurement,
$x(j) = j$th position (wavelengths),
K_x = spatial frequency (cycles/λ) = $\sin(az)$,
$K = 2\pi/\lambda$ = wavenumber,
i = square root of -1,
n = number of measurements.

The situation for two-dimensional transformations is slightly more complicated. The spatial frequency is defined in terms of a three-component vector with elements K_x, K_y, and K_z. K_x is the horizontal component, K_y is a vertical component, and K_z is a depth component. K_x, K_y, and K_z also are known equivalently as the u, v, and w components. The norm (length) of this vector must be equal to one cycle/wavelength for energy traveling by free-space propagation.

Equation (2.11) defines a filter that yields in complex form (i.e., as a phasor) the amount of RF energy traveling at a given azimuth angle. The filter can be modified to two dimensions to determine the energy traveling in a specified azimuth and elevation direction. To do this, we first determine the energy traveling in a direction corresponding to a horizontal and vertical spatial frequency. This type of transform has a "K space" output and allows us to view certain types of multipath and evanescent energy. The transformation of the measured near-field phase front to an equivalent far-field angular response $A(K_x, K_y)$ at a given horizontal and vertical spatial frequency (K_x, K_y) is given by

$$A(K_x, K_y) = \frac{1}{n} \sum_{j=1}^{n} E(j)\, e^{-iK(x(j)K_x + y(j)K_y)} \qquad (2.12)$$

where

$E(j)$ = complex voltage for jth measurement,
$x(j)$ = x probe position for jth measurement,
$y(j)$ = y probe position for jth measurement,
K = $2\pi/\lambda$ = wavenumber,
K_x = horizontal spatial frequency (cycles/λ),
K_y = vertical spatial frequency (cycles/λ).

The transformation of the phase front measured on a planar surface to all possible angles can be defined in terms of the classical two-dimensional Fourier transform (see Appendix D). The relationship between a two-dimensional field distribution $f(x, y)$ and a two-dimensional angular spectrum $F(K_x, K_y)$ is

$$F(K_x, K_y) = \int \int f(x, y)\, e^{-i(K_x x + K_y y)}\, dx\, dy \qquad (2.13)$$

$$f(x, y) = \int \int F(K_x, K_y)\, e^{i(K_x x + K_y y)}\, dK_x\, dK_y \qquad (2.14)$$

where

x = x position (wavelengths),
y = y position (wavelengths),
K = $2\pi/\lambda$ = wavenumber,

K_x = azimuthal spatial frequency (cycles/λ),
K_y = elevation spatial frequency (cycles/λ).

A far-field transform of a raster data set can be implemented by solving (2.12) at all angles for which far-field data are required. This would be quite slow, however. The algorithms actually used to perform the far-field transformations are direct descendants of the two-dimensional spatial filter. These algorithms will be described later in Chapter 3.

For most applications, the transform output in angle space is preferred. Many transforms operate by first transforming the measurements into the K space and then using a remapping or interpolation scheme to convert the K space output into angle space.

2.4 DOPPLER BEAM FORMING

The near-field measurement and data reduction process can be described in terms of doppler frequency shifts. Energy received by the near-field probe is doppler shifted by an amount related to the direction of energy arrival. A spectrum of the directions of energy arrival is equivalent to an angular spectrum or far-field pattern. The doppler shift results from the motion of the probe antenna relative to the AUT. The maximum doppler shift occurs when the probe is traveling in the direction of propagation.

The amount of doppler shift (Δf) is a direct function of the RF frequency (f), probe velocity (v), and the direction of arrival (θ) relative to the probe velocity vector:

$$\Delta(f) = fv/c \, \sin\theta \tag{2.15}$$

Equivalently, the doppler shift is equal to probe velocity (v) measured in wavelengths per second times the sine of the direction of energy arrival:

$$\Delta f = v \, \sin\theta \tag{2.16}$$

The doppler-shifted energy can be analyzed to derive an equivalent far-field response for the AUT. As an example, assume a transmitter frequency of 11.803 GHz (1 in. wavelength) and a relative velocity of 12 in. per s. Table 2.5 lists doppler frequency offsets corresponding to various angles of relative motion.

A spectrum analyzer can be used to sort the different doppler frequencies. Each frequency corresponds to a particular angle of arrival. For example, if energy at a doppler frequency offset of 10.39 Hz is present, then energy is arriving from an angle of 60°. Likewise, a bandpass filter tuned to 10.39 Hz will pass only energy arriving from a 60° angle.

Table 2.5
Doppler Shift due to Probe Motion

Angle (θ)	Doppler Shift $\Delta f = 12 \sin\theta$ (Hz)
90°	12.00 Hz
60°	10.39 Hz
30°	6.00 Hz
0°	0.00 Hz
−30°	−6.00 Hz
−60°	−10.39 Hz
−90°	−12.00 Hz

The concept of doppler filtering is used extensively in airborne radar systems and is the foundation of synthetic aperture and doppler beam-sharpening techniques. These types of radars analyze the aircraft motion-induced doppler shift to the received radar return signal. By processing the received signal with a spectrum analyzer, the direction of signal arrival relative to the aircraft velocity vector can be determined.

In a similar manner, the near-field measurement probe antenna flies past the AUT. Energy arriving at different directions relative to the probe motion will undergo different doppler shifts. Energy approaching the probe antenna from the left will be shifted up in frequency, due to the doppler principle, if the probe antenna is moving to the left. A bandpass filter tuned to the doppler frequency will detect energy coming from that direction only.

A spectrum of energy arrival directions is equivalent to a far-field angular spectrum, as electromagnetic energy propagates in a straight line. Because the probe moves in two dimensions, the doppler spectrum is computed by a two-dimensional Fourier transform. The two-dimensional Fourier transform implements a set of bandpass doppler filters that will separate the doppler frequencies corresponding to the different directions in the angular spectrum. This concept is also known as *doppler beam forming.*

The far-field angular spectrum is obtained easily from the doppler spectrum, which is the Fourier transform of the received complex doppler signal from the near-field probe. The conversion between the angular $A(\theta)$ and doppler $A(S)$ spectra is simply

$$A(\theta) = A[\arcsin(S)] \tag{2.17}$$

where

$S = f/\lambda$ (cycles/λ),
f = doppler frequency (Hz).

The arcsine function simply converts a beam tilt to the equivalent angle. The angular spectrum derived from the probe doppler signal corresponds to an angular spectrum in the near field. An angular spectrum in the near field is identical to an angular spectrum in the far field, except for the inverse square-law decrease in power and the phase delay. The power decrease and phase delay are described by a Green's function (see Appendix B). In antenna measurements, the angular spectrum is normalized as gain relative to an isotropic radiator. The Green's function is identical for both the AUT and equivalent isotropic source. Both the inverse square-law effect and phase delay are eliminated by normalization. The normalized near-field and far-field angular spectra are identical.

The *intermediate frequency* (IF) response of the receiver can modify the doppler spectrum resulting in a distorted far-field pattern. A narrow IF bandwidth relative to the received doppler signal causes the derived antenna pattern to appear narrower than it actually is, because the wide-angle doppler components are attenuated excessively. The required IF bandwidth for most applications is simply the scan velocity measured in wavelengths per second. For example, if the probe is traveling at 12 in/s and the test wavelength is one inch, the required IF bandwidth is 12 Hz.

Intentionally introduced doppler filters can be used to modify the probe pattern. Because the probe antenna often is less sensitive to energy arriving from the side, the far-field pattern will be distorted. This effect can be removed by "probe correction," as will be described later.

2.5 APERTURE SYNTHESIS

The measurement of the far-field performance of an antenna requires that it be illuminated with a source that appears to be at a large or infinite distance. Under these conditions, the energy arriving at the AUT will be parallel rays that define a planar phase front.

The simplest way to produce a plane wave is to move the source to a distance at which the spherical phase front approximates a plane wave across the antenna aperture, often a distance of many miles. This is the method used by the far-field ranges.

Another method of producing a plane wave is to use a lens, parabolic reflector, or phased (conventional or endfire) array as a collimator (see Table 2.6). A collimator converts the spherical phase front of a feed antenna into a planar phase front. An antenna tested with a planar phase front, by definition, is being tested in the far-field region. A collimator can be used either to transmit or receive, producing identical results. This is a direct consequence of the principle of reciprocity.

If the collimating element is a parabolic reflector, the setup is called a *compact range*. (An example is shown in Figure 2.7.) The design criterion for most compact

Table 2.6
Source and Aperture Characteristics of Test Ranges

Test Range	Source	Aperture
Far-field range	distant	real
Compact range	collimated	real (parabolic)
	collimated	real (phased array)
Near-field range	collimated	synthetic (phased array)

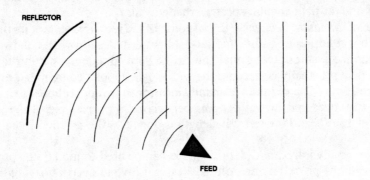

Figure 2.7 Compact range.

ranges is virtually identical to that of a low-sidelobe off-axis parabolic reflector antenna.

A collimated test range can be built by using a phased array antenna instead of a feed and parabolic reflector. A phased array antenna generally consists of an array of small antennas, called *elements,* covering a surface. The elements are connected through a beam former, which consists of phase adjusters and summers. The phase shifters can be used to steer the beam electronically to various angles.

Assume that a set of ideal antenna elements spaced uniformly in a plane are illuminated by an on-axis plane wave (see Figure 2.8). The output of all elements are in phase and at a constant amplitude. By summing the output of all elements, all energy is coherently added with the total energy equal to the energy entering one element times the total number of elements.

The situation is different if the phased array antenna is illuminated by an off-axis plane wave. Because the plane wave illumination strikes the antenna elements at an oblique angle, the phases of the elements will be different. If the plane wave strikes the antenna at an angle that results in an 180° or odd multiple phaseshift between adjacent elements, then, when coherently summed, the output of adjacent elements will cancel each other out. The phased array antenna output for plane waves arriving from other directions can be determined from the magnitude of the

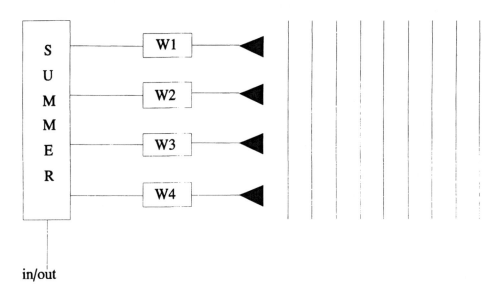

Figure 2.8 A phased array antenna illuminated by an on-axis plane wave.

energy striking the elements and the phase angle between the element outputs for a given direction.

The phased array antenna can be "steered" by connecting a phase shifter in series with each phased array element, as in Figure 2.9. The phase shifter commands required to steer the antenna to a given direction are equal to the negative of the plane-wave phase offsets between a reference element and the given element. The combination of the phase shifters and summer is called a *beam former*. The beam can be steered as fast as the phase shifters can be commanded. Beam-steering times can be less than 1 μs.

The output from the phased array elements can be fed simultaneously to more than one beam former. An example is the TDRSS satellite in which the outputs of 27 elements on the spacecraft are brought simultaneously to 20 beam formers in the ground station.

The near-field range system is equivalent to a synthetic aperture compact range system. The near-field antenna uses the concept of aperture synthesis to produce a collimating antenna large enough to accept all energy emitted from the AUT. For a low-gain antenna such as a spacecraft omnidirectional *telemetry, tracking, and control* (TT&C) antenna, the aperture may need to envelop the AUT completely. In this case, the synthetic aperture is often shaped as a sphere or cylinder, which is similar to the concept of conformal phased arrays.

The synthetic aperture is formed by coherently integrating the output of a small antenna that is moved throughout the aperture region. The synthesized

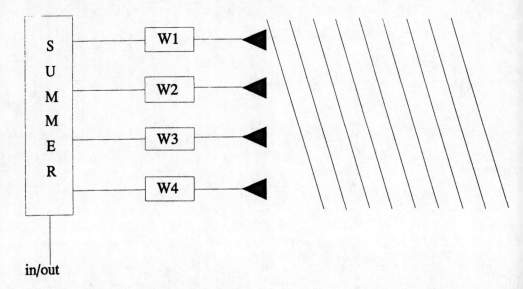

Figure 2.9 A phased array antenna with beam steering.

antenna is steered (using the far-field transform) to all angles for which far-field information is required. The far-field transform uses Fourier techniques to determine the gain in a given direction. The Fourier transform applies phase shifts to the individual elements (data records) and then sums the resulting elemental outputs to determine the gain in a given direction. In one sense, the near-field range is a multibeam synthetic aperture version of the compact range. The near-field range uses a phased array rather than a parabolic reflector.

A phased array antenna can be formed synthetically by moving a single antenna element into the position where each element would be and recording the amplitude and phase. The phase reference for the element can be derived from another reference antenna element or simply through a cable connected to the transmitter. The amplitude and phase measurement for each element is summed in a computer. The technique of moving an antenna throughout the region of a desired aperture and coherently forming a beam from recorded amplitude and phase measurements is called *aperture synthesis*. In summary, the synthetic phased array antenna is formed by completing these steps:

1. Move a single antenna element sequentially to each position where an element is required.

2. Measure the antenna element output (transmission) in complex (I/Q) form at each position.
3. Combine the measurements in a beam former. Because the amplitudes and phases for all elements are individually available, any number of beam formers can be used. The beam formers can be efficiently implemented by computer using the Fourier transform [2].

The near-field range uses a single probe antenna element. A synthetic aperture phased array requires a phase reference for the moving antenna element. This may be provided by either a cable connected to the transmitter or a reference antenna. Typical values of near-field range aperture synthesis are as follows:

Synthetic aperture diameter: Same as scan diameter

Focal distance: Infinity

Number of feed elements: Same as number of measurement points

Element type: Horn antenna

Element arrangement: Starburst or raster

Element spacing: 0.4–5 wavelengths

Number of beam formers: $91 \times 91 = 8281$

Method of beam formation: Fourier transform

Beam-former hardware: Digital computer

Each AUT requires a different synthetic aperture. In the near-field antenna measurement system, the parameters that define the properties of the synthetic aperture are these:

1. Far-field beam steering angles,
2. Scan shape (i.e., planar, cylindrical, spherical, or conformal),
3. Scan dimensions (i.e., height and width),
4. Probe antenna and absorber selection,
5. Sampling pattern (i.e., raster, polar, or random),
6. Sampling density.

The user designs the test by designing a synthetic aperture phased array to test the AUT, which is accomplished by specifying these parameters.

2.6 OTHER RELATED TECHNOLOGIES

Fourier optics, aperture synthesis, and doppler processing concepts lead to identical equations and results. These fundamental concepts are used in many areas of science and technology [3, 4] and often have been extended in particular areas to solve specific problems. Some of the technologies using phase-front and spatial frequency concepts include the following:

- Antennas:
  near-field measurements
  antenna design
- Radio astronomy:
  aperture synthesis
  very long baseline interferometry
  plane polar (starburst) far-field transforms
- Radar:
  synthetic aperture
  doppler beam sharpening
  pulse compression
- Oceanography:
  sonar imaging
  beam forming
- Medicine:
  imaging ultrasound
- Seismology:
  migration and stacking
  velocity filtering
- Optics:
  holography
  Fourier optics

Table 2.7 compares equivalent terminology used in several of these areas.

Figure 2.10 shows a *very large array* (VLA), which is a radio telescope that forms images of distant astronomical radio objects. The VLA is conceptually and mathematically equivalent to a 27-mile aperture near-field antenna measurement system. The AUT corresponds to the radio object. Images are formed by converting the measured phase front into an angular spectrum, using Fourier transform methods similar to those in near-field antenna measurements [5–7]. Even larger arrays exist, some with aperture dimensions larger than the earth [8].

All of these techniques process the phase front of a real or synthetic array to derive useful information. Many of the technologies use unique extensions to derive more information from the phase front and improve the accuracy of the measurements. Some of the extensions to phase-front processing with potential application to near-field antenna testing follow:

- Radioastronomy [5, 7, 8]:
  Starburst (plane polar) far-field transformations (VLA)
  Antenna surface shape measurements
  Precise antenna position determination

Table 2.7
Terminology Equivalences

Near-field Measurements	Radar (SAR)	Radio Astronomy	Seismology
Near field	focused		normal moveout
Spatial frequency	doppler	spatial frequency	
Measurement plane	synthetic aperture	UV plane	v, t space
Spatial frequency	doppler frequency	phase tilt	velocity
Spatial filter	doppler filter	beam former	veloc. filter
Far-field transform	beam former	beam former	stacking
Aliasing	ambiguity	grating lobes	
Undersampling	ambiguity	grating lobes	
Probe antenna	antenna	element	geophone
Probe pattern	antenna pattern	element pattern	
Probe correction	array factor	deconvolution	deconvolution
Source	transmitter	source	source, shot
Receiver	receiver	receiver	geophone
Scan pattern		array	array
Measurement set			gather

Figure 2.10 Very large array radio telescope. (Photo courtesy of NRAO.)

    Correction of atmospheric effects (VLBI)
    Very long-distance phase reference links (VLA, VLBI)
- Radar [4, 9–11]:
    Antenna path errors and corrections
    Near-field antenna operation (focusing)
    Near-field radar cross-section measurements

Multipath detection and suppression
Real-time processing
- Seismology [3, 4, 12]
Measurement of reflecting surfaces
Nonuniform sampling
Anisotropic media
- Oceanography [13]
Nonuniform sampling
Anisotropic media
- Medicine [4]:
Anisotropic media
- Optics [4, 14–17]:
Real-time processing
Off-axis reference beams

REFERENCES

1. Ulaby, F., R. Moore, and A. Fung, *Microwave Remote Sensing,* vol. 2, Artech House, Norwood, MA, 1982. Discusses synthetic aperture concepts from a variety of viewpoints.
2. Steyskai, H., "Digital Beamforming Antennas," *Microwave J.,* January 1987. This article describes the basics of digital beam forming antennas, which use concepts very similar to near-field methods. The DBF antenna is a real aperture version of the synthetic phased array used by the near-field range. This article also discussed the signal-to-noise ratio and process gain associated with the beam forming.
3. Haykin, S., *Array Signal Processing,* Prentice-Hall, Englewood Cliffs, NJ, 1985. Discusses array processing in seismic, radio astronomy, and other areas.
4. Lee, H., *Imaging Technology,* IEEE Press, New York, 1986. A collection of articles intended to show the similarity in the phase-front processing in various disciplines. Chapters cover holography, optical processing, acoustic imaging, microwave imaging, and seismic processing.
5. Hjellming, R., *An Introduction to the NRAO Very Large Array,* National Radio Astronomy Observatory, Socorro, NM, 1983. A technical description of the theory and operation of the VLA radio telescope in New Mexico. The VLA, in essence, is a 27-mile diameter near-field range array using a starburstlike scan pattern. The AUT are distant stars and galaxies.
6. Napier, P., *et al.,* "The Very Large Array: Design and Performance of a Modern Synthesis Radio Telescope," *Proc. IEEE,* Vol. 71, No. 11, November 1983, pp. 1295–1320; reprinted in *Instrumentation and Techniques for Radio Astronomy,* IEEE Press, 1988. Description of the VLA radio telescope.
7. Thompson, A.R., and J. W. Moran, *Interferometry and Synthesis in Radio Astronomy,* John Wiley and Sons, New York, 1986. Discusses a variety of subjects relevant to near-field measurements including interferometry, phase coherent receivers, atmospheric effects, aperture synthesis, and geodetic measurements.
8. Readhead, A., "Radio Astronomy by Very-Long-Baseline Interferometry," *Scientific American,* June 1982. A well-written introduction to VLBI concepts. Discusses the concept of aperture synthesis and the transformation of a phase-front into an angular spectrum.
9. Kovaly, J., *Synthetic Aperture Radar,* Artech House, Norwood, MA, 1976. A collection of papers

that describe various aspects of synthetic aperture radar and related concepts such as doppler beam forming.

10. Mensa, D., *High Resolution Radar Cross-Section Imaging,* Artech House, Norwood, MA, 1990. Describes synthetic aperture concepts and the related processing algorithms. A classic in the field.

11. Stimson, G., *Introduction to Airborne Radar,* Hughes Aircraft Co., El Segundo, CA, 1983. Probably the best introductory book covering phasors, Fourier transforms, pulse compression, synthetic apertures, and other related concepts.

12. Walter, W., *et al., Seismic Imaging Atlas 1976,* Geophysical Corporation, Pasadena, CA, 1976. A description of techniques used to determine the position of underground seismic reflectors. Covers the theory of aplanatic wave functions.

13. Sutton, J., "Underwater Acoustic Imaging," *Proc. IEEE,* Vol. 67, No. 4, April 1979. Describes the concepts and techniques for underwater acoustic imaging. This article is part of a special issue on acoustic imaging.

14. Goodman, J., *Introduction to Fourier Optics,* McGraw-Hill, New York, 1968. A senior level textbook that covers the basics of Fourier optics.

15. Harburn, G., *et al., Atlas of Optical Transforms,* G. Bell and Sons, London, 1975. An unusual book, which consists of many images of two-dimensional Fourier transform pairs. These images provide insight into the near-field measurement process.

16. Koch, W., *Lasers and Holography,* Dover, New York, 1981. A basic book that describes the fundamentals of wavefronts, including several excellent photographs of both acoustic and microwave phase fronts.

17. Shulman, A., *Principles of Optical Data Processing for Engineers,* NASA Technical Report #TR R-327, Goddard Space Flight Center, Greenbelt, MD, 1970. A well-written explanation of Fourier optics, the foundation of the near-field process, with many good illustrations.

Chapter 3
NEAR-FIELD MEASUREMENT THEORY

This chapter provides a discussion of several topics related to the theory of near-field measurements. In the area of near-field sampling theory, we will discuss the sampling theorem, scan pattern dimensions, spatial filters, probe antennas, and the sampling pattern. This leads us to the planar far-field transformation algorithms: the 2-D Fourier transform (planar raster), the interpolation and FFT (plane polar), and the factored DFT (planar raster and polar). We conclude the chapter with a look at probe correction.

3.1 NEAR-FIELD SAMPLING THEORY

For the antenna test to be performed accurately and rapidly, the user of near-field range measurements must correctly define the following scan parameters:

Scan shape (planar, cylindrical, spherical)

Scan dimensions (height, width, radius, *et cetera*)

Probe antenna specifications (type, gain, polarization, *et cetera*)

Scan pattern (raster, starburst, spiral, random)

Scan parameters (sample spacings)

These parameters are most easily determined by realizing that the near-field range system is conceptually equivalent to a multiple beam, synthetic aperture, phased array compact range system (see Chapter 2). As such, the scan parameter determination can be accomplished by a basic understanding of phased array antenna design principles. This means that we need to accomplish the following:

1. The synthesized near-field aperture must be large enough to accept all significant energy from the AUT.
2. The phase front should be sampled with elemental positions that satisfy the Nyquist sampling theorem. The combined response of the AUT and near-

field range should have no grating lobes in regions of interest. Grating lobes are caused by violations of the sampling theorem.

3. The near-field range should have a classic diffraction limited Airy disk response if illuminated by a uniformly illuminated circular aperture.

The following steps are taken to meet these requirements. A detailed discussion will come later.

1. The synthesized near-field aperture surface must be capable of accepting all significant energy emitted from the antenna under test. The usual scan surface shapes are planar, cylindrical, or spherical. Planar surfaces normally are used for high-gain antennas that transmit energy over a small angular extent. Spherical and cylindrical surfaces are normally used for low-gain antennas that transmit energy more broadly.

2. The dimensions of the synthesized near-field aperture must be large enough to accept all significant energy from the antenna under test.

3. The probe antenna needs to be specified, as its selection can greatly influence the measurement quality and speed. The selection criteria is based on minimizing the number of sampling points by using the probe pattern to suppress grating lobes. The probe selection also influences the accuracy of the microwave interferometer.

4. The discrete positions in which the probe antenna will sample the near field must be defined. The sample points (corresponding to element positions in a phased array antenna) normally are arranged in a two-dimensional grid or a radially symmetric starburst pattern when a planar scan is used. The element pattern and spacing are used to suppress the grating lobes that result in spurious sidelobes.

3.1.1 Synthetic Aperture Surface Shape

The probe antenna is moved by the near-field robot over a path that captures all significant microwave emissions from the AUT. The path of motion is usually constrained to a surface that can be planar, spherical, cylindrical, or arbitrary, as long as it collects all significant energy. The actual points where the measurements are taken define the elements of a synthetic aperture phased array antenna. The design of the synthetic aperture or scan pattern can significantly affect the quality and acquisition time of the phase-front measurements.

Common scan surfaces include planes, cylinders, and spheres (see Table 3.1). The planar scan surface generally is preferred for high-gain spacecraft antennas because all significant plane-wave energy is usually within 10° of the boresight axis and alignment is quite simple. Other advantages of planar scan surfaces include simple probe correction and better zero gravity simulation because the antenna

Table 3.1
Near-Field Scan Surface Comparison

Parameter	Planar	Cylindrical	Spherical
High-gain antennas	excellent	good	good
Low-gain antennas	poor	poor	excellent
Antenna feed elements	good	good	excellent
Stationary AUT	yes	possible	possible
Zero gravity simulation	excellent	poor	variable
Alignment ease	simple	difficult	difficult
Transform	simple	moderate	moderate
Probe correction	simple	complex	complex
Speed	fast	slow	slow

under test is stationary. Conversely, a spherical scan is used for low-gain antennas and antenna feed elements because the energy is captured at large angles from the AUT boresight axis. Cylindrical surfaces are often used with television broadcast antennas and certain spacecraft TT&C omni antennas, which have a narrow pattern on one axis and a broad pattern on a second axis.

The scan area should be large enough to accept all significant near-field energy (energy above the desired sidelobe measurement noise level). The correct scan dimensions for a near-field measurement sequence can be determined from three rules:

1. For planar near-field ranges and the linear axis of a cylindrical near-field range, the correct scan height is based on the physical geometry (i.e., RF energy travels in a straight line from the antenna edges):

$$\text{Scan height} = D + P + 2Z \tan\theta \qquad (3.1)$$

where

D = antenna height,
P = probe height,
Z = AUT-probe distance,
θ = maximum processing angle from boresight.

For gain measurements of highly directive antennas with insignificant sidelobe energy, the aperture dimensions are slightly larger than the physical dimensions of the AUT antenna aperture. The scan angle for cylindrical and spherical near-field measurements based on the physical geometry is

$$\text{Scan angle} = \min\{2[\theta + \arctan(D/2Z)], 360°\} \qquad (3.2)$$

2. The RF signal level should be at a level below the lowest sidelobe level of interest at the scan edges. Typical values are 25 to 45 dB down at the scan pattern edges.

3. The scan pattern should not be significantly larger than the first two rules indicate. Excessive overscanning consumes time and disk storage and can result in poor quality data due to noise, particularly for the starburst scan, as will be explained later.

Excessive truncation of the scan pattern results in rapidly deteriorating measurement quality at the larger far-field angles and a general increase in sidelobe levels. The decrease in measurement quality at far angles is explained by the test geometry. The increase in sidelobe levels is due to the spatial step function (scan truncation), which is convolved with the electromagnetic field measurements. This effect, called *Gibb's ripple,* is a well known phenomena in the study of Fourier transformations. It sometimes can be countered by artificially windowing the near-field measurements with a window function.

3.1.2 Sampling Theorem

The sampling theorem, also known as the Nyquist sampling criterion, states that a spatially band-limited signal of finite energy, which has no spatial frequency components higher than W cycles per wavelength, is completely described by specifying the values of the signal at distance intervals of less than 180° of phase change for the highest spatial frequency present. A near-field phase front is correctly sampled if the phase of the highest spatial frequency present changes by less than 180° between two adjacent samples. In the starburst (plane polar) scan, two adjacent samples are two points along a ray or two points at equal radius on two adjacent rays.

The sampling theorem has several important consequences:

1. If no multipath or evanescent energy is present, there is no need to sample the phase front more densely than at $\lambda/2$ plus 1 sample intervals. This is because the electromagnetic field variation is inherently band-limited to one cycle per wavelength by free-space propagation. The required sampling density for a cylindrical and spherical scan is established by a cylinder or sphere with a radius equal to the maximum radial extent of the AUT. The angular sampling density is at a $\lambda/2$ sample spacing on a surface with a radius equal to the maximum radial extent.

2. If the phase front is further band-limited by a spatial filter, the sampling density often can be reduced by one to two orders of magnitude.

3. If the sampling theorem is violated, energy will appear at spurious angles in the far field. This is aliasing, and it is equivalent to grating lobes in phased array antennas.

4. Oversampling is generally not advised because more time and disk storage are required. Oversampling can provide advantages in certain cases by increasing the signal-to-noise ratio (SNR) and minimizing evanescent and multipath effects. If oversampling is used, a prefilter, such as is used in SAR, may be used to reduce the processing time and quantity of data stored to disk.

Satisfying the Nyquist criterion simply requires that the phase-front samples be taken at intervals of less than half the shortest distance (highest frequency) spatial frequency present. Energy in free space propagation is limited to a spatial frequency of one cycle per wavelength. Equivalently, the phase of an RF signal cannot change by more than 360° in one wavelength of motion. Two samples per wavelength would satisfy the Nyquist criteria. If measurements are taken in the evanescent region very close to the antenna under test, the phase may change more rapidly than 360° per wavelength.

Energy in the evanescent region of an antenna can vary rapidly in phase, resulting in very high spatial frequency components. At distances greater than a few wavelengths and ignoring certain artificial multipath effects, no spatial frequencies higher than one cycle per wavelength can exist. This is because free space propagation is a form of spatial frequency filtering. Other types of spatial filters may either degrade or improve the quality of near-field measurements.

Spatial filters modify the spatial frequency spectrum. Spatial filters are functionally equivalent to angular filters both in concept and effect (see Table 3.2). Many spatial filters are unintentionally introduced into the system. As an example, an excessively narrow receiver IF bandwidth will distort the far-field pattern by

Table 3.2
Examples of Spatial Filters

Scalar horn	low pass
Dish antenna	low pass
Receiver IF filter	low pass (doppler beam sharpening)
Free-space propagation	low pass (as compared to evanescent propagation)
Multibeam antenna	band pass (if steered off-axis)
Phased array	band pass (if steered off-axis)
Autotrack dish	band pass
Autotrack feed	high pass
Nulling antenna	band reject
Probe antenna	low pass, high pass, band pass, band reject, and others: low pass for most applications
Near- to far-field transform	band pass (n simultaneous filters)
Computer generated	low pass, high pass, band pass, band reject, and others

Note: Low-pass filters become bandpass filters if tilted.

decreasing the apparent AUT beamwidth and increasing the directivity (see the section in Chapter 1 on doppler beam forming). Spatial filters can be used to improve the quality of the near-field measurements. For example, a high-gain probe antenna can be used to reduce the sampling density for certain tests. All spatial filters, whether intentional or not, affect the measured far-field response. Ignoring the effects of spatial filtering can result in gain errors, pattern distortions, antenna boresight shifts, and beamwidth errors.

The spatial filter response can be suppressed by deconvolution. The deconvolution operation is in itself a spatial filter with a complementary response to the original spatial filter. The most commonly used deconvolution is the so-called probe correction, in which the spatial filtering effect of the probe antenna is deconvolved from the measured response. This will be described later.

3.1.3 Probe Antenna

The careful selection of a near-field probe antenna, in certain cases, can significantly improve the quality and speed of the data acquisition process. A carefully selected probe antenna will improve the measurement accuracy by

1. Minimizing aliasing,
2. Enhancing the SNR,
3. Minimizing multipath effects,
4. Improving the sidelobe measurement accuracy.

The selection of a probe antenna is based on an understanding of the probe spatial filtering properties. In the near-field viewpoint, the probe antenna is a spatial filter. Equivalently, in the far-field viewpoint, the probe antenna is an angular filter.

The probe angular response can be tailored to enhance or suppress energy arriving from certain directions. This is true irrespective of whether the probe antenna is in the near or far field of the antenna under test. As an example, energy arriving from certain directions may cause aliasing resulting in a corruption of the far-field pattern. Equivalently, in a phased array antenna design, the element pattern can be used to suppress grating lobes. These two concepts are identical.

The rationale for probe antenna selection is based on an understanding of the concepts of spatial and angular filtering. A filter modifies a spectrum by differentially attenuating certain signal components. For example, an angular bandpass filter, such as a parabolic dish antenna, will pass energy arriving from a certain direction. The parabolic dish antenna is an angular bandpass filter because it accepts energy from only a certain direction. An angular band reject filter will reject energy arriving from a certain direction. Angular band reject filters include monopulse and nulling antennas.

An electromagnetic field has both electric (**E**) and magnetic (**H**) field components. The vector cross product between the **E** and **H** fields results in the Poynting vector (**S**), which is aligned with the direction of propagation:

$$\mathbf{S} = \mathbf{E} \times \mathbf{H} \tag{3.3}$$

Outside of the reactive (evanescent) near-field region, the E and H fields are related by the characteristic impedance of free space (377 Ω). The units on the E and H fields are volts per meter (V/m) and amperes per meter (A/m), respectively. The Poynting vector describes the power density of the electromagnetic field, which is in watts per square meter (W/m).

The near-field probe antenna measures either the **E** or **H** field of the antenna under test. The other field can be derived from the measured field after the transformation of the measured field into a derived plane-wave spectrum. The basic types of probes used in near-field measurements are these:

1. *Open-ended waveguide.* The open-ended waveguide provides an omnidirectional measurement of the E field with minimal disturbance to the electromagnetic field. Because of these properties, the open-ended waveguide is very popular. In some cases, the waveguide is dielectrically loaded to further reduce the cross-sectional area. For planar near-field ranges, other probe antenna designs often can provide significant advantages including higher quality and faster measurement.
2. *Loop antenna.* The loop antenna measures the H field instead of the E field. Otherwise, it is similar to the open-ended waveguide.
3. *High-gain antenna.* High-gain antennas include horns, dishes, endfire, log periodic, and so on. The high-gain probe is generally preferred for most high-gain spacecraft antenna measurements made on planar near-field ranges. An excellent probe antenna for most high-gain spacecraft antennas has proven to be a spare feed horn from the antenna under test.
4. *Monopulse antenna.* The monopulse antenna can provide significant advantages in the measurement of low sidelobes.
5. *Synthetic probe antenna.* By moving any of the previously described probe antennas, its response can be modified. For example, axial mutual coupling between the probe and antenna under test can be suppressed by moving the probe antenna between two positions separated by $\lambda/4$ along the z axis for each measurement point and forming an appropriately weighted sum. This concept is discussed further in Chapter 4. The main disadvantage is the additional time required to move the probe antenna.

In planar near-field measurements of high-gain spacecraft antennas, the recommended probe antenna is usually a horn antenna with a gain of 15 to 25 dB and polarization properties similar to the antenna under test. We will show why by analyzing a typical near-field test of a high-gain antenna such as a geosynchronous spacecraft downlink antenna. The subtended angle of the earth's disk from a geosynchronous orbit is 18° or a half-angle of 9°. Often far-field data are not needed beyond 9°. For this example, we want to know the antenna gain and sidelobe structure to a maximum angle of 9° from the boresight.

Because we have no interest in energy beyond 9° from the boresight, we select a probe antenna that rapidly attenuates energy beyond 9° from the boresight direction. This probe antenna operates as a low-pass spatial-angular filter that attenuates energy beyond 0.16 cycles/λ, or 9°. An example of a probe meeting the 9° cutoff requirements is a scalar horn antenna. Several advantages result from using a scalar horn instead of the more conventional open-ended waveguide probe.

1. The higher gain scalar horn will have a significantly lower insertion loss than the open-ended waveguide probe. The gain of the scalar horn is approximately 25 dB. The gain of the open-ended waveguide is approximately 6 dB. The difference of 19 dB results in a 19 dB higher SNR.
2. Fewer sample points are required to satisfy the Nyquist sampling criteria. The highest spatial frequency present has been lowered allowing the required sampling density to be reduced by the sine of 9° (0.16). For a two-dimensional raster scan this results in a 50-fold reduction in the number of sample points. The sample interval is increased by a factor of 6.4 to 3.2λ.
3. Any multipath energy arriving at angles greater than 9° will be rejected (assuming a brick-wall response).
4. The x and y axis positioning accuracy requirements are not as severe as the reciprocal of the sine of 9° (6.4) (Z accuracy requirements are unaffected).

A few disadvantages also occur:

1. Probe correction is generally required. This is easy to do.
2. The probe is heavier, particularily at low frequencies.
3. Better probe attitude stabilization is required, as the probe response is not omnidirectional. The attitude stabilization requirements are not difficult and are easily handled by most near-field scanners.
4. The larger probe antenna is more prone to mutual coupling with the antenna under test. Several methods can be used to minimize the problem:

   • An absorber should cover up surfaces behind the probe aperture.
   • The edge of the probe antenna should be thin and sharp to minimize the reflective area.
   • An isolator or attenuator should be used at the probe data input to reduce VSWR reflections.

- Maintain a 20 dB or greater differential between the AUT and probe gains (see Yaghjian [6]).
- Range gating techniques can be used to entirely eliminate the mutual coupling problem. These techniques are described later in detail.
- Coherently sum two different scans at a pair of Z distances separated by λ/4 into a single, combined pattern. This requires phase correction, which is a particularly effective technique if the AUT is moved instead of the probe antenna. Dual bounce reflections from the probe antenna, scanner mechanism, and facility are quite effectively suppressed by this technique.
- Tilt the scan plane relative to the antenna under test. This will steer the multipath energy away from the antenna boresight axis.

When testing high-gain antennas at high frequencies, the probe antenna gain should also be high to reduce the aperture mismatch loss and reduce measurement time. High-gain probes operate as low-pass spatial filters in the near field, requiring fewer sample points to satisfy the Nyquist criterion. Scalar horns provide low sidelobe levels, implying minimal response to off-axis energy from the AUT and multipath distortions. High-gain probes require better attitude stabilization than low-gain probes but do not require as good x, y positioning accuracy. The Z accuracy requirements are not affected by probe gain. A good probe antenna for most high-gain spacecraft antennas tests is a spare feed horn from that antenna. The feed covers the frequency band, has approximately the correct gain, and usually can provide two polarization measurements simultaneously.

Low-gain probe antennas are used when far-field data are required at larger angles and lower frequencies, because the AUT gain is lower and the scannar may have a limited payload weight capability. For broadband operation the probe can be a log periodic antenna or a broadband horn, although the cross-polarization performance generally is not good.

Spherical near-field ranges almost always require the use of a low-gain probe antenna because the energy often arrives at steep angles relative to the probe boresight axis. Probe correction is more difficult in spherical measurements. Generally a symmetical pattern with good cross-polarization properties is required. For the same reason, cylindrical near-field ranges require a low gain on the azimuth axis. The probe gain along the linear axis may be high, however. The low-gain probe antenna is the most common and must be used for wide-angle far-field data.

Low-sidelobe measurements can be made more easily in the near-field range by using a probe with an on-axis null. This type of probe is similar in design to an autotrack or monopulse feed. The on-axis null reduces the receiver linearity requirements as spatial frequency components corresponding to low sidelobe levels are a larger component of the received signal. Receiver nonlinearities can result in the generation of spatial harmonic and intermodulation distortion products.

Evanescent and mutual coupling energy may appear at very high spatial frequencies. The apparent upper spatial frequency limits for various near-field signal components follow:

Evanescent propagation   infinity
Mutual coupling effects   infinity
Free space propagation   1 cycle/λ
Multipath   1 cycle/λ

Multipath and mutual coupling result from unwanted reflections of the microwave energy. A distinction is made in this book between reflections caused by moving and stationary reflectors. Mutual coupling is defined as reflections between the moving probe antenna, other moving assemblies, and the stationary AUT. Multipath coupling is defined as reflections between stationary objects only. This distinction is made to simplify the analysis of the effects of reflections. For example, propagating multipath energy will always have a spatial frequency no greater than one cycle per wavelength, which is not true for mutually coupled energy.

The probe antenna does not spatially filter the evanescent or mutual coupling energy in a predictable manner. Therefore, measurements usually are taken outside the evanescent region. Likewise, mutual coupling is often suppressed by using a physically small probe antenna, increasing the probe to AUT separation, tilting the scan plane, using multiple scan planes, or minimizing the probe antenna VSWR.

The probe antenna, like the antenna under test, always should be connected directly to an isolator or attenuator. Both the transmitter and receiver may have a significant VSWR. Because the transmission lines and related components also may have some VSWR, the isolator or attenuator should be mounted as close to the antenna as possible. Any VSWR in either the probe or AUT results in multiple reflections (mutual coupling) between the probe antenna and AUT. The probe to AUT multiple reflections can be the most significant of all multipath mechanisms in the near-field environment. The isolators or attenuators can reduce this effect by 10 dB or more.

The mutual coupling effects can also be minimized by summing, with phase adjustments, a pair of scans at two distances separated by $\lambda/4$ (see Chapter 4), or by tilting the scan surface. A tilted scan surface will cause the mutually coupled energy to rotate to an angle different than the AUT beam rotation angle, where it can be filtered out by computer processing (see Table 3.3). For example, if a scan plane is rotated by 10° relative to the AUT boresight axis, the three-trip multipath boresight energy will be rotated to 31.4°:

$$\arcsin(n \sin\theta) = 31.4° \tag{3.4}$$

Table 3.3
Beam Angle and Spatial Frequency Equivalences

Far-Field Half-Angle θ	Spatial Frequency (Cycles/λ) $sin\theta$	Nyquist Sample Interval (λ) $0.5/sin\theta$	Probe Gain (dB)
90°	1.000	0.500	0
60°	0.866	0.577	2
45°	0.707	0.707	4
30°	0.500	1.000	8
20°	0.342	1.462	11
15°	0.259	1.932	14
10°	0.174	2.879	18
5°	0.0872	5.737	24
1°	0.0175	28.649	37
0.1°	0.0017	286.479	58

where

n = multipath to direct path length ratio = 3,
θ = scan plane tilt = 10°.

3.1.4 Scan Pattern

The electromagnetic field must be sampled at discrete points within the synthetic aperture. After defining the synthetic aperture shape, dimensions, and the probe antenna properties, the sampling points on the aperture surface need to be selected. The arrangement and spacing of the points is called the *scan pattern*. The sampling points correspond to the element positions in a phased array antenna. The most common sampling element arrangement is a two-dimensional grid, called a *raster*. The scan pattern needs to meet two constraints:

1. The scan pattern must meet the Nyquist criterion if grating lobes are to be suppressed. The minimum scan density is established by the Nyquist sampling theorem, which states that the phase of any spatial frequency component must shift by less than 180° between adjacent samples.
2. The scan pattern should not be any denser than required by the Nyquist criteria. This will minimize data acquisition time and storage requirements.

These constraints are true whether the scan surface is planar, cylindrical, spherical, or arbitrary (conformal). Violating the Nyquist criteria will result in the generation of grating lobes, causing spurious sidelobe energy in the far-field pattern.

The electromagnetic field is sampled at discrete points within the synthetic aperture. The most common sampling pattern is a two-dimensional grid of points on a planar surface with a $\lambda/2$ spacing. Aliasing can be positively eliminated by sampling at less than $\lambda/2$ and remaining outside the evanescent region. A more efficient technique, useful when far out sidelobe measurements are not needed, is to spatially prefilter the phase front. This can result in a significantly lower sampling density. Spatial prefiltering can be accomplished by appropriate probe antenna selection, as described in the previous section. Typical sampling intervals range from 0.5 to 10λ.

Large radially symmetric antennas generally have radially symmetric phase fronts. One property of the Fourier transform is that the Fourier transform of a radially symmetric function will also be radially symmetric. A relative of the Fourier transform, called a *Hankel transform,* can be used to transform a single radial cut of a radially symmetric antenna into the equivalent far-field pattern.

Real symmetric antennas often have aperture illuminations that are almost perfectly radially symmetric. The phase of any spatial frequency component changes very slowly with the ϕ (clock) angle in a θ, ϕ coordinate system. Because of this, the angular sampling density can be very low. An increase in scanning efficiency therefore can be obtained by acquiring the antenna phase front measurements in a polar reference frame. A relatively low number of rays need to be measured. This scan pattern is defined by a set of rays emerging from a common reference point (see Figure 3.1). This scan pattern, called a *plane polar* or *starburst scan,* can result in a significantly lower sampling density for radially symmetric antennas.

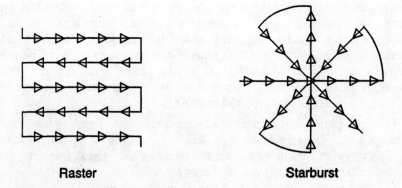

Raster

Starburst

Figure 3.1 Raster and starburst scan trajectories.

The starburst scan often provides a higher scanning efficiency for radially symmetric antennas because the higher order circular Fourier coefficients approach zero very rapidly. Only very low-frequency circular spatial frequency components are significant. This allows a wide angle between sample points without inducing aliasing. A high sampling efficiency is obtained by acquiring the phase front in a polar coordinate system as a set of rays emerging from a common center. The sampling density along a cut is determined by the spatial filter cut-off frequency of the probe and usually varies between 0.5 and 10λ.

The number of cuts in a starburst scan is determined by the symmetry of the far-field radiation pattern of the antenna under test. Typical values used for solid reflectors are 8 cuts for sum patterns and 16 cuts for autotrack patterns. A higher number of cuts may be required for deployable mesh antennas, such as those used on the TDRSS and Galileo spacecraft, due to the periodic gore structure, particularly if sidelobe levels need to be characterized. The required number of cuts can be determined experimentally by comparing far-field results for different numbers of cuts per scan. Typically the number of cuts should be greater than the number of gores. No changes to the far-field pattern should occur if the number of cuts is sufficient. Normally this test is performed by decimating an existing measurement data set.

A starburst data point is radially weighted to normalize the variation in the sampling density across the aperture [1, 2], as the sampling density is lower at the outer edge of the scan. The starburst pattern is more sensitive to overscanning than is the raster pattern, where all measurements are weighted equally (see Table 3.4).

Table 3.4
Comparison between Planar Raster and Starburst Scans

	Raster	Starburst
Large antennas (low-gain probe)	slow	good
Large antennas (high-gain probe)	good	good
Low-gain antennas	good	poor
Asymmetric antennas	good	poor
Wide-angle patterns	good	poor
Measurement speed (6 dB probe)	1 ×	16 ×
pattern	128 × 128	128 × 8
Measurement speed (25 dB probe)	114 ×	170 ×
pattern	12 × 12	12 × 8
Transform time	faster	slower
Process gain (noise reduction)	higher	lower
Transform complexity	lower	higher
Scan alignment requirements	simpler	harder
Robustness	higher	lower

Notes:
1. Starburst scans often take an order of magnitude fewer data points. This is particularly true for low-gain probe antennas, which can result in substantial savings of time and disk space.
2. Starburst scans are quite prone to aliasing and other problems when low-gain antennas are tested.
3. The starburst scan cannot be used for asymmetrical antennas.

It is important that the scan pattern not be excessively larger than the size of the AUT aperture or a reduction of the sidelobe SNR noise ratio will result.

Radial sampling densities need not exceed ($\lambda/2$) + 1 sample for assuming space propagation with no mutual coupling. Sampling densities can be reduced further by using appropriate probe antennas to spatially prefilter the RF energy. Representative starburst scan pattern parameters for various spacecraft and ground antennas are listed in Table 3.5. The listed values are based on the Nyquist sampling criterion, using the probe antenna as a brick-wall low-pass filter.

The following sampling parameters are recommended:

$$\text{Probe gain} = 0.5[\pi/\tan(M/1.03)]^2 \tag{3.5}$$

$$\text{Scan width} = D + P + 2Z\tan(M) \tag{3.6}$$

$$\text{Sample delta} = 0.5(n/n + 1)\lambda/\sin(M) \tag{3.7}$$

$$\text{Number of samples/ray} = \text{sample delta/scan width} = n \tag{3.8}$$

where

D = AUT aperture diameter,
M = maximum far-field angle,
P = probe antenna aperture,
Z = probe to AUT separation,
λ = wavelength.

We assume an AUT brick-wall cut-off at the maximum far-field angle (M).

3.2 FAR-FIELD TRANSFORMATION ALGORITHMS

The transformation of a phase front into an angular spectrum is often called a *near-to far-field transformation*. This is a misnomer because the most common formulations of the transforms do not transform data from one distance to another. Unfortunately, the use of this terminology is so widespread that we shall continue to call it a *far-field transformation*. The transform input and output are at the same location, the location at which the measurements were made. The transform converts only between a phase front and an angular spectrum (i.e., the spectrum of directions in which the energy is traveling) at the same position in space. The transformation results in the equivalent of a far-field pattern because the radiated near-field energy components are always traveling in a straight line at any distance from the AUT.

Table 3.5
Representative Antennas and Starburst Scan Parameters

Antenna	Frequency (GHz)	Diameter (ft)	Maximum Far Field	AUT Gain (dB)	Probe Gain (dB)	Z Distance (ft)	Scan Width (ft)	# Cuts	Sample Delta (in)	Samples/ Cut
SGH	10.70	.25	45°	17	6	.41	.45	8	0.78	10
LANDSAT	15.00	6	5°	47	25	3	7.1	8	4.5	22
ACTS	29.75	9	5°	57	25	5	10.9	16	2.27	60
TDRSS SA	15.00	15	5°	56	25	5	17.4	16	4.51	48
STDN	2.30	210	5°	61	25	50	240	16	29.4	100
Arecibo	430.00	1000	5°	59	25	250	1200	16	157.	92

Two basic types of scans are performed in planar near-field measurements: raster and plane polar (starburst). The relative advantages of each type were previously described.

3.2.1 Raster Far-Field Transform

The raster far-field transform will be described only briefly because it is relatively straightforward. The most common and efficient method uses the *fast Fourier transform* (FFT) to derive a spatial frequency spectrum that is then mapped into an angular spectrum. The procedure is as follows.

1. Perform a 2-D Fourier transform of the measured phase front:
   Input—uniformly sampled phase front;
   Output—measured spatial frequency spectrum.
2. Apply probe correction to the spatial frequency spectrum. In small angles with no cross-polarization components, this is accomplished by dividing the measured spatial frequency spectrum by the probe spatial frequency spectrum. A division in the Fourier domain is equivalent to a deconvolution in the input domain:
   Input—measured and probe spatial frequency spectrum;
   Output—AUT spatial frequency spectrum.
3. Interpolate if required. Interpolation should be band limited and usually is performed by using zero-padding Fourier transform techniques (transform the signal, increase size by appending zeros to the data and inverse transform):
   Input—AUT spatial frequency spectrum;
   Output—AUT spatial frequency spectrum.
4. Convert spatial frequency spectrum to an angular spectrum by mapping through an arcsine function: $f(\theta) = f[\arcsin(kx)]$. For a two-dimensional elevation over the azimuth reference frame the elevation angle is $\arcsin(Ky)$ and the azimuth is $\arctan(Kx/Kz)$, as will be discussed later:
   Input—AUT spatial frequency spectrum;
   Output—AUT angular spectrum.

The fast Fourier transform is a computer algorithm that is quicker than the *discrete Fourier transform* (DFT). The FFT takes advantage of certain redundancies in the DFT by factoring the DFT exponent rotations into powers of 2.

Other transform methods include the DFT and *factored discrete Fourier transforms* (FDFT). These are compared in Table 3.6. The DFT has the advantage of being very simple and flexible with the disadvantage of a significantly slower processing speed. The FDFT transform capabilities lie between the DFT and FFT. Both the DFT and FDFT and will be described further.

Table 3.6
Transformation Techniques Compared

	2-D FFT	FDFT	DFT
Speed	fast	medium	slow
Round-off errors	good	good	poor
Real time	no	possible	no
Multiplexed beams	yes	yes	yes
Vectorization code	yes	yes	yes
x, y, z error compensation	interpolation	partial	yes
Angle output	2-D interpolation	1-D interpolation	yes
Plane polar	2-D interpolation	yes	yes
Zoom area	2-D interpolation	partial	yes

3.2.2 Plane Polar Far-Field Transform

Three basic methods have been developed to transform a plane polar sampled phase front into an equivalent far-field angular spectrum (see Table 3.7):

1. Interpolation and FFT,
2. Weighted FDFT, and
3. Fourier/Jacobi Bessel Expansion.

The first two techniques will be described in some detail starting with the interpolation and FFT technique.

Table 3.7
Plane Polar Transform Methods Compared

	Fourier-Bessel	Interpolation and FFT	FDFT
Speed	medium	fast	medium
Complexity	difficult	medium	simple
Real time	no	no	possible
Multiplexed beams	marginal	yes	yes
Vectorization code	no	yes	yes

Angular Spectrum by Interpolation and FFT

The angular spectrum (far-field response) can be computed from a measured plane polar phase front by interpolation to a raster form. The raster form can then be processed using the previously described 2-D fast Fourier transform method.

This method is used extensively in the processing of radio astronomy visibility data (phase front) into the equivalent brightness function (angular spectrum or far-field response). The phase front is sampled in a variety of ways, one of which is virtually identical to the starburst pattern often used in antenna near-field measurements. These concepts and the related algorithms are described in more detail in. [1, 2]. The production of an angular spectrum by interpolating a polar sampled function onto a raster grid has also been used in synthetic aperture radar to focus the synthetic array [3]. The selection of the interpolation method is critical to the success of this method. The interpolation should be spectrally band limited. Gaussian weighted $(\sin x)/x$ and Lagrange interpolation methods have been used [1, 2, 4].

Plane Polar Angular Spectrum by DFT

The angular spectrum can be determined by a direct integration of the phase front modified by a radial weighting function. This method was used in radioastronomy [1, 2]; however, the interpolation and FFT method proved to be much faster. A significant performance increase, however, can be attained by a partial factorization of the DFT, as described later. The FDFT provides a throughput comparable to the more complex Fourier-Bessel transform technique. Therefore, we will initially develop the DFT formulation.

The transformation of the measured planar raster or plane polar near-field phase-front data into an equivalent far-field K-space response $A(K_x, K_y)$ can be described by the following discrete Fourier transformation:

$$A(K_x, K_y) = \frac{1}{nw} \sum_{j=1}^{n} E(j)W(j)R(j) \tag{3.9}$$

where

$$W(j) = e^{-iK(K_x x(j) + K_y y(j) + K_z z(j))}$$
$$Kz = \sqrt{1 - K_x^2 + K_y^2}, \text{ for } K_x^2 + K_y^2 < 1$$
$$0, \text{ for } K_x^2 + K_y^2 \geq 1$$

$x(j) = x$ probe position for jth measurement,

$y(j) = y$ probe position for jth measurement,

$z(j) = z$ probe position for jth measurement,

$E(j) = j$th measured complex amplitude,

$R(j) =$ area weight (to be defined shortly, but equal to 1 for planar raster scan),

$K = 2\pi/\lambda =$ wavenumber,

$n =$ number of measurements,

w = transform gain (to be defined later, but equal to 1 for planar raster scan),

K_x = horizontal spatial frequency (cycles/λ),

K_y = vertical spatial frequency (cycles/λ),

K_z = depth spatial frequency (cycles/λ).

For conventional planar near-field measurements, $z(j)$ is always zero (as the surface is planar), allowing us to drop the K_z term. With $R(j)$ and w set to 1, the DFT (3.9) transforms a conventional raster data set into a K-space output. Transformation of plane polar data sets requires computing a position-dependent radial weighting term, $R(j)$, to account for the lower sampling density as the radius increases. The weight of each point can be determined from the scan geometry. For the starburst scan, the area associated with each point is shown in Figure 3.2.

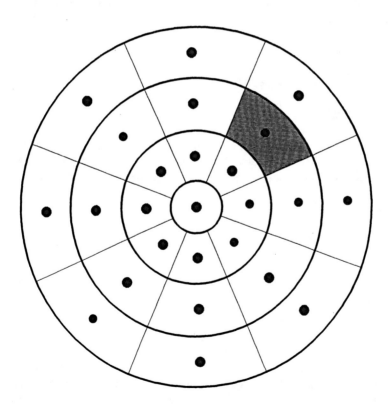

Figure 3.2 Area associated with each point in a starburst scan.

The radial weights for the starburst scan can be derived by solving for the area associated with each point. Ignoring the center point, the area (A) associated with a sample point can be derived by solving for the area of a ring segment centered at the scan origin with a width equal to the sample spacing. The ring area is the difference between two circular areas. The segment area $R(j)$ is the ring area divided by the number of rays:

$$R(j) = \{\pi(r + \delta/2)\}^2/n - \{\pi(r - \delta/2)\}^2/n \qquad (3.10)$$

where

    r = radius to point,
    δ = radial point spacing,
    n = number of rays.

By expanding the terms in (3.10), the equation for the segment area can be simplified to

$$R(j) = 2\pi r\delta/n \qquad (3.11)$$

The center point is a special case, with a weight of

$$R(j) = 2\pi(\delta/2)^2/n \qquad (3.12)$$

The weighting operation affects the gain of the transform. The transform gain (w) can be determined by Parseval's theorem (see Appendix D) or by adding the weights associated with each point. The transform output is divided by the transform gain.

$$w = \sum_{j=1}^{n} R(j) \qquad (3.13)$$

Conversion between Angles and Spatial Frequency

The previously described DFT (3.9) output is in the K-space domain. In general, we want an angle space output corresponding to far-field measurements acquired on a far-field elevation over azimuth positioner. The spatial frequency can be defined in terms of a unit length three-component vector in a right-handed coordinate system with elements K_x, K_y, and K_z. K_x is the horizontal component; K_y is the vertical component; and K_z is the depth component. K_x, K_y, and K_z also are known equivalently as the u, v, and w components. The norm (length) of this vector must be equal to 1 cycle/λ for electromagnetic energy traveling by free-space propagation.

Alternately, the K_x, K_y, and K_z components can be defined in a spherical coordinate system, where θ is the angle of the vector relative to the z axis and ϕ is the CCW clock angle of the vector around the z axis. The ϕ angle is measured relative to the $+x$ axis.

$$K_x = \sin\theta \cos\phi \tag{3.14}$$

$$K_y = \sin\theta \sin\phi \tag{3.15}$$

$$K_z = \cos\theta \tag{3.16}$$

The K_x, K_y, and K_x components can be described in terms of elevation (el) and azimuth (az) angles. An elevation over azimuth geometry, such as in a far-field antenna range, is used:

$$K_x = \sin(az) \cos(el) \tag{3.17}$$

$$K_y = \sin(el) \tag{3.18}$$

$$K_z = \cos(az) \cos(el) \tag{3.19}$$

By relating azimuth and elevation angles to the spherical coordinate system, θ and ϕ can be defined in terms of the azimuth and elevation angles:

$$\theta = \arccos[\cos(el) \cos(az)] = \arccos(K_z) \tag{3.20}$$

$$\phi = \arctan[\tan(el)/\sin(az)] = \arctan(K_y/K_x) \tag{3.21}$$

Conversely,

$$az = \arctan[\tan(\theta) \cos(\phi)] = \arctan(K_x/K_z) \tag{3.22}$$

$$el = \arcsin[\sin(\theta) \sin(\phi)] = \arcsin(K_y) \tag{3.23}$$

By substituting equations (3.17), (3.18), and (3.19) into (3.9), the DFT output will lie directly in the angle space and be fully band limited. Although quite slow, this form of a DFT makes an excellent reference model to which other transform algorithms can be compared:

$$A(az, el) = \frac{1}{nw} \sum_{j=1}^{n} E(j)W(j)R(j) \tag{3.24}$$

---

where

$$W(j) = e^{-iK\{\cos(\text{el})[\sin(\text{az})x(j)+\cos(\text{az})z(j)]+\sin(\text{el})y(j)\}}$$

$x(j) = x$ probe position for jth measurement,

$y(j) = y$ probe position for jth measurement,

$z(j) = z$ probe position for jth measurement,

$E(j) = j$th measured complex amplitude,

$R(j) =$ Area weight,

$K = 2\pi/\lambda =$ wavenumber,

$n =$ number of measurements,

$w =$ transform gain,

$K_x =$ horizontal spatial frequency (cycles/λ),·

$K_y =$ vertical spatial frequency (cycles/λ),

$K_z =$ depth spatial frequency (cycles/λ).

When conventional planar measurements are made, $z(j)$ is zero. In this case, the last term in the exponential can be eliminated. In other cases, retaining the z term can be useful. A constant nonzero $z(j)$ corresponds to a z translation of the measurement plane, leading to the development of holographic back projections (see Chapter 5). Alternately, the $z(j)$ term can be used to compensate for measured scanner z position errors. A first-order correction for x and y position errors can be achieved by passing the measured x and y points directly to the DFT. Full correction requires the determination of the area, $R(j)$, associated with each point. The distorted positions must be close enough to the target positions that the Nyquist sampling theorem is not violated. The processing of nonuniformly spaced plane polar measurements can be considered to be an example of a severely distorted raster scan. The Nyquist theorem in this case is satisfied by spatial prefiltering.

In principle, the $x(j)$, $y(j)$, and $z(j)$ terms can define surfaces acquired on cylindrical or spherical surfaces. Tests to date indicate that this method can be used to process cylindrical and spherical measurements although several unresolved issues remain. A weighting function similar to that used in the starburst transform is required to compensate for the differing sampling densities near the poles of the spherical and cylindrical surfaces.

Factored DFT Algorithm

Although the DFT algorithm has many advantages, the direct two- or three-dimensional integration of the electric field by this method can be very time consuming. Two techniques may be combined for vastly improving the throughput of the basic DFT algorithm while retaining many of the DFT advantages:

1. The angle to spatial frequency mapping is precomputed.
2. The complex weights are factored into a series of uncoupled products.

The DFT can be factored into a computationally efficient form by using a single complex multiplication and addition per polarization in the inner loop. The factorization is used to uncouple the far-field azimuth and elevation angles, allowing independent calculation of the exponential terms. The exponentials can be efficiently combined later with a single complex multiply. For a square matrix output of dimension $N \times N$, this typically results in a reduction of the number of complex exponential calculations by several orders of magnitude from N^2 to $2N$ per iteration. By using a typical output matrix format of 91×91 elements, the complex exponential calculation is reduced by a factor of 45 from 8281 to 182 times per point. The factorization is accomplished by converting an exponent sum into a product of complex exponentials:

$$e^{i(\theta_1 + \theta_2)} = e^{i(\theta_1)} e^{i(\theta_2)} \qquad (3.25)$$

To factor the DFT, it is necessary that the factorization terms be independent. There are several ways of uncoupling the azimuth and elevation angles. For this example we will drop the cos(el) term from equation (3.24). This results in an elevation-dependent azimuth distortion of the transform output, which can be corrected by a series of one-dimensional azimuth interpolations. Z-position correction is limited to small angles although the entire scan plane can be translated readily by an elevation-phase adjustment. Generally, no interpolation is required for all angles on the principal cuts and for elevation angles less than 30°. This form of the partially factored DFT far-field transform is described by

$$A(\text{az, el}) = \frac{1}{nw} \sum_{j=1}^{n} W_1(j) W_2(j) \qquad (3.26)$$

where

$$W_1(j) = e^{-iK[\sin(\text{el})y(j)]} E(j) R(j),$$
$$W_2(j) = e^{-iK\{[\sin(\text{az})x(j)] + [\cos(\text{az})z(j)]\}},$$

$x(j) = x$ probe position for jth measurement,
$y(j) = y$ probe position for jth measurement,
$z(j) = z$ probe position for jth measurement,
$E(j) = j$th measured complex voltage,
$R(j) = j$th measurement weight,
$K = 2\pi/\lambda =$ wavenumber,
$n =$ number of measurements,
$w =$ transform gain.

An example of a factored DFT transform capable of processing both raster and plane polar measurements is listed in Appendix E. This transform implements (3.28) without the large-angle azimuth or Z correction. This program has provided almost identical results as the output of a plane polar Fourier-Bessel expansion. The gain agreement between transforms was within 0.02 dB when using measured spacecraft antenna data over a processed ± 10° span. Contour plots could be overlayed with only a slight disagreement at the −40 dB sidelobe level. The FDFT algorithm provides a simple and efficient solution to many near-field transformation applications.

The factored direct integration transformation for planar near-field measurements, listed in Appendix E, operates as follows:

1. Build a set of two tables containing the normalized spatial frequencies for the far-field azimuth and elevation directions.

$$K_x = \sin(az)$$

$$K_y = \sin(el)$$

Initialize a two-dimensional matrix that will contain the far-field data to zero.

2. Read a data file record containing a pair of amplitude and phase measurements corresponding to the vertical and horizontal components of a given sample point. Also read the xy position where that point was taken. Convert both amplitude and phase measurements into complex voltages.
3. If a plane polar scan pattern was used, apply a weight proportional to the radius to the complex voltages.
4. Build a table of complex weights corresponding to the far-field azimuth angles and the x coordinate of the measurement point.
5. Compute the complex weight for the current y coordinate and a given elevation angle. Multiply this complex weight times the radially weighted voltage measurements.
6. Form the complex products for all combinations of the two complex weights. Add the complex weights to a matrix that will contain the far-field pattern. Return to Step 5 until all y values have been processed. Return to Step 2 until all points have been processed.
7. Output the matrix in whatever form is required for the next program.

3.3 PROBE COMPENSATION

The true angular response of the antenna under test is distorted by the convolution between the AUT and probe angular responses, particularly when high-gain and axial null probes are used or measurements are processed to wide angles. This concept is equivalent to the convolution between the element and array patterns in a phased array antenna.

If the probe orientation in space remains fixed during a scan, the probe response can be deconvolved from the AUT by dividing the complex AUT angular spectrum by the complex probe angular spectrum. This is true for planar near-field ranges but not for cylindrical or spherical near-field ranges.

The angular spectrum is the two-dimensional Fourier transform of the phase front. A convolution of two functions is equivalent to the product of the Fourier transforms of the two functions. The deconvolution is the inverse operation. This operation is known as *probe correction* when the probe response is deconvolved. It is accomplished by dividing the AUT complex angular spectrum by the probe antenna complex angular spectrum.

The probe correction for a scan with a constant orientation probe can be understood more easily through a simple example. Assume that the uncorrected far-field pattern for an antenna under test indicates a relative gain of 20 dB at 5° from the boresight and the probe antenna has a measured relative gain of −3 dB at 5° from the boresight. The −3 dB gain means that the true measurement is 3 dB too low (see Table 3.8). The corrected gain for the antenna under test is simply the difference in levels or for this example 23 dB at 5° from the boresight. A pattern corrected for a typical probe antenna response will be broader than the uncorrected pattern.

Table 3.8
Probe Correction Example (constant probe orientation)

Angle	Probe Gain (g)	Correction (c = |g − 20|)	Uncorrected AUT Gain (G)	Corrected AUT Gain (G + c)
−10°	6 dB	14 dB	−5 dB	9 dB
−5°	17 dB	3 dB	20 dB	23 dB
0°	20 dB	0 dB	50 dB	50 dB
5°	16 dB	4 dB	20 dB	24 dB
10°	4 dB	16 dB	0 dB	16 dB

If the probe antenna has a cross-polarized component, the planar probe compensation (deconvolution) becomes slightly more complex. The near-field measurement is the convolution between the AUT and probe response. A convolution in the near-field domain corresponds to a product in the Fourier domain:

$$I_x = E_p E_{p1} + E_c E_{c1} \tag{3.27}$$

$$I_y = E_p E_{c2} + E_c E_{p2} \tag{3.28}$$

where

I_x = measured principal response,
I_y = measured cross-polarized response,

E_p = true principal AUT response,
E_c = true cross-polarized AUT response,
E_{p1} = probe 1 principal response
E_{c1} = probe 1 cross-polarized response,
E_{p2} = probe 2 principal response,
E_{c2} = probe 2 cross-polarized response.

Equations (3.27) and (3.28) assume that different probes are used to measure the I_x and I_y components. If a single probe is rotated to measure the cross-polarization component, the following equations can be appropriately simplified. Rewriting (3.27) and (3. 28) as a vector matrix product results in

$$\begin{bmatrix} I_x \\ I_y \end{bmatrix} = \begin{bmatrix} E_{p1} & E_{c1} \\ E_{c2} & E_{p2} \end{bmatrix} \begin{bmatrix} E_p \\ E_c \end{bmatrix} \tag{3.29}$$

The actual deconvolved antenna pattern E_p and E_c components can be found by inverting the matrix in (3.29):

$$\begin{bmatrix} E_p \\ E_c \end{bmatrix} = \frac{1}{\delta} \begin{bmatrix} E_{p2} & -E_{c1} \\ -E_{c2} & E_{p1} \end{bmatrix} \begin{bmatrix} I_x \\ I_y \end{bmatrix} \tag{3.30}$$

where

$$\delta = E_{p1}E_{p2} - E_{c1}E_{c2}$$

There are a number of definitions of cross polarization. Three common forms are often known as Ludwig types 1, 2, and 3 [5]. The cross-polarization values of an antenna can be substantially different in the three coordinate systems.

Ludwig type 1 corresponds to a rectangular coordinate system with one unit vector in the direction of the reference polarization and another in the direction of the cross polarization. Planar near-field measurements are of this form.

Ludwig form 2 corresponds to spherical coordinate system in which the unit vectors are tangent to the surface of a sphere. Energy leaving a theoretical dipole antenna would have no cross-polarization component in this coordinate system.

Ludwig form 3 corresponds to what is measured on a conventional far-field antenna measurement range. Because most antenna measurements have been made in this reference frame, Ludwig form 3 is generally the most commonly used definition.

Another form, often used in theoretical work, is called the "E theta E phi" definition. It is the same as Ludwig form 3 except that this form rotates with the ϕ angle.

The probe correction is implemented by transforming the probe measurements into the transform output polarization form (Ludwig form 1) and then using (3.30) to deconvolve the probe response. The result can hence be transformed into Ludwig form 3 or another desired form.

REFERENCES

1. Hjellming, R., *An Introduction to the NRAO Very Large Array,* National Radio Astronomy Observatory, Socorro, NM, 1983. A technical description of the theory and operation of the VLA radio telescope in New Mexico. The VLA in essence is a 20-mile diameter near-field range using a starburst scan pattern. The "antennas under test" are distant stars and galaxies.

2. Thompson, A.R., and J.W. Moran, *Interferometry and Synthesis in Radio Astronomy,* John Wiley and Sons, New York, 1986. Discusses a variety of subjects relevant to near-field measurements, including interferometry, phase coherent receivers, plane polar (starburst) transforms, atmospheric effects, aperture synthesis and geodetic measurements. Highly recommended.

3. Mensa, D., *High Resolution Radar Imaging,* Artech House, Norwood, MA (1981); *High Resolution Radar Cross-Section Imaging,* Artech House, Norwood, MA, 1990. Describes synthetic aperture concepts and the related processing algorithms. It is a classic in the field.

4. Gatti, M., and Y. Rahmat-Samii, "FFT Applications to Plane-Polar Near-Field Antenna Measurements," *IEEE Trans. on Antennas and Propagation,* Vol. AP-36, No. 6, June 1988. Describes a plane polar transformation based on bivariate Lagrange interpolation and FFT processing.

5. Ludwig, A., "The Definition of Cross Polarization," *IEEE Trans. on Antennas and Propagation,* Vol. AP-21, No. 1, January 1973. A classic paper that describes three basic definitions of cross-polarization coordinate systems.

6. Yaghjian, A., "Approximate Formulas for the Far-Fields and Gain of Open-Ended Rectangular Waveguide," NBSIR 83-1689, National Institute of Standards, May 1983. Document provides mathematical pattern models for open-ended rectangular waveguide probes.

7. Repjar, A., *et al.,* "Accurate Determination of Planar Near-Field Correction Parameters for Linearly Polarized Probes," *IEEE Trans. on Antennas and Propagation,* Special Issue on Near-Field Scanning Techniques, June 1988, p. 855. A detailed measurement procedure for probe calibrations.

Chapter 4
MICROWAVE INTERFEROMETER

This chapter describes the RF instrumentation used in near field antenna measurements. The RF system components (source, antennas, cables, receiver, *et cetera*) form a two-path microwave interferometer (shown in Figure 4.1).

The concept of a two-path microwave interferometer is discussed first. This concept is then applied to the vector network analyzer. A discussion of RF sources, phase reference methods, and novel receiver designs follows. We conclude with a discussion of pulse, pulse compression, and SAR radar techniques as applied to near-field measurements.

In near-field antenna measurements, a microwave interferometer (often in the form of a vector network analyzer) measures the interference between a pair of microwave signals that have traveled through two separate paths, only one of which includes the antenna under test. The interferometer output is a measure of the complex gain (amplitude and phase response) of the AUT–probe antenna transmission path relative to a reference path. The near-field measurement system then uses a computer to transform the measured phase-front data to the far-field angular equivalent, producing the desired antenna electrical property measurements. The antenna phase front and far-field angular spectrum are a Fourier transform pair.

Interference occurs when wavefronts traveling through more than one path arrive at a common detector. Interference, as a physical phenomena, works the same way for RF, light, sound, ocean waves, and so on. As the relative path lengths

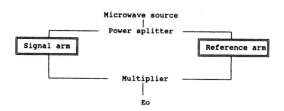

Figure 4.1 Microwave interferometer.

change, the intensity of the signal at the detector output fluctuates in a periodic manner.

Wave fronts can be combined in the detector by addition or multiplication. Interfering ocean waves at the beach and optical holography using photographic film are examples of additive interference. In near-field measurements, a multiplicative technique is used to combine the interfering signals. The multiplicative technique provides much higher sensitivity.

4.1 VECTOR NETWORK ANALYZERS

Many modern near-field measurement systems use a *vector network analyzer* (VNA) to implement a major portion of the microwave interferometer. VNAs are a form of a two-arm interferometer that measures the transmission and reflection characteristics of components providing the results as relative amplitudes and phases. Scalar network analyzers measure the amplitude response only and generally are not suitable for near-field measurements.

A vector network analyzer consists of three basic subsections:

1. Microwave source,
2. Test set,
3. Phase coherent receiver.

The microwave source provides the RF energy for the system. The test set contains two interferometer paths. One path contains the *device under test* (DUT). In antenna measurements, the DUT is the combination of the test and probe antennas. The other path is a fixed reference path. The two paths are combined in the VNA receiver by using multiplicative interference. The receiver output is the amplitude ratio and phase difference between the two interferometer arms.

Figure 4.2 shows a simplified block diagram of a typical vector network analyzer. The source (HP 8340) at the left side of the figure produces the RF test signal. The test set (HP 85XX) splits the RF signal from the source into two paths. One path is routed to the DUT. The other path is routed directly to the reference channel of the receiver. The test set additionally couples energy transmitted or reflected by the DUT to the second channel of the receiver.

The receiver following the test set performs an amplitude and phase comparison between the two RF channels. The network analyzer receiver consists of an IF detector and display processor. The IF detector coherently down converts the DUT signal from the HP 85XX test set to zero frequency with the output in an *inphase/quadrature* (*I/Q*) format. A rectangular to polar conversion of the *I/Q* format within the display processor results in an amplitude and phase output. The IF detector unit operates as follows.

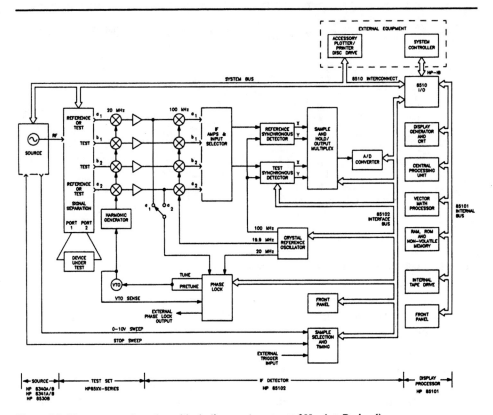

Figure 4.2 Vector network analyzer block diagram (courtesy of Hewlett-Packard).

The reference channel signal from the RF source is down-converted to a 20 MHz IF by a harmonic mixer. After IF amplification, this signal is phase compared with a 20 MHz crystal oscillator. The resultant phase error signal phase locks the LO source located in the test set. The result is that the LO and IF signals are coherently related to the reference signal. The reference IF signal is further coherently down-converted to a 100 kHz IF.

The signal from the DUT is down-converted to a 20 MHz IF in a similar manner using the same LO signal. A second coherent down conversion to a 100 kHz IF is then performed. The 100 kHz IF signal from the DUT channel is combined with the 100 kHz reference signal in a quadrature detector resulting in I and Q outputs.

The display processor is a microcomputer-based unit that sequences the measurements, applies corrections, and then displays the measurements. Additionally, the microcomputer can be used to implement a Fourier transform pulse compression operation that converts the swept frequency measurements into time-domain plots [1]. Figure 4.3 shows a representative postdetection signal processing flow.

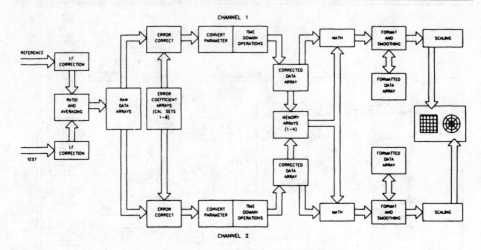

Figure 4.3 Postdetection digital signal processing (courtesy of Hewlett-Packard).

Because of the diversity of vector network analyzer applications, several different types of test sets have been developed. Each has different advantages in antenna measurement systems:

1. *S-parameter test set.* The S-parameter test set normally is used for two-port component measurements. As such, it has two connections (S_1, S_2). Two separate transmission measurements (S_{12}, S_{21}) and two separate reflection measurements (S_{11}, S_{22}) are possible. The separation of these measurement components requires RF switching and a reflectometer bridge. Figure 4.4 shows a representative design. The S-parameter test set has the advantages of being able to completely characterize antenna and component mismatch errors as

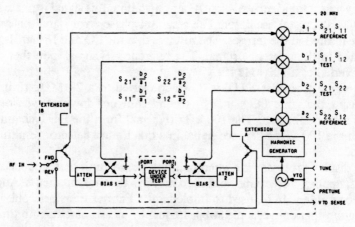

Figure 4.4 *S*-parameter test set (courtesy of Hewlett-Packard).

required for gain measurements and to measure cable flexure effects (gated S_{11} or S_{22} measurements).

2. *Frequency converter.* The frequency converter test set is essentially an *S*-parameter test set with the reflectometer components removed. The frequency converter includes only the first LO and mixers. A representative design is shown in Figure 4.5. The frequency converter test set has several advantages. The frequency converter test set is typically 20 dB more sensitive than the *S*-parameter test set because the reflectometer bridge losses are not present. Three test inputs can be selected without additional hardware. The frequency converter test set is least expensive.

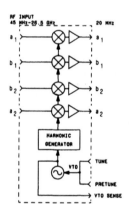

Figure 4.5 RF converter (courtesy of Hewlett-Packard).

3. *Remote mixer configuration.* The frequency converter test set performance can be improved by separating the mixers and placing them near the DUT. This is the basic concept behind the remote mixer configuration [2] shown in Figure 4.6. The remote mixer configuration provides the highest sensitivity when long cables are needed. The mixers can be located near the DUT. Furthermore, the remote mixer configuration supports test frequencies outside of the range of the other test sets. However, in the remote mixer configuration, care is required to ensure that the LO signals to the mixers are extremely well isolated from each other. If not, a leakage signal will be added to the measurements. The leakage signal is produced when the LO signal is modulated at the IF due to lack of mixer isolation in the reference channel. If this modulated LO signal is coupled to the signal channel LO, the lack of mixer isolation will result in coupling to the signal channel mixer IF line. An equivalent path exists in the opposite direction. This problem is easily solved by

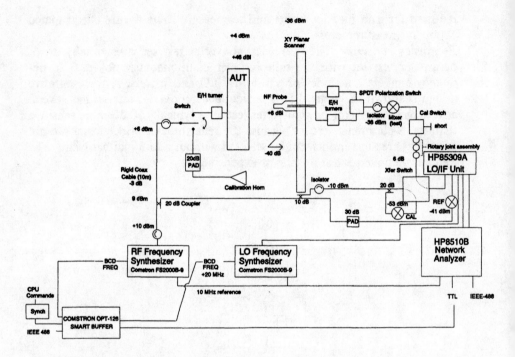

Figure 4.6 Remote figure configuration.

using isolators or LO isolation amplifiers in series with the mixer LO lines, as shown in Figure 4.6.

A path-loss analysis (see Chapter 9) should be performed to determine the minimum test set requirements. Often the addition of a simple RF preamplifier can mitigate the need for a more complex test set. The RF frequency converter configuration is generally best for smaller systems, as it is simple, accurate, and lower in cost than other configurations. Large systems operating at high frequencies often benefit from the remote mixer configuration.

4.2 MICROWAVE SOURCES

A near-field antenna measurement system generally uses a microwave frequency synthesizer to provide the required stable frequency reference to the microwave interferometer.

Millimeter wave test frequencies generally are obtained by using probe or AUT-mounted varactor frequency multipliers driven by a frequency synthesizer.

The multiplier input is often in the X or Ku band (8.2 to 18 GHz) region. This method of obtaining millimeter-wave frequencies has worked quite well and is recommended. This method also is compatible with limited bandwidth cable and fiber optic phase reference links. The preferred frequency multiplier is a simple varactor unit driven by a small solid-state power amplifier. The use of phase-locked loop frequency multipliers is less desirable because they introduce significant phase noise at all frequencies outside of the phase-locked loop bandwidth. This is of particular concern when measurements with a short integration time are made.

High-power *traveling wave tube* (TWT) and other amplifiers generally are not required in near-field measurement systems. The transform process gain (see Chapter 10) can provide a substantial signal-to-noise ratio improvement in the derived far-field data. Excessively low SNR values usually result from incorrect test design, probe selection, or receiver operation. If a noisy power amplifier is used, the phase reference for the receiver should be taken from the amplifier output rather than the input. The power amplifier's phase noise will be better suppressed if the power amplifier is not in one arm of the interferometer.

Other RF sources including Gunn oscillators, IMPATT diodes, and klystrons have been used in the past, particularly in the millimeter frequencies. The use of these devices is discouraged because of amplitude and frequency instabilities. Certain receivers may not correctly phase-lock onto such sources. The successful use of these devices requires careful attention to the path length matching of the two interferometer arms (i.e., the AUT-probe and reference cable path lengths).

The path length match between the two interferometer arms can be determined from swept frequency measurements if a receiver with time-domain capability and compatible source is used. The path length differential is determined by taking the Fourier transform of the swept frequency measurements. This operation, called *time-domain mode* or *pulse compression,* is described later in this chapter (also see [3]). Many vector network analyzers such as the Hewlett-Packard 8510B and 8720 and Wiltron 360 can perform the required pulse compression internally. Some near-field data acquisition programs provide an equivalent pulse compression capability using swept frequency measurements.

When the source is coupled to either the probe or test antenna, care must be used to ensure the VSWR of the device driving the antenna is low. The VSWR of the transmitter can be high, particularly if a varactor multiplier is used. The output of the transmitter must be coupled through an isolator or attenuator to minimize mutual coupling between the AUT and probe antenna. Mutual coupling occurs when energy entering the transmitting or receiving antenna is reflected. An isolator or load instead will absorb the reflected power. A missing isolator or attenuator from either of the antennas may increase the reflection level by an order of magnitude. The receiver should also have an isolator or attenuator at the receiver input for the same reason.

4.3 PHASE REFERENCE CABLE

A single cable is needed to carry a phase reference signal between the moving probe antenna and stationary RF equipment, irrespective of whether the probe is used for transmitting or receiving. The phase and amplitude stability requirements of the phase reference cable are severe. Any change in the electrical length of the phase reference cable during scanner motion is equivalent to a z-plane position error in the scanner; z-plane accuracies of some ultra-high-precision millimeter-wave near-field scanners exceed 0.0002 inch.

Even worse is the tendency of the phase reference cable errors to be systematic with probe position. The systematic errors result in processing errors in the near-to-far-field transformation. For example, the dominant error in a set of measurements of a satellite earth coverage antenna was an excessive variation in the axial ratio when using a linearly polarized probe. In one case, a semirigid cable introduced a systematic phase error of 1° at 44.5 GHz, which corresponds to a path length change of 0.00074 inch.

A variety of methods have been used or proposed to carry the near-field interferometer phase reference signal. The methods can be broadly separated into three categories: direct RF transmission, RF modulated optical transmission, and free-running stabilized oscillators. Some of the methods used or proposed are listed in Table 4.1. Currently, *polytetrafluoroethylene* (PTFE) RF cables and waveguide and rotary joint systems are the most common. Compensated coaxial cables, compensated fiber optic cables, and atomic frequency standards will probably become the popular phase references as the technology develops.

Table 4.1
Methods of Carrying the Interferometer Phase Reference Signal

Method	User
Flexible and semirigid cables	various
Waveguide and rotary joints	various
Compensated coaxial cable	NIST, others
Free-space RF	Bell Labs
Fiber optic cables	various
Fiber optic cables, compensated	LEP, LAPIS
Free-space, optical	none
Free-space, compensated	R&D (LAPIS)
Atomic frequency standard	radioastronomy

Flexible Cables

Flexible cables are the most common phase reference. Semirigid coaxial cable has been used for many years. Semirigid coaxial requires careful placement and validation to ensure a minimum phase error inducing stresses. In addition, semirigid coaxial cable has a relatively high temperature coefficient around 80 ppm/°C.

The newest PTFE cables from various manufacturers generally work quite well. The current generation of PTFE cables largely perform better than semirigid coaxial line. PTFE dielectric flexible waveguides have been developed, which support frequencies in excess of 100 GHz. A representative PTFE cable (P3S01S01) manufactured by Gortex is 0.290 inch in diameter and is made rugged with a spring wrap and polyurethane jacket. This cable provides reasonable low-loss performance with a temperature response of 40 ppm/°C. The cables also are fairly stable with flexing, inducing less than 1° phase change with bending at 5 GHz.

In large systems, other cables can provide a much lower temperature coefficient. As an example, a temperature coefficient of 7 ppm/°C has been reported for a ⅞-inch LDF5-50 foam dielectric Heliax cable [6]. Heliax cable is available with temperature coefficients as low as 2 ppm/°C over moderate (40°C) temperature ranges. These very low thermal coefficients are achieved by a differential thermal action. The copper conductor expands with increasing temperature, causing the physical length to increase. The dielectric constant of the foam dielectric decreases with increasing temperature and the density of the foam determines the inverse temperature coefficient. By correctly selecting the foam density, the difference can result in a cable of very stable phase with varying temperature. This type of cable is moderately stable with flexure, and can be attached to a rigid structure and combined with rotary joints to minimize this error source. A representative FSJ4P-50B, ½-inch diameter cable provides a 10.5 GHz bandwidth with low-loss performance of 9 dB/100 feet at 5 GHz and a temperature coefficient of 7.2 ppm/°C.

Thermal expansion of the phase reference cable can be minimized by using similar types and lengths of cable in both interferometer arms, although much care would be required to ensure similar thermal environments. Generally, a thermally stabilized environment is much better than to match cable lengths for thermal reasons.

Rotary Joints

The success of the waveguide and rotary joint phase reference links is heavily dependent on the quality of the rotary joints. Millimeter-wave tests at 44.5 GHz with rotary joints have shown systematic 5° phase errors. These errors, if stable with time, can be mapped and applied as corrections to the RF measurements. The rotary joint angles can be determined with potentiometers, resolvers, encoders, or simply from a knowledge of the geometry. Others have reported significantly better performance with the rotary joints from specific vendors. Advantages include millimeter-wave operation and moderate accuracy. Disadvantages include rotary joint wear and additional connections with their associated discontinuities.

Rigid cables and waveguide can be used when rotary joints are available. Copper waveguide can be used to provide a thermal expansion coefficient near 16 ppm/°C. Typical losses are 1–2 dB/100 feet. The thermal model is relatively simple, allowing length compensation if the temperature history is known. In large precision near-field systems, the cable or waveguide should be wrapped in thermal insulation.

Free-Space RF

Transmission of the phase reference through free space is an attractive concept. The only known use of this technique for microwave near-field measurements were some early near-field imaging experiments by Bell Laboratories although a beam waveguide variation has been proposed for a submillimeter-wave application. The Bell Laboratories system transmitted the phase reference signal from a small reference antenna. This technique has not been used widely because of receiver limitations, software incompatibility (off-axis phase reference), and potential multipath problems. Another subtle problem occurs from geometric aberrations in the position of the effective phase center of the phase reference antenna. Conversely, this is the most popular technique for far-field ranges and optical holography.

Very strong analogies exist between near-field measurement systems and the VLA and similar systems used in radioastronomy [5]. In the VLA, a phase reference is produced from cross-correlations between antenna pairs. A similar technique has been proposed to measure the system level performance of an EW interferometer system by using near-field methods. Alternately, the free-space system can be augmented with a beam waveguide system.

One advantage of the free-space RF link is the simplicity and low cost of the link and phase measurement receiver. The Bell Labs receiver was simply a crystal detector. The phase information is carried in the additive amplitude interference pattern as sensed by the crystal detector. Hilbert transform techniques can be used to extract both amplitude and phase. The receiver performance is relatively poor, however, because of the large dc bias resulting from the additive rather than multiplicative interferometer design and the lack of a consistent LO signal level.

The advantages of free-space transmission include a virtually unlimited bandwidth and low cost. In certain cases (EW interferometer system test), this method can provide a uniquely simple and elegant solution. Its disadvantages include multipath problems, signal level variations, antenna phase aberrations, receiver limitations, and troublesome geometry.

Fiber-Optic Cable

Fiber-optic phase reference systems are currently in the developmental stage. Performance depends heavily on the careful selection of the fiber optic cable. The phase stability of jacketed optical fibers seems to be similar to that of PTFE cables; however, both are improving with time. As yet unclear is whether fiber optical phase reference systems offer a significant advantage over conventional RF cables made of PTFE.

Fiber optic cables are essentially waveguides that operate at optical rather than microwave frequencies. The fiber optic link operates by amplitude modulating an optical carrier with the microwave reference signal, transmitting the modulated light to another location by means of a fiber optic waveguide, and then converting the modulated light into a microwave signal in a photodetector, as shown in Figure 4.7. The fiber optic link consists of a modulated light source, the fiber optic waveguide, and a photodetector.

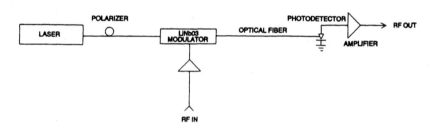

Figure 4.7 Fiber optic link (courtesy of Hewlett-Packard).

The light source is amplitude modulated by the microwave phase reference signal. Either a directly modulated diode laser or a laser modulated by an external electro-optic modulator may be used. The directly modulated lasers are lower in cost and simpler. The indirectly modulated systems have a wider bandwidth, better *signal-to-noise ratio* (SNR), and are more reliable.

The directly modulated InGaAlP (indium gallium arsenide aluminum phosphide) laser diodes typically operate at a wavelength in the vicinity of 1.3 μm with an output power of 50 mW. A laser diode is smaller than a grain of sand and emits the optical energy from a region 6 μm in diameter. The laser diode is modulated by varying the laser current. The laser diode has an impedance of only a few ohms. The RF modulation is usually from a 50 Ω source. The source match is accomplished by a 48 Ω resistor in series with the laser diode, supporting wideband operation. Because of the series resistor, there is approximately a 20 dB coupling loss in microwave energy. The optical fiber is bonded directly to the laser output surface. The fiber accepts energy within a 6 μm area. The fiber positioning relative to the active laser region is extremely critical and performed during manufacture. The coupling loss between the optical fiber and the laser diode is approximately 6 dB. Current direct modulation bandwidths limits are on the order of 6 to 12 GHz, but are rapidly becoming larger. Noise produced by the laser establishes an upper limit on the link SNR. The laser noise power density is on the order of -100 dBm/Hz or -50 dBm over a 100 kHz bandwidth.

Indirectly modulated systems use a separate laser and modulator. The laser can be selected from a variety of choices including diode and neodymium yttrium aluminum garnet (Nd:YAG) lasers. Primary considerations in the choice of laser are its power, wavelength, and stability. Desirable operating wavelengths are near 1.3 to 1.5 μm due to modulator and fiber optic characteristics. Stability requirements are based on allowable phase and amplitude noise in the interferometer. A 40 dB SNR normally is adequate. Laser noise can be further suppressed, if necessary, by feedback intensity stabilization systems.

The high modulation frequency currently limits the choices of optical modulator technologies to the lithium niobate (LiNbO$_3$) modulator and certain variations. The LiNbO$_3$ modulator (shown in Figure 4.8) internally consists of an electro-optical phase modulator and Mach-Zender interferometer that converts the phase modulation into amplitude modulation. Modulation bandwidths are in the range of 10 to 20 GHz.

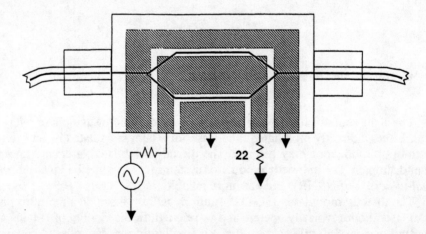

Figure 4.8 Lithium Niobate electro-optical modulator (courtesy of Hewlett-Packard).

The intensity modulated light is transmitted through a fiber-optic cable to the optical receiver. The characteristics of the fiber are of critical importance to the phase reference link. Current evidence suggests that the highest performance is achieved with the single-mode, polarization-maintaining fiber.

Several tests performed at C and X band indicate varying levels of phase instability induced by cable flexure:

1. Single mode fibers are significantly more phase stable than multimode fibers because of mode switching durable cable flexure.

2. Polarization maintaining fibers are more phase stable, according to research in fiber optic sensors. The improved stability is due to suppression of rotation of the single TEM_{00} (transverse electromagnetic) mode.
3. Phase stability is affected by temperature variations, because the glass fiber has a nonzero thermal expansion coefficient. The near-field environment is normally thermally stable. Thermal compensation can be obtained by using similar cables in both arms of the interferometer.
4. Some optical fibers are sensitive to stress. Optical fibers are very small (50 μm) and therefore enclosed in a jacket. The design of the jacket affects the stresses on the optical fiber. Heavily jacketed types with silicone oil seem to provide the best performance, and some brands of optical fiber provide significantly better phase stability than others.

Compensated Fiber Optic Cable

The compensated fiber-optic system is similar to the normal fiber optic link except that the length of the fiber is monitored and corrected in real time. Several different variations exist. A technique used in particle accelerators is an optical equivalent to RF coaxial schemes developed for radioastronomy [7]. Another scheme is used by the proposed LAPIS near-field measurement system [8]. The compensated fiber optic link provides the advantage of very high accuracy and will probably become a preferred method in the future.

Free-Space Optical Methods

Transmission of the phase reference through free space is an attractive concept. This technique currently has not been used because of incompatibility with existing software programs (off-axis phase reference) and complexity. The advantages of these methods include very high accuracy. Their disadvantages include geometry issues, the previously mentioned software problems, inability to fulfill laser safety requirements, lack of sufficient development, and cost. The estimated accuracy is 2.0 ppm of the path length. For a 20-foot scan at 100 GHz, the rms phase accuracy would be approximately 1.4°.

Compensated Free-Space Optical Methods

Atmospheric effects put an upper limit on the phase accuracy of a normal free-space optical link. Variations in atmospheric temperature, pressure, and humidity affect the dielectric constant or refractive index of the atmosphere. The phase accuracy of a free-space optical link in a typical near-field environment is limited to approximately 2 ppm. By using a technique that instantaneously identifies the errors induced by variations in the refractive index, the phase accuracy can be improved to better than 0.1 ppm of the path length. For 20-foot scan at 100 GHz, the phase accuracy would be 0.07°.

The compensated free-space optical link uses multifrequency dispersion measurements to solve for the instantaneous line integral value of the dielectric constant along the free-space transmission path. A variation of this scheme is used in a synergistic combination with a compensated fiber optic system in the proposed LAPIS near-field measurement system [8]. Its advantages include virtually unmatched accuracy, but at a very high cost, laser safety problems, and incomplete development.

Atomic Frequency Standard

The phase synchronization of microwave radioastronomy receivers separated by intercontinental distances has been successfully achieved through the use of atomic frequency standards. An atomic frequency standard such as the Hydrogen maser can achieve a frequency stability of 1 part in 10^{15} or a phase drift of 1° in 277 s at a frequency of 10 GHz.

In near-field measurement, one frequency standard is installed near the probe antenna. A second unit is installed near the test antenna. The units are synchronized while stationary. The accuracy is dependent on time. Its advantages include no multipath problems and unlimited separation. Its disadvantages include high cost and weight and the requirement for frequent calibrations. This method is likely to become common in the future as low-cost, lightweight, ultra-high-stability frequency references are developed.

Electrical Cable Length Measurement

Phase errors due to flexure in a RF or optical reference cable can be directly measured and used to suppress measurement phase errors. This technique has been used in near-field measurements by the National Institute of Standards (NIST), providing an order of magnitude improvement in some cases [15]. Their method was based on introducing a significant mismatch at the far end of the cable and monitoring the phase angle of the reflection with a microwave bridge. Variations and extensions to this basic concept have been used in radio astronomy [4, 5, 16] and to synchronize nuclear particle accelerators [6]. A network analyzer designed by EIP apparently also incorporated cable length monitoring. Such monitoring to improve phase accuracy is likely to become quite popular in the future.

The basic concept behind all electrical cable length measurement systems is the same. A reference signal at one end is transmitted to the other end. The signal at the other end is compared with the transmitted signal. The difficulty is in returning the signal from the far end to the near end so that the signal comparison can be made. Most systems return the far end signal through the same cable, equivalent to an S_{11} measurement.

In the case of S_{11} measurements, one problem is that other reflections within the cable can produce spurious return signals, corrupting the desired signal. This problem is more severe as the cable becomes longer because the distant reflections are differentially attenuated by the cable losses. Consider a phase reference cable that has a 25 dB loss in a given direction. The cable will have a round-trip loss of 50 dB. The issue is even more complex in that the internal cable reflections actually affect the effective cable length in a normal near-field (S_{12}) measurement, but not in the same way as indicated by an S_{11} measurement.

Various schemes have been developed to reduce the response to spurious S_{11} measurement reflections including amplitude, phase, and frequency coding and range-gating. While these schemes improve the measurement quality by suppressing nearby discontinuities, they generally ignore the range-dependent distortion of the discontinuity returns. This issue will be discussed further in this section.

The following is a list of methods which can be used for the measurement of the electrical cable length. The first two methods use a separate return path, the others use a shared return path.

1. Separated return path with a second cable:
   Advantages—Simplicity;
   Disadvantages—Unknown errors due to cable differences.

   - The electrical delay of a cable can be monitored by bringing the signal at the far end back to the near end and monitoring the phase. In one approach, the signal is returned by using a second matched cable. The problem with this method is the general inability to acceptably prove that the cables are suitably matched.

2. Overdetermined multiple return paths [8]:
   Advantages—Synergistic solution accurate in certain cases;
   Disadvantages—Very complex.

   - This system uses a multiplicity of optical wavelength air return paths to solve for a fiber optic cable length. Least-squares methods are used to self-calibrate the system, providing synergistic advantages in a very specific, large, near-field measurement application [8], but it is quite complex.

3. Large discontinuity and RF bridge [15, 17]:
   Advantages—Simple, real time;
   Disadvantages—Low SNR, no rejection of other reflections.

   - This method has been used by NIST providing a 10× improvement in some cases. Their particular implementation was both simple and quite clever. Because there is no rejection or modification of reflections at other positions, this method does not provide a complete cancellation of length errors, particularly when the cable path has a high attenuation loss.

4. Amplitude modulated discontinuity [4]:
   Advantages—High SNR;
   Disadvantages—Care is required to prevent leakage into the primary measurement system and incorrect processing of discontinuities within the phase reference cable.

   - This method is an extension to the third method, where the discontinuity is amplitude modulated. The amplitude modulation serves to separate this discontinuity from others that are not modulated. This method is relatively simple and provides a substantial, although not complete, rejection of unwanted reflections.

5. Transponder, no frequency shift:
   Advantages—Relative simplicity;
   Disadvantages—Stability and minimal rejection of other reflections.

   - In this method, an amplifier and circulator are used to enhance the return from the far end of the cable. This system provides a somewhat stronger return and better SNR than the third method. The performance should be higher than the latter method, although the system is still sensitive to other unwanted reflections. The fourth method will generally provide better results than this technique when long cables are used. Care is required to ensure that the transponder does not oscillate.

6. Transponder frequency shift [5]:
   Advantages—High SNR, rejection of other reflections.
   Disadvantages—Complexity, sensitive to dispersion, incorrect processing of internal cable discontinuities.

   - This type of design can provide a very high accuracy. The system is relatively complex.

7. Range gated discontinuity:
   Advantages—Simple hardware, very high SNR, path compensation possible;
   Disadvantages—Generally non-real-time, unless a fast receiver such as the HTI design, outlined later in this chapter, is used.

   - This method is a modification of a pulse compression time-domain reflectometer. The concept and implementation are generally quite straightforward. A discontinuity is connected to one end of the cable. The other end of the cable is connected to a directional coupler or circulator to allow an S_{11} measurement. The interferometer (network analyzer) is operated in a swept frequency, pulse compression mode.
   - After transforming the swept frequency measurements into a range domain by an inverse fast Fourier transform, the measurements are weighted as a

function of the range loss. In free space, the range loss is simply an inverse square-law function. In the case of the phase reference cable, the range loss is a somewhat arbitrary monotonic function of range. The specific range-loss function can be determined by insertion loss or TDR measurements to various parts of the cable and knowledge of the cable properties. A plot of the weighted return signal as a function of range provides a graphic display of the cable performance and helps localize faults.

- After applying the range-loss compensation, the range-domain signal is Fourier transformed into the frequency domain. The electrical distance to the discontinuity is subtracted by a phase derotation. The residual phase (in the frequency domain) provides a direct measure of both the absolute delay and dispersion.

- This method is relatively simple to implement and provides extensive information about cable quality. The accuracy is high because of the correct range-loss compensation and the high process gain within the system. A representative accuracy with a modern network analyzer would be approximately 0.2°.

4.4 PHASE REFERENCE THERMAL COMPENSATION

Significant phase errors even can occur with a cable having a thermal stability of 7 ppm/°C. With a 75-foot path length typical of large systems, a 1°C temperature change over the measurement time will result in a 0.001-inch change of path length. Some improvement can be gained by wrapping the cables in thermal insulating material. Thermally induced errors can be minimized by decreasing the measurement time and improving the facility thermal control. For example, destratification fans or ducting can be used. The effects of vertical temperature gradients can be reduced by minimizing the length of vertical cable segments. The effective measurement time can be further minimized through the use of tie scans, as will be described below. Other potential sources of thermally induced problems are high RF power levels and the associated power dissipation in the cable.

As an example, a representative near-field measurement system is thermally stabilized with a diurnal variation ±2°C. The maximum temperature rate of change is approximately 4°C/6 hours or 0.66°C/hour. A scan takes 6.8 hours to complete. A temperature change of 4°C is possible during the scan. For this large system, the length of the phase reference cable to the probe is approximately 100 feet, and the AUT cable adds another 50 feet for a total cable length of 150 feet. With a temperature coefficient of 7 ppm and a 4°C temperature change, the effective cable length can change by 0.05 inch. This corresponds to an electrical phase change of 18° at X-band.

In this system, a single vertical line scan takes 40 s to complete. During this time period, the temperature could vary by as much as 0.0073°C. The thermally induced variation in cable length would be 9.2×10^{-5} inches or 0.033 electrical degrees. By allowing the drift to occur and correcting it by a tie scan, the phase drift during an entire scan can be effectively suppressed. The maximum phase error after the tie scan is the sum of the following terms.

1. The thermally induced phase noise during a 40 s vertical cut is 0.033° at 11.803 GHz.
2. The thermally induced phase noise during a 2.8 min horizontal tie scan is 0.064° at 5.3 GHz. Assuming the temperature is changing at a constant rate, this term can be substantially reduced by performing two measurement cuts in opposite directions and coherently averaging. This effectively suppresses any thermally induced phase shifts with constant rate of change.
3. The receiver phase noise during the tie scan must be very low. Unlike in a conventional near-field scan, no process gain is present in the tie scan. SNR of 60 dB is required to maintain a 0.06° phase noise level. While this SNR is relatively easy to maintain in the regions where the aperture is well illuminated, this is generally not possible over the entire region. Several solutions are possible:

   • Do not apply the correction when the SNR is below an acceptable level;
   • Decrease the receiver noise bandwidth by decreasing the IF bandwidth, increasing averaging, *et cetera;*
   • A thermal model can be developed by performing bidirectional tie scans at a periodic rate (five minute to one hour intervals). The sample rate is based on the Nyquist sampling theorem. Because a thermally insulated cable has a very long time constant, a low sample rate is suitable. By using an amplitude weighted least-squares fit, one can solve for a cable phase history. The thermal model is then used to apply a time-based phase correction to the measured near-field data. The least-squares measurement residual provides a direct measure of the model accuracy.

4.5 MICROWAVE RECEIVERS

The microwave receiver is a critical part of the near-field interferometer. The receiver measures the complex (amplitude and phase) response of the probe-AUT combination. A variety of receiver designs have been developed to measure the near-field phasefront:

1. Vector network analyzers; for example, Hewlett-Packard 8510B, HP-8720, Wiltron 360.
2. Antenna range receivers; for example, Scientific Atlanta 1795, 1780, Orbit.
3. Special designs; for example, Hilbert transform based receivers, phase modulated interferometers, homodyne receivers, crystal detector receivers.

The vector network analyzers are the most commonly used receivers. These analyzers currently provide very high quality *continuous wave* (CW)-measurements at rates of up to 2000 measurements per second. Multifrequency measurements generally are much slower because of synthesizer tuning limitations and receiver phase-lock time. With fast switching synthesizers, measurement speeds approaching the CW speed are possible. The synthesizer tuning slew rate must be limited to ensure that the receiver remains in the phase-lock state.

Specialized receiver designs can be used for very high throughput or low cost [8–10]. Low-cost, high-performance, high-accuracy phase measuring receivers suitable for many antenna and *radar cross section* (RCS) measurement applications can be built quite easily. These receivers are based on a superheterodyne design with digital IF signal processing. *Hilbert transform-based receivers* (HTR) or self-calibrating *phase modulated interferometry* (PMI) techniques (see Table 4.2 and Figures 4.9 and 4.10) are used to derive the quadrature signal component. These receivers use a minimum of hardware, primarily a mixer, a phase shifter and a computer interface. The receiver IF and baseband signal processing is purely via computer software.

Low-cost homodyne receivers using a zero (dc) IF have been used in some systems. Although the design is outwardly similar to the much higher performance Hilbert transform and PMI designs, the homodyne receiver does not perform nearly as well, because of dc leakage, drift, and excessive $1/f$ noise at the dc IF.

Although not obvious, a crystal detector receiver can provide both amplitude and phase information through additive interferometry. The crystal detector receiver's primary advantage is its very low cost; however, it suffers from the same problems as homodyne receivers.

This section will concentrate primarily on the Hilbert transform-based receiver, phase modulated interferometer, and crystal detector receiver designs. The ideal receiver inputs, with microwave signals at the test frequency, are the signal channel and the reference channel. The ideal receiver outputs, digital data to com-

Table 4.2
Typical Phase Modulated Interferometer Performance (6 GHz, 5 ms integration)

Parameter	Value	
Amplitude stability	0.01	dB/hr
Phase stability	0.2	°/hr
Amplitude noise	0.01	dB rms
Phase noise	0.2°	rms
Linearity	0.001	dB/dB
AM-to-PM conversion	0.01	°/dB
PM-to-AM conversion	0.10	dB
Dynamic range	75	dB

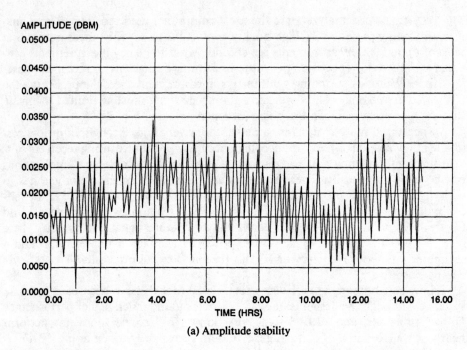

(a) Amplitude stability

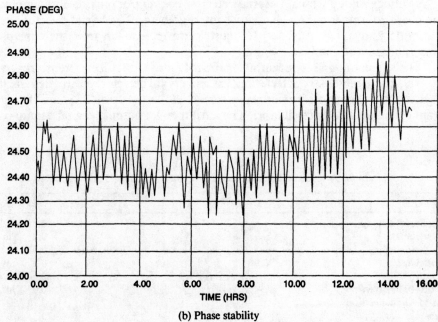

(b) Phase stability

Figure 4.9 PMI receiver amplitude (a) and phase (b) stability over a 15 hour interval, HP 8672 source.

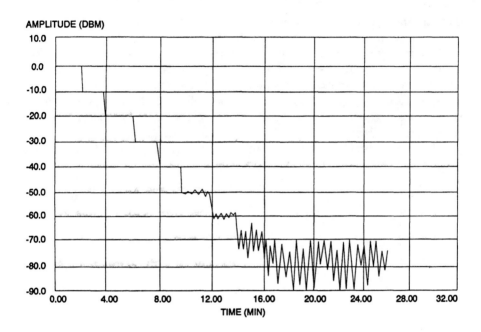

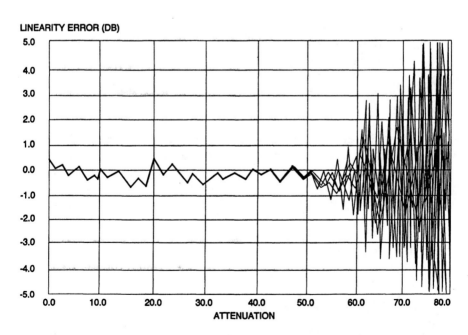

Figure 4.10 PMI linearity plots. Periodic structure in plot (a) is due to test attenuator nonlinearity.

puter, are the signal channel to reference channel amplitude ratio, and the signal channel phase relative to the reference channel.

The receiver output is a phasor corresponding to the complex ratio between a signal channel input phaser and a reference channel phasor (see Chapter 2). As the input from both is real, the required complex phasors can be developed by Hilbert transforms of the input signals. The Hilbert transform (Appendix D) is mathematically equivalent to a broadband 90° phase shifter or quadrature hybrid, and it is used to derive the quadrature signal component.

The ideal amplitude and phase measuring receiver has the following transfer function:

$$\text{Amplitude } (t) = 20 \log |\mathbf{E}(t)| \text{ (dB)} \tag{4.1}$$
$$\text{Phase } (t) = \arg [\mathbf{E}(t)]$$

where

$$\mathbf{E}(t) = \frac{S(t) + iH[S(t)]}{R(t) + iH[R(t)]}$$

and

$$S(t) = \text{signal channel input,}$$
$$R(t) = \text{reference channel input,}$$
$$t = \text{time,}$$
$$i = \text{square root of} -1,$$
$$H(f) = -i \text{ sgn}(f) \, G(f) \text{ (Hilbert transform),}$$
$$f = \text{RF.}$$

The complex division of the signal channel by the reference channel results in a measure of the DUT transfer function. If the reference channel signal is constant in amplitude, the complex division can be replaced by a complex conjugate multiplication (see Chapter 2). A balanced mixer then can be used as a multiplier to form the product of the two RF signals. Figure 4.11 shows the fundamental concept behind many phase measurement receivers.

We will first discuss a swept frequency receiver design using a Hilbert transform to derive the quadrature signal component. We then extend this design to a CW interferometer using PMI techniques.

4.5.1 Hilbert Transform-Based Receiver Designs

The Hilbert transform-based receiver is a digital IF single-sideband (SSB) super-heterodyne receiver optimized for swept frequency antenna and RCS measurement

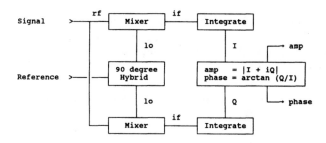

Figure 4.11 Basic coherent receiver block diagram.

[8]. This type of receiver is capable of making multifrequency or swept frequency measurements at rates exceeding 100,000 measurements per second. Several design variations exist. The receiver IF and product detector stages are implemented largely in computer software, resulting in a minimum amount of hardware. The lack of hardware means high performance, accuracy, flexibility, and low cost.

The Hilbert transform-based receiver is functionally quite simple (see Figure 4.12), consisting of only a few hardware components. The internal operation of the HTR is most easily understood by analyzing it in the context of a microwave interferometer. The main interferometer RF components include a computer-controlled RF source and a balanced mixer. The two mixer input ports (signal and LO) are connected directly to the signal and reference channels. The reference channel serves as the mixer LO signal and is provided by the microwave source. The mixer IF output is amplified, digitized, and further processed within the computer system.

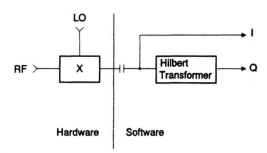

Figure 4.12 Hilbert transform-based receiver.

A microwave interferometer measures the interference pattern resulting from a microwave signal that traveled through two separate paths. In this case, the signal path is through the AUT-probe combination and the reference path is from the synthesizer to the mixer LO input port. The interference occurs at the point where the two signals are recombined. The recombination of the signals to produce the interference pattern can be achieved by addition or, in this case, multiplication. The combined signal is called an *interferogram*.

We initially assume that the signal path is longer than the reference path and that the two interferometer paths will be combined multiplicatively in a balanced microwave mixer. Both the signal and reference paths start at the frequency reference shown in Figure 4.13.

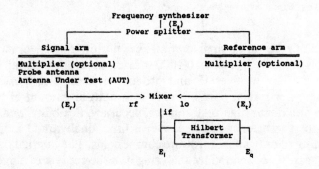

Figure 4.13 Hilbert transform-based microwave interferometer.

The frequency synthesizer produces a cosinusoidal voltage waveform (E_s) as a function of time:

$$E_s = \cos(2\pi f t) \text{ (reference signal)} \qquad (4.2)$$

where

f = RF frequency,
t = time

The receiver input signal is the transmitter output signal modified by the effects of the path length (time delay) and path (insertion) loss. The phase shift due to path length will be 360° or 2π rad per wavelength of path length. The receiver (mixer) input signal therefore will be

$$E_r = K_r \,[\cos(2\pi f t) \quad \text{(path loss and transmitting signal)}$$
$$+ \, 2\pi R_r/\lambda] \quad \text{(path length)} \qquad (4.3)$$

where

K_r = signal path loss,
λ = wavelength,
R_r = signal path length.

The LO (reference) signal to the receiver is similar to the received signal, except that the path length and loss values are different:

$$E_t = K_t \, [\cos(2\pi ft \quad \text{(path loss and transmitting signal)}$$
$$+ \, 2\pi R_t/\lambda)] \quad \text{(path length)} \tag{4.4}$$

where

K_t = LO path loss,
R_t = LO path length.

A balanced mixer can be modeled as a multiplier forming the mathematical product between the RF and LO ports with a scale factor or conversion loss (K_m). The inphase (I) mixer output (E_i) is

$$E_i = K_m E_t E_r$$
$$= K_m K_t \, [\cos(2\pi ft \quad \text{(reference signal)}$$
$$+ \, 2\pi R_t/\lambda)] \quad \text{(lo path length)} \tag{4.5}$$
$$K_r \, [\cos(2\pi ft \quad \text{(received signal)}$$
$$+ \, 2\pi R_r/\lambda)] \quad \text{(signal path length)}$$

Using the cosine product rule,

$$E_i = .5 K_m K_t K_r \qquad \text{(sum frequency)} \tag{4.6}$$
$$\{\cos[4\pi ft + 2\pi(R_r + R_t)/\lambda]\}$$
$$- .5 K_m K_t K_r \qquad \text{(difference frequency)} \tag{4.7}$$
$$\{\cos[2\pi(R_r - R_t)/\lambda]\}$$

The upper sideband is in the microwave spectrum and is not passed by the IF preamplifier; therefore, only the difference frequency is used. E_i can be rewritten using $\delta = R_r - R_t$ to symbolize the interferometer path length differential between the signal and LO path lengths:

$$E_i = -0.5K_mK_tK_r\,[\cos(2\pi\delta/\lambda)] \tag{4.8}$$

Equation (4.8) states that the mixer output voltage is equal to the amplitude of the received signal multiplied by the mixer conversion loss and the cosine of the phase difference between the received signal and the LO signal. This is equivalent to the dot product between the two signal phasors. The mixer output voltage is equal to the real in-phase (I) signal component of the interferogram signal.

The separation of the amplitude and phase information requires additional information in the form of an imaginary (quadrature) signal (E). This signal can be derived in a manner similar to the previously derived in-phase signal (E_i):

$$E_q = -0.5K_mK_tK_r\,\sin(2\pi\delta/\lambda) \tag{4.9}$$

The quadrature (Q) signal is similar to the I signal except that a sine function is used instead of the cosine function. The I and Q signals form a complex vector whose magnitude is the amplitude of the signal. The phase angle of the signal is the arctangent of the Q signal divided by the I signal.

The quadrature signal can be derived in a variety of ways. All methods involve some form of a 90° phase shifter (quadrature hybrid, dome filter, Hilbert transform, *et cetera*). The methods can be separated into hardware and software techniques. These hardware methods are used:

1. A quadrature hybrid and a second mixer can produce the quadrature component. There are several variations on this theme with varying levels of complexity. Figure 4.11 shows this type of system. The approach generally is used in network analyzers. Its disadvantages include high cost and low accuracy.
2. The transmitting signal or receiver input can be phase modulated or serrodyned. By appropriately synchronizing the receiver output to the serrodyning signal, the quadrature component can be extracted. This concept will be discussed later.
3. A dome filter can be used at the mixer output if certain conditions hold; for example, no negative frequencies can be present. This method is similar to the Hilbert transform method described next but has several disadvantages.

The primary software method is based on the Hilbert transform. This method (Appendix D) can be used to analytically derive the quadrature component from the I channel signal if negative frequency components can be suppressed. The method is quite simple, accurate, and very effective. Its use was demonstrated in an ISAR radar [18].

Receivers based on the Hilbert transform can provide first-rate performance at a very low cost although, because of the negative frequency restriction, some care is required in their use. This type of receiver provides a very simple and elegant solution when fast multifrequency measurements are required. An extension (PMI), described later, provides conventional CW measurement capability. The simpler multifrequency concept will be discussed first.

The Hilbert transformer is a broadband, 90° phase shifter operating on the I channel mixer output. The Hilbert transform is implemented numerically in the digital computer and defined for a function of $G(f)$ as $H(f)$ where f is a frequency and i is the square root of -1.

$$H(f) = -i \operatorname{sgn}(f) G(f) \qquad (4.10)$$

The Hilbert transform is described in more detail in Appendix D. Correct operation of the receiver requires the absence of all negative frequency components. Because the Hilbert transform shifts all frequencies by 90°, any energy at a negative frequency would incorrectly appear to be positive. Negative frequencies correspond to clockwise rotating phasors. In swept frequency interferometer measurements, no negative frequencies are present if the following constraints are met:

1. The signal path is longer than the reference path.
2. Swept frequency steps are small enough to eliminate aliasing due to path length. The frequency step is small enough when the phase of the longest path length component changes by less than 180° per frequency increment. The maximum frequency step size (f) must be less than

$$f = c/2\delta$$

For example,

$$f = 4.918 \text{ MHz} \qquad (4.11)$$
$$\delta = 100 \text{ ft}$$

3. If the probe is in motion during the test, the sum of the most negative spatial frequency and the positive IF produced by the path differential should be positive. Generally, this is no problem.

Given no negative frequencies, the Q channel is simply the Hilbert transform of the I channel. The Hilbert transform operates by suppressing the negative frequencies in the real I channel output. This can be shown by remembering that the Fourier transform of a real (I) signal must be even symmetric. Likewise the Fourier transform of an imaginary (Q) signal must be odd symmetric. The Hilbert transform multiplies the negative frequencies by -1 resulting in a change from an even to an odd function of frequency. The sum of the Fourier transform of a real signal and its Hilbert transform results in the suppression of all negative frequencies. This can be shown by forming the sum:

$$G(f) + iH(f) = \begin{cases} 2G(f), f > 0 \\ G(0), \quad f = 0 \\ 0, \quad\quad f < 0 \end{cases} \tag{4.12}$$

The inverse Fourier transform of this sum is a rotating phasor consisting of I and Q parts and called an *analytic* or *preenvelope signal*. The analytic signal is a rotating phasor that when converted to polar form, provides the amplitude and phase of the received signal as a function of frequency.

Hilbert transform methods still can be used in certain cases, even when the nonswept (CW) measurements are performed. For example, the Hilbert transform can be used in the spatial frequency domain instead of the temporal frequency domain. The requirement here is to ensure no negative spatial frequencies. For narrow angle antennas, this can be done by tilting both the test and probe antennas. The probe antenna can be further used as a spatial filter to reject any negative spatial frequencies. The I channel near-field measurements are Fourier transformed in only two dimensions. Because the measurements are real, the transform output is even symmetric on both axes. The transform output corresponding to the negative spatial frequencies is zeroed. The result is the far-field pattern at one-quarter scale.

In another variation, the I channel measurements are acquired only in two measurement planes separated by ¼ λ. The measurements are phase corrected and processed by a 2-D FFT, resulting in the far-field pattern. Additionally, this method suppresses the axial multipath; it is discussed later in this chapter and in reference [11].

4.5.2 Phase Modulated Interferometry

In the swept frequency version of the Hilbert transform-based receiver, the path length difference between the two interferometer arms results in the generation of an IF signal shifted in frequency away from dc. The dc drift, leakage, and $1/f$ noise can be readily suppressed by an IF filter. The HTR is a form of a superheterodyne receiver.

In the latter two receiver configurations using CW spatial domain Hilbert transforms, the measurements are essentially acquired with a homodyne (IF at zero frequency) receiver. As was previously mentioned, the homodyne receiver suffers from excessive dc drift, leakage, and $1/f$ noise. A simple solution is to AM or PM modulate the RF signal at a rate beyond the $1/f$ corner frequency (typically 1 to 100 kHz). This concept with some extensions leads to the development of the phase modulated interferometer. The PMI is a general-purpose receiver supporting both CW and multifrequency operation (see Figure 4.14). The multifrequency operation is handled by the previously described Hilbert transform method.

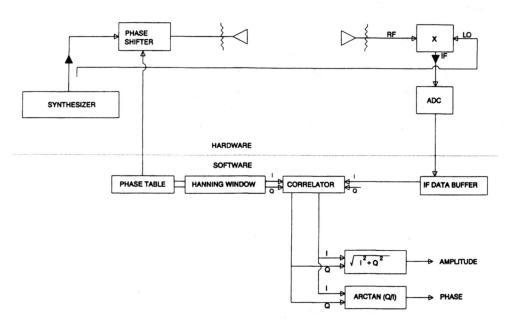

Figure 4.14 Phase modulated interferometer.

Negative spatial frequencies can be up-converted to an appropriate IF devoid of $1/f$ noise by swept frequency unequal path length interferometry techniques or, alternately, through the use of a computer-controlled phase shifter. The phase shifter is used to introduce a frequency shift into the interferometer resulting in an IF beyond the $1/f$ noise break frequency. The phase shifter is not required for swept frequency measurements as the system reverts to a Hilbert transform-based configuration.

For a PMI CW interferogram to contain no negative frequencies, the phase shifter step size must be less than 180°, and the doppler shift of the sum of any spatial frequency and the IF frequency produced by the phase shifter should be positive during scanner motion. As in the swept frequency case, this generally is no problem.

The receiver input is coupled to a balanced or harmonic mixer. The mixer LO is provided by the same microwave frequency synthesizer that drives the transmitter. The transmitter signal passes through a digitally controlled phase shifter.

The phase shifter is used to "serrodyne," or frequency shift, the transmitter signal. The amount of frequency shift is equal to the receiver IF, nominally 20 kHz. The serrodyne operation shifts the phase at a constant rate equivalent to a frequency offset of the transmitter. The serrodyne is accomplished by driving the phase shifter with a sawtooth or staircase phase command. A minimum of three phase states is required, although four or more phase states may be used, depending on specific computer algorithms. If error spectrum methods are used (these will be described later) as many as 32 states may be required.

Phase shifter VSWR variations as a function of the commanded phase shift can result in a power variation at the mixer LO port. The LO power variation can leak into the IF port due to poor mixer isolation. This leakage is coherent and appears as a bias at the receiver output. The spurious IF leakage can be coherently suppressed in the computer but drift is likely.

A better solution is to fully eliminate coherent LO power variations by installing the phase shifter in series with the transmitter rather than the LO side of the interferometer. Additionally, an isolator or a broadband amplifier is installed between the source and phase shifter input. This problem and solution is similar to LO leakage problems encountered in remote mixer VNA configurations.

The mixer output corresponds to a coherent down conversion from the microwave center frequency to the serrodyne or IF frequency, nominally 20 kHz. Sidebands in the mixer IF output are induced by the doppler-shifted AUT energy as sensed by the moving near-field probe (see Chapter 2). The mixer output is in either real or complex form, depending on whether a balanced or quadrature mixer was used. In either case, the received energy spectrum is centered at the serrodyne frequency with doppler components at both positive and negative frequency offsets. Positive doppler frequencies correspond to plane wave far-field components and result in decreasing range during probe travel.

The mixer output is passed to a data acquisition computer that uses a software correlator to suppress receiver errors. A Hanning or Kaiser-Bessel weighted integrate and dump IF filter is used instead of a more conventional IF filter with an exponentially mapped past response. The integrate and dump correlator more closely approximates the ideal matched filter response for the dynamically moving probe antenna. The receiver sampling rate is 100 kHz.

The mixer may have systematic errors including dc bias and nonlinearity caused by mixer compression. Differential IQ gain-phase (circularity) errors also are introduced if a *quadrature IF mixer* (QIFM) is used. Furthermore, the phase shifter has frequency and phase shift dependent gain and phase linearity (circularity) errors. These errors can be identified and suppressed by several different methods:

1. Hilbert transform calibration,
2. Statistical methods,

3. Least-squares methods,
4. Error spectrum methods.

Hilbert transform methods can be used for precisely determining the phase shifter weights (phase and amplitude values) for a series of temporal or spatial frequencies. The receiver is calibrated by operating in the previously described HTR mode and monitoring the receiver output while selecting different phase states. The derived weights then are used to orthogonalize (circularize) the phase shifter commands and QIFM (if used). The phase shifter and QIFM weights can be separated by first orthogonalizing the phase shifter using the I channel and then determining the QIFM quadrature errors. Residual circularity errors in either device can be handled by orthogonalization matrices.

Alternately, the phase shifter weights and orthogonalization matrix can be determined statistically. Random noise is introduced into the system. Lack of circularity at the receiver output can be readily detected. A quadrature gain unbalance exists when the integrated I and Q noise powers are different. A phase unbalance exists when the integrated sum of the I and Q noise voltages does not equal the integrated difference between the I and Q noise voltages.

Least-squares methods can be used to orthogonalize the receiver if the computer controlled phase shifter is built as a series of decoupled binary weights. This method is used in a precision vector network analyzer [12].

Receiver circularity, nonlinearity, and various bias errors can be detected by transforming the phase modulated IF signal into an error domain [13] via a Fourier transform process. By transforming the measurements into an error domain, uncorrupted measurements can be separated from the errors.

The receiver output is transformed into the error domain by applying a ramp function in-phase angle to the transmitted signal and performing a Fourier transform of the mixer output. The mixer output as a function of phase shift and error space are a Fourier transform pair. The error spectrum can be derived from the mixer outputs (either I or I and Q) by a complex Fourier transform:

$$E(n) = \int f(\Phi)\, e^{-i2\pi\Phi n}\, d(\Phi) \qquad (4.13)$$

where

$E(n)$ = energy at nth harmonic,
$f(\Phi)$ = receiver mixer output,
Φ = commanded phase angle,
n = serrodyne harmonic ratio,
i = square root of -1.

The phase ramp results in the generation of a frequency shift resulting in the production of a *single sideband* (SSB) signal by the phasing method with the opposite sideband suppressed (if a QIFM is used). Circularity errors in both the phase modulator and QIFM (if present) result in the loss of sideband suppression. Under ideal conditions, the mixer output is a real (I) signal (if a balanced mixer is used) or a complex (I/Q) signal (if a QIFM is used) of the receiver input shifted to a 20 kHz center frequency (IF).

With a fixed-frequency, constant-amplitude receiver input, the receiver's IF output should be a constant amplitude vector rotating at a constant rate corresponding to the SSB offset (serrodyning) frequency. The complex Fourier transform of this rotating vector should result in energy only at the SSB offset frequency produced by the phase shifter. Any errors in the QIFM mixer or phase shifter result in a modulation of the length of the rotating vector resulting in the generation of energy at spurious frequencies. Gain and phase errors in a QIFM will result in the loss of sideband suppression and appear in the error spectrum at the image frequency. Bias errors appear in the spectrum at dc. Receiver nonlinearities are revealed as harmonic distortion lines in the spectrum. The noise level between serrodyne harmonic lines corresponds to the receiver noise level. Phase shifter errors result in a broadening of the error spectral lines and the production of spurious spectral lines (see Figure 4.15).

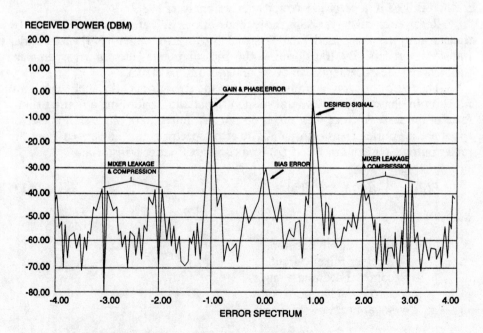

Figure 4.15 Example of an error spectrum derived by a Fourier transform of a SSB signal. The X axis scale corresponds to the serrodyne harmonic number.

Better separation of the error spectral lines is possible if the data are convolved with a window function. The window function is used to minimize the effects of truncating the received IF signal. The window minimizes crosstalk between the transformed error spectral lines. The receiver currently uses a Hann (or Hanning) window, but a Kaiser-Bessel window will probably be used in the future as it has somewhat better sidelobe characteristics.

Suppression of receiver errors, in principle, can be accomplished by transforming the measurements into an error domain, filtering out the errors, and then performing the inverse transform. Note that all negative serrodyne frequencies, which are all error terms, are set to zero. As shown earlier, this is equivalent to performing a Hilbert transform that results in the production of a pure analytic or preenvelope (I/Q) signal. The resultant error free IF signal can then be down converted to dc resulting in an uncorrupted I/Q signal.

Some care is required to make this method work well as the error spectrum can become distorted by unmodeled terms. For example, phase shifter step size nonlinearities introduce high-order harmonics and harmonic sidebands into the error spectrum. This effect can be reduced by predistorting the phase shifter commands or by individually orthogonalizing the measurements at each phase state.

If the voltage response is required for only a single error line, the Fourier transform can be efficiently replaced by a complex cross-correlation. The first harmonic of the serrodyne frequency corresponds to the center of the uncorrupted receiver output. The exponential term in the Fourier transform is a complex weight. Using de Moivre's theorem, the Fourier transform can be rewritten as

$$E(n) = \int f(\Phi) \ W(\Phi)n \ d(\Phi) \qquad (4.14)$$

where

$W(\Phi)$ = phase shifter complex weight,
  = $e^{-i2\pi\Phi}$ (commanded value).

This cross-correlation function is between the mixer output and the Hann or (Hanning) weighted, commanded phase shifter angles. The cross-correlation technique is quicker and easier to perform, and it is used in the PMI receiver instead of a full Fourier transform. Additionally, the correlator can be slightly chirped for better acceptance of the doppler sidebands.

The microwave phase-front measurements can be distorted by a doppler beam sharpening induced by the motion of the RF probe (see Chapter 2). The off-axis AUT spatial frequencies are differentially attenuated according to the frequency response of the receiver error suppression filter that establishes the IF bandwidth. This is equivalent to a convolution between the AUT spatial frequency spectrum and the IF response. The effective probe directivity is increased because the sharpening of the doppler beam decreases the effective probe beamwidth along the direction of travel. The result is an erroneous reduction of sidelobe energy off the boresight axis. This effect results in a modification of the far-field angular spectrum similar to that caused by the angle-dependent gain of the probe antenna.

The doppler beam-sharpening distortion can be minimized by selecting an error-domain filter with a response that is flat over all measured spatial frequencies. The previously mentioned chirp correlator can provide a flat response. Equivalently, the doppler beam sharpening can be removed by a deconvolution similar to that used in "probe correction."

The width of both the desired signal and error lines in the error spectrum are the sum of several effects. These include gain and phase nonlinearities in the receiver and the doppler bandwidth of the near-field data. Receiver phase nonlinearities result in the generation of FM sidebands and are caused by hardware tolerances in the QIFM and phase shifter. The near-field data bandwidth is established by the doppler shift of the spatial frequencies produced by the AUT-probe combination. The highest possible near-field doppler frequency, f_d (assuming no evanescent or multipath effect) is simply the velocity measured in wavelengths (cycles) per second:

$$f_d = v/\lambda \tag{4.15}$$

where

v = scan velocity,
λ = wavelength.

For a near-field range operating at 26.5 GHz with a scan velocity of 24 in. per s, the maximum doppler frequency is 54 Hz. To separate the uncorrupted measurement from the receiver errors, the error energy should not overlap the measurement energy. The error spectrum line is broadened by both the receiver phase nonlinearities and the near-field doppler signal components. The serrodyning frequency must be at least twice the doppler frequency corresponding to the highest spatial frequency of the AUT. If this rule is violated, the width of the lines in the error spectrum will be larger than their spacing, and the uncorrupted measurement cannot be separated from the errors.

4.5.3 PMI Hardware Design

The hardware design of a Hilbert transform-based receiver or PMI system is straightforward (see Figure 4.16). The following components are required:

1. Balanced or harmonic mixer,
2. Phase modulator (PMI configuration only),

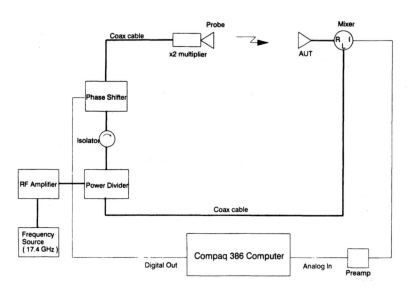

Figure 4.16 A 34.8 GHz phase modulated interferometer used in a millimeter wave near field antenna measurement system.

3. IF preamplifier and integrator,
4. Computer interface,
5. Miscellaneous RF components (isolators, power splitters, *et cetera*).

Mixer

Both the HTR and PMI receivers use a balanced or harmonic mixer to convert the RF signal to an IF signal. Harmonic mixers can be used in millimeter-wave systems. The mixer RF input should cover the frequency range of interest and allow an IF between dc and 1 MHz.

Phase Modulator

A computer-controlled phase modulator or shifter is required in the PMI configuration but not in the HTR configuration. The phase shifter should cover the LO frequency band. The required phase shifter resolution depends on the particular calibration method used and the harmonic ratio if harmonic mixers are used. A representative computer-controlled phase shifter manufactured by RHG covers 2 to 26 GHz with 5 bits of resolution. The phase switching time is less than 1 μs.

IF Preamplifier

The IF signal from the mixer needs to be amplified and filtered prior to the analog-to-digital (A/D) conversion. In the case of the PMI, the IF is equal to the serrodyning rate. In the case of the HTR, the IF is a function of the path difference and frequency slew rate. In both cases, the IF amplifier should be ac coupled with a high-pass filter so that dc biases and $1/f$ noise are rejected. The preamplifier gain is typically between 10 and 500. Additional IF channels can be used if multiple receiver channels are simultaneously used to record multiple antenna polarizations or beams.

The best receiver performance will occur when the sampling is synchronous and the IF amplifier output is integrated over the frequency step interval (HTR) or phase step interval (PMI). This results in a matched filter response with excellent out-of-band rejection.

Computer Interface

The computer interface digitizes the IF signal and controls the phase shifter, if CW, or synthesizer, if multifrequency measurements are made. The computer interface uses *direct memory access* (DMA) techniques to achieve a high throughput and minimize timing jitter. The high conversion rate increases the IF, resulting in less $1/f$ noise. The high throughput also is required to support continuous path operations. A representative computer interface is either a DMA A/D converter and DMA parallel-port board set or a DSP processor board. Digital signal processing boards that can digitize at 320 kHz are readily available. When combined with a Comstrom synthesizer, 320,000 frequency measurements per second can be acquired. Table 4.3 shows some comparisons.

Table 4.3
Representative Configurations

	Broadband 2 to 26 GHz Receiver	*34.8 GHz Millimeter-Wave Receiver*
LO frequency	Same as test frequency	¼ of test frequency
Mixer	Norsal DBM 1-26	Spacek Labs 2M28-35
Phase shifter	RHG QDD2-26 phase shifter	RHG QDD2-26

Multiple receiver channels are easily added by paralleling additional mixers and preamplifiers. To maintain high performance, a DSP or array processor should be added to the computational system.

Variations of PMI techniques have been used in optical interferometry. Figure 4.17 shows an example of such a system. The frequency source is a laser. The test and reference beams are separated by beam splitters. Lenses are used to convert spherical phase fronts to planar phase fronts and *vice versa*. The phase shifter is implemented as a piezoelectrically displaced mirror. Interference is by additive methods in an imaging photodetector array.

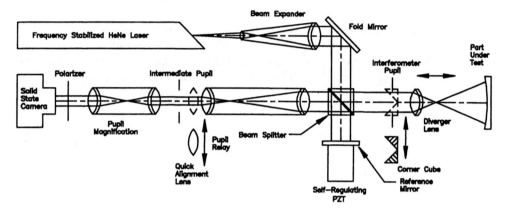

Figure 4.17 Optical phase modulated interferometer (courtesy of Breault Research Organization).

4.5.4 Crystal Detector Receiver

A very simple design for a near-field phase measurement receiver consists of nothing more than a crystal detector connected to a preamplifier. The preamplifier output is digitized by an A/D converter connected to the data acquisition computer. The concept behind this receiver is very similar to the concepts used in optical holography. Both the holographic film and crystal detector measure power. The phase information is imbedded in a fringe pattern caused by the interference between an object phase front and a reference phase front.

A variety of designs are possible. As an example we will examine the configuration in which the crystal detector and probe antenna assembly are illuminated simultaneously by the AUT and an off-axis reference antenna. The phase reference signal must be coupled into the same input as the probe antenna signal as the detector has only a single RF input. The phase reference signal can be carried by a cable, but, in this case, it will be supplied by an additional reference antenna near the AUT.

This design, although very workable, has several disadvantages: lower sensitivity, certain restrictions on the test geometry, and a somewhat involved computer processing. The latter two points relate to the use of the Hilbert transform to derive the phase information. The lower sensitivity is due to the amplitude mismatch between the AUT and reference signals. The crystal detector receiver must meet the following requirements to provide valid amplitude and phase information:

1. The reference beam power incident on the detector must always be greater than the signal power, because this will prevent loss of phase information created by a loss of RF detector bias.
2. The reference beam must come from an angle greater than any angle from which energy from the AUT arrives—this must be true for all probe positions—as it is required to ensure that all received spatial frequencies are positive (a requirement of the Hilbert transform that will be used to produce the analytic signal).

The crystal detector provides a voltage output proportional to the square root of the incident power. The incident power is the sum of the object signal (AUT) and reference signal power. The RF measurements are converted into an equivalent phase front by a variety of methods.

4.6 RADAR IMAGING AND MULTIPATH SUPPRESSION TECHNIQUES

The identification and suppression of facility multipath errors by radar techniques is an attractive concept rarely applied to near-field measurements. This will change in the future. Additionally, multipath within an antenna can be observed providing additional insights to the antenna operation. Three types of radar processing for the imaging, identification, and suppression of multipath will be described: pulse radar, pulse compression radar, and synthetic aperture radar.

Pulse Radar

A pulse radar operates by transmitting a short pulse and plotting the received signal as a function of time. For example, assume that a 1 ns wide pulse with a 1 GHz bandwidth is being transmitted from an antenna under test. A 1 ns pulse propagating at the speed of light in free space will have a width of 1 foot. If the received signal level is plotted as a function of time a peak will occur at the delay time corresponding to the direct path. In this example, multipath energy appearing at delays separated by more than 1 foot can be suppressed.

The input to the receiver can be enabled for the instant that the direct signal arrives and inhibited at all other times, suppressing the multipath signal. The primary disadvantages of this technique are the difficulties in rapidly enabling and inhibiting the receiver and the decreased SNR caused by the narrow pulsewidth.

Pulse Compression Radar

The pulse compression radar uses swept frequency chirp techniques to overcome the problems of producing and detecting short pulses and the attendant loss in SNR. This method is used by most vector network analyzers (time-domain mode) and certain other receivers.

Synthetic Aperture Radar

Mutual coupling can be identified by observing fluctuations in the receiver output as the probe antenna is moved toward the antenna under test. The movement of the probe antenna along the z axis produces a synthetic aperture form of endfire array antenna. Multipath signals can be significantly reduced by coherently processing a pair of near-field scans separated by $\lambda/4$; other forms of SAR processing can also be used.

The first two techniques suppress signals that arrive at delays other than the main path. An important parameter is the path length resolution, which is directly related to the bandwidth of the pulse or frequency sweep. One common definition of pathlength resolution is simply the propagation velocity divided by the signal bandwidth. For example, a microwave signal with a swept frequency bandwidth of 4 GHz allows a path length resolution of 3 inches. We cannot have high-range resolution with a narrow bandwidth antenna.

The advantages of range gating are as follows:

1. Range gating techniques can effectively eliminate multipath signals, mutual coupling, and reflection problems. The use of range gating techniques for far-field antenna measurements has been successfully demonstrated with the HP-8510 network analyzer.
2. Radar techniques can identify the actual reflection paths, particularly if both down-range and cross-range (SAR) techniques are used.
3. Pulse compression range gating techniques can provide phasefront information simultaneously at numerous frequencies. This can eliminate the need for repeatedly scanning an antenna under test.
4. The microwave interferometer receiver may be simplified to only an I channel design because the phase information may be readily recovered by a Hilbert transform.
5. Intentional multiple propagation paths within antennas can be resolved if the antenna bandwidth is sufficient.

The disadvantages of range gating are as follows:

1. Radar adds another level of complexity to the near field measurement system. To solve this problem, a swept frequency pulse compression range gate can

be implemented using a fast frequency or sweeper synthesizer and a Hilbert transform-based receiver. The largely software-based Hilbert transform-based receiver is composed of a mixer, preamplifier, and A/D converter. The phase is derived mathematically through the use of a Hilbert transform. This approach actually requires less hardware than in the CW case.

2. A narrow antenna transmission bandwidth will prevent the radar from achieving a reasonable range gating resolution, as it is impossible to obtain high-range resolution with a narrow band antenna. To solve this problem, use CW SAR techniques such as staggered Z scans [11] or CW SAR variations that develop a cross-range resolution. The latter case is closely related to conventional near-field measurements except that subapertures are processed.

3. Smearing of the phasefront is likely if the swept frequency pulse compression techniques are used during scans. To solve this problem, the previously described swept frequency interferometer design can measure 300,000 frequencies per second. A frequency sweep can be completed in a few milliseconds. This design is an extension of the previously described Hilbert transform-based receiver.

4. The receiver SNR will be reduced with a short integration time; however, postintegration processing in the transform will recover the loss in SNR.

5. Certain antennas, such as log-periodic designs, are frequency dispersive. The dispersion will distort the radar pulse causing a loss of range resolution. However, pulse dispersion in antennas can be handled readily by modifying the pulse compression algorithm, resulting in the full theoretical path-length resolution.

6. Real-time swept frequency range gating cannot be implemented on ranges by using existing receivers because they will not remain phase-locked during a fast sweep. To solve this problem, the existing receiver can be replaced with a very simple, low-cost Hilbert transform-based receiver design, which contains no phase-locked loops. Alternately, the phase-locked loop can be bypassed by using a coherently related LO frequency synthesizer.

The range gate width and delay needs to be set to pass the desired energy and reject unwanted multipath energy. Some multipath energy occurs within an antenna and *must not* be suppressed. The identification of different multipath mechanisms is discussed in Chapter 9. Range gating techniques should not be used unless the multipath mechanisms are well understood.

There are two basic techniques for range gating: pulse gating and pulse compression. Pulse gating equipment can be added to any system without changes to the receiver or software, although some sensitivity and dynamic range is lost. Pulse compression techniques require only software changes if a swept frequency receiver system is used. The pulse compression technique generally provides better performance and resolution, although most network analyzers are not fast enough to efficiently acquire swept frequency data.

Pulse gating systems consist of a pair of fast rise time (1 to 5 ns rise time) RF switches controlled by a pulse generator. One RF switch is connected in series with the transmitter; the other RF switch is connected in series with the receiver. The pulse generator sends a pulse to the transmit switch followed by a pulse to the receive switch. The pulse timing is adjusted so that the gated direct path transmitting energy passes through the receiving switch during the time when it is enabled. The multipath energy arrives at a different delay after the switch is closed. The pulse compression technique is generally simpler and can provide much better range resolution when broadband antennas are tested.

Swept frequency measurements can provide near-field phase-front measurements at many different test frequencies. A more important use, however, is measuring and suppressing multipath energy by pulse compression methods. In this technique, a multifrequency measurement set (or interferogram) is acquired at each measurement point by using a swept frequency interferometer.

Effective use of swept frequency pulse compression techniques in a near-field measurement system requires a high throughput, beyond the capability of current network analyzers. Swept frequency pulse compression interferometers are capable of measuring 300,000 frequencies/s. Typically 100 to 500 frequencies are used in a pulse compression operation. This number allows acquisition of a complete interferogram in 0.3 to 2 ms. Computer processing then performs the pulse compression and range gate operations. A block diagram of a high performance swept frequency interferometer is shown in Figure 4.18.

This swept frequency microwave interferometer is an unequal path length design that generates an interference pattern between the signal (AUT-probe) and LO (reference) paths. By using a longer arm in the signal channel of the interferometer and a suitable frequency step size, only positive frequencies as required by the Hilbert transform will be produced.

The system operates as follows. The RF can be either stepped or continuously swept, providing nearly identical results as the mixer output is sampled at discrete times. A longer receiver integration time can be used in the stepped mode, providing a slight increase in SNR. In this case, the computer sends a series of uniformly spaced frequency commands to a fast Comstrom frequency synthesizer while digitizing the mixer output. The mixer input is connected to the DUT. The mixer LO signal, corresponding to the interferometer reference channel, is provided by the microwave source. The mixer forms the mathematical product between the received and LO signals. This product is an interferogram in the form of a time series. The interferogram corresponds directly to an in-phase (I) channel receiver IF signal. The quadrature signal component will be derived in the computer by a Hilbert transform.

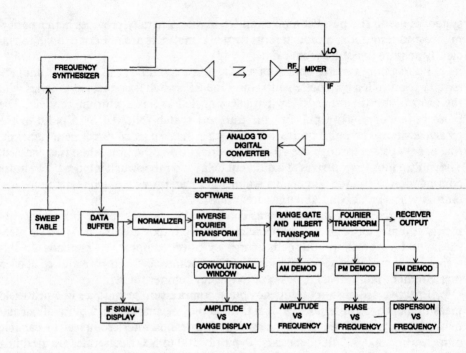

Figure 4.18 Swept frequency, pulse compression interferometer.

The mixer output is only a function of the insertion loss, the relative path length, and the wavelength of the microwave signal. If the microwave signal is linearly stepped in frequency, a sampled cosine wave will be produced at the mixer output. The swept frequency chirp as functions of RF and path length are a Fourier transform pair. The I channel receiver output for a constant path length during a linear RF sweep will appear to be a constant frequency sine wave. Longer paths correspond to higher frequency sine waves. Dispersion, if present, will cause the sine wave frequency to change during the sweep time. An inverse Fourier transform is used to convert the constant frequency to an equivalent $(\sin x)/x$ pulse in the path-length domain. A convolutional window (typically Kaiser-Bessel) then can be applied in the path-length domain to reduce the path-length sidelobes of the compressed pulse. This operation is known as *pulse* or *range compression* [3, 9, 13].

The quadrature (Q) channel of the chirp (swept frequency) signal can be derived by a broadband 90° phase shifter operating at baseband because no negative frequencies are present. In this case, the broadband 90° phase shifter is implemented in digital form by a Hilbert transform after transformation to the path-length domain. The signal magnitude can be plotted as a function of path-length delay. This type of plot corresponds to the time-domain plots obtained from vector network analyzers.

Multipath energy can be suppressed by applying an appropriate range-gate window in the path-length domain. Next a Fourier transform of the path-length domain signal is computed, resulting in a multifrequency range-gated data set. This data set is an analytic or preenvelope signal containing I and Q components. The analytic signal is a rotating phasor that, when converted to polar form, provides the amplitude and phase of the received signal as a function of frequency.

The amplitude of the analytic signal corresponds to the DUT frequency response at the measurement point. The derivative of the phase of the analytic signal with respect to frequency provides a measure of the group delay of the RF path. The group delay measurement is particularly useful in tracking the phase center of broadband antennas. For computational efficiency, the IFFT, Hilbert transform, range gate, and FFT can be replaced by an appropriate digital filter.

Amplitude and frequency errors in the received signal created by source errors, cable errors, and antenna dispersion can be corrected by a complex multiplication between the received signal and a complex weighting function. This operation is similar to SAR focusing, except that this operation focuses the pulse compressor [1]. Alternately, the test frequencies can be spaced nonuniformly to compensate for the frequency-dependent dispersion delay.

4.6.1 Time-Delay Imaging

Time-delay imaging can be accomplished by converting a near-field measurement system into a FMCW SAR radar. If range gating is combined with near-field measurements, far-field performance measurements and holographic images corresponding to different delay times and frequencies can be computed. In addition to sorting the energy arrival by azimuth and elevation, one can simultaneously sort the energy by path delay time and frequency, which can be useful in identifying both antenna and test facility anomalies.

Time-delay imaging can be accomplished by making a set of multifrequency transmission measurements with the previously described swept frequency interferometer at each point. The multifrequency measurements are range gated. A single frequency is extracted and processed by conventional near-field methods. A representative multifrequency data set might consist of 256 frequencies at each point of a 50×50 element scan (640,000 measurements). Alternately, conventional near-field methods can be used in conjunction with a pulse gating system, although the performance will generally be lower. Properly understood and used, this type of system can provide keen insight into the operation of antennas and more control and rejection of multipath disturbances.

4.6.2 SAR Processing

The pulse and pulse compression techniques enable us to sort different path lengths. Similarly, synthetic aperture radar techniques can enable us to sort different energy arrival directions. The basic near-field measurement is a certain form of a two-dimensional CW SAR radar (see Chapter 2). Although not common, SAR techniques can be used with CW signals [9]. One advantage of CW SAR techniques is their inherent compatibility with narrow bandwidth antennas. Examples of relevant CW SAR techniques include

1. Conventional near-field testing;
2. Staggered Z scanning for multipath suppression;
3. SAR imaging (RCS testing, anechoic chamber multipath imaging, far-field range multipath imaging, EMI leakage imaging).

All of these CW SAR techniques can be combined with pulse or pulse compression waveforms to provide path-length gated versions. The elimination of multipath and clutter by pulse and pulse compression processing can provide a substantially higher SNR.

An unusual CW SAR technique, called *staggered z* or *volumetric scanning,* can be used to substantially reduce axial mutual coupling between the near-field scanner and the antenna under test. This technique is of particular value in testing low sidelobe antennas. A 25 dB reduction of the axial mutual coupling interference has been achieved by this method for a small planar phased array antenna [11], see Figures 4.19 and 4.20. In a certain sense, this method operates by forming a synthetic aperture endfire probe antenna.

In one variation of this method, the AUT is scanned normally although the probe antenna or AUT is moved between two alternate positions separated by $\lambda/4$ along the axial direction. The axial direct-path signal component is shifted in-phase by 90° as the probe and AUT are separated by $\lambda/4$. The mutual coupling signal is shifted in-phase by 270° as separation between the probe and AUT is increased by $\lambda/4$. The increased phase shift for the mutual coupling component is caused by the energy traveling three times between the probe or scanner and AUT for the first reflection.

The set of measurements can be processed so that the direct signal component is coherently added while the multipath signal component is coherently subtracted. A phase adjustment of 90° on the component shifted $\lambda/4$ causes the direct-path measurement phase to be the same as the unshifted component. Conversely, the 90° phase of the axial multipath component results in a signal shifted by 180° relative to the unshifted component. Coherently summing these phase adjusted measurements cancels the axial mutual coupling component. Alternately, the mutual coupling signal component can be extracted by coherently subtracting the phase-adjusted data sets.

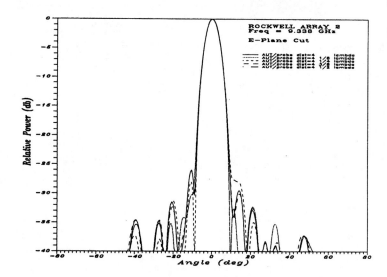

Figure 4.19 This plot shows a series of *E*-plane cuts of a small phased-array antenna taken at different probe separation distances. (Note: The differences in the traces are due primarily to axial mutual coupling between the AUT and probe-scanner.)

The staggered *z* scan technique works well on the near-field boresight axis (see Figure 4.20). As the angle from the near-field boresight increases, the suppression efficiency decreases and, at certain larger angles, can become worse than unsuppressed measurements. This method generally works well in planar near-field measurements, as the axial mutual coupling component is generally much larger than the wide-angle multipath component. The suppression efficiency as a function of the angle from boresight is directly related to the pattern of a synthetic two-element endfire probe antenna. A real aperture version of this probe antenna could be designed (using a pair of spatially staggered elements and a quadrature hybrid or a reflector) that would provide a very low mutual coupling with a conventional near-field measurement system.

4.6.3 SAR Imaging

The near-field measurement system, with minor modifications, can be used as a radio camera to identify multipath and leakage sources within an anechoic chamber or a far-field measurement system. It also can be used to measure the phase flatness in the quiet zone of a compact or far-field range or for CW RCS measurements. A variation of this technique is described in [9]. Small, portable near-field measurement systems as described in Chapter 6 are best suited for this application.

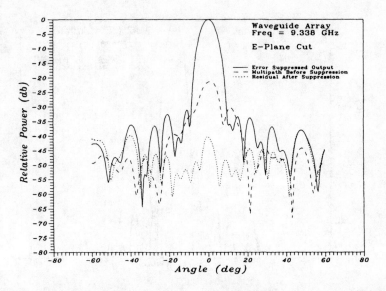

Figure 4.20 This plot shows a far-field *E*-plane cut after axial multipath has been suppressed by the staggered *Z* scan technique. (Note: The middle trace shows the multipath component that was suppressed. The lowest trace shows the residual uncompensated multipath error. This latter trace was derived by repeating staggered *z* scans at different *z* distances.)

A conventional near-field measurement system can be considered a form of two-dimensional CW SAR radar. The grid of sampling points form a two-dimensional synthetic aperture antenna array. The uniformly illuminated aperture used in near-field antenna measurements must be modified into a low sidelobe design by tapering the illumination at the aperture edges. This is handled by the additional step of applying a Kaiser-Bessel or similar window function [14] as a function of spatial position to the DUT measurements. The scan pattern can be of virtually any type, including planar raster, plane polar, cylindrical, and spherical. The sample positions correspond to element positions in a synthetic aperture phased array antenna.

A representative test would be performed by placing a planar scanner in the quiet zone area. The scan plane would be tilted slightly (5°) in azimuth and elevation relative to the predicted phase front to allow viewing internal receiver leakages. The network analyzer would be connected to make an S_{12} or S_{21} measurement between the distant source antenna and the scanner mounted probe antenna.

The measurement software is configured for the test by selecting a Kaiser-Bessel or other window function for tapering the synthetic aperture. The procedure at this point would be very similar to conventional near-field processing. The raw near-field measurement data set could be plotted and is equivalent to the phase-front in the probed region. The near-field plots typically are scaled to a full-scale range of a few dB, as opposed to the typical 40 or 50 dB ranges when used for conventional antenna near-field measurements. The phase range also tends to be quite small ($\pm 10°$). X and Y cuts could be used to measure the phase curvature in the test region.

The far-field (Fourier) transform then would be used to convert the measured phasefront into an angle or K space representation. As a significant difference from conventional near-field processing, the data into the Fourier transform must be tapered by a window function to suppress sidelobes in the synthetic aperture.

The output of the transform would be the received energy in either angle or K space. An ideal anechoic chamber should show a small illuminated region slightly off boresight (see Figure 4.21). A beam precisely on-axis would correspond to a coherent on-axis leakage source, receiver quadrature unbalance, or often an LO leakage in a remote mixer configuration. Beams at other angles would be caused by reflections from lights, supports, walls, and so on.

If the transform output is in angle space, we can read the direction of an interference path and transfer the coordinates to a theodolite. The theodolite, when

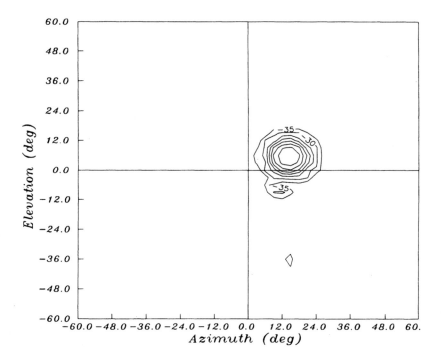

Figure 4.21 Image of a "clean" chamber.

positioned at the scanner position and aligned with the scanner reference frame, will point along the interfering path. The K space mapping is somewhat like a fish-eye-lens image of the same thing. There should be no energy outside a K space circle of radius one. If energy is present, it is created by a multipath mechanism.

Figure 4.22 shows the performance of a degraded anechoic chamber. The desired energy from the illumination horn arrives from the upper right-hand quadrant. The energy at the exact center corresponds to a severe RF leak within the receiving system. The xy scanner was tilted intentionally to allow this leakage signal to be observed. The lower peaks correspond to reflections from a mounting panel, and the upper peaks correspond to the location of a light fixture.

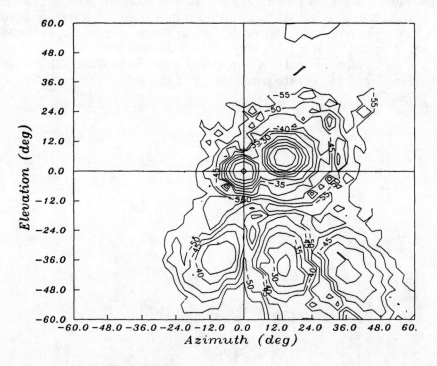

Figure 4.22 Image from a "dirty" chamber.

Other applications of this technique include imaging EMI and other leakage sources in structures, avionics, and other electronic equipment. This technique can be combined with the previously described time-delay imaging technique to provide multipath images at different path delay times. Additionally, holographic processing can be used to further project the field to other locations.

REFERENCES

1. *Using the Option 02 Time Domain Software for the Model 360 Vector Network Analyzer,* AN360-6, Wiltron Corp, Morgan Hill, CA, 1989. Discusses time-domain processing in vector network analyzers.
2. Boyles, J., "Choosing the Proper Mixing Technique for Antenna Testing," Microwaves and RF Magazine, March 1988. Discusses harmonic and remote mixer VNA configurations.
3. Stimson, G., *Introduction to Airborne Radar,* Hughes Aircraft Co, El Segundo, CA, 1983. Probably the best introductory book covering phasers, Fourier transforms, pulse compression, synthetic apertures, and other related concepts.
4. Swarup, G., and K.S. Yang, "Phase Adjustment of Large Antennas," *IRE Trans. Antennas Propag.,* Vol. AP-9, pp. 75–81, 1961. Discusses a method for correcting errors in phase reference cables.
5. Thompson, A.R., and J.W. Moran, *Interferometry and Synthesis in Radio Astronomy,* John Wiley and Sons, New York, 1986. Book discusses a variety of subjects relevant to near-field measurements, including interferometry, phase coherent receivers, atmospheric effects, aperture synthesis, and geodetic measurements. Highly recommended.
6. Schwarz, H., and J. Weaver, "The RF Reference Line for PEP," *IEEE Trans. on Nuclear Science,* Vol. NS-26, No. 3, June 1979. Describes a phase stabilized reference line for a nuclear particle accelerator. The phase stabilization technique is directly applicable to stabilizing the near-field phase reference line. This technique is used by the EIP receiver.
7. Peschardt, E., and J.P.H. Sladen, "Transmission of a Stabilized RF Phase Reference over a Monomode Fiber-Optic Link," *Electronic Letters,* Vol. 22, No. 16, July 1986. Describes a stabilized optical fiber phase reference for a particle accelerator. The fiber-optic phase reference monitors the change in optical path length by sensing the RF phase of a reflection at one end of the optical fiber.
8. Slater, D., "Large Area Precision Inspection System," TRW internal report, June 30, 1986. A detailed technical description of the proposed LAPIS near-field range. The LAPIS is designed to test large spacecraft antennas with dimensions approaching 400 feet. The LAPIS uses an unusual assortment of inertial and laser sensors for precisely determining the position of the payload.
9. Mensa, D., *High Resolution Radar Cross-Section Imaging,* Artech House, Norwood, MA, 1990. Describes pulse compression, synthetic aperture concepts, and the related processing algorithms. A classic in the field.
10. Richardson, P., "Pulsed, Computer-Controllable Receiver and Exciter Having Wide Instantaneous Bandwidth for Testing Active-Element Phased Arrays," AMTA Conference Proceedings, Melbourne, FL, 1985. Covers the hardware design and Fourier calibration technique used in a high-speed near-field measurement receiver.
11. Hindman, G., and D. Slater, "Error Suppression Techniques for Near-field Antenna Measurements," AMTA Symp., Antenna Measurement Techniques Association, Monterey, CA, 1989. Describes a simple and effective multipath suppression technique using volumetric scanning and processing.
12. Gartner, E., and B. Scheik, "Automatic Homodyne Network Analyzer with Phase Shift Keying and Baseband Data Sampling," 14th European Microwave Conference, Liege, Belgium, 1984. Describes a precision vector network analyzer using phase modulated interferometry techniques.
13. Churchill, P., "The Correction of I and Q Errors in a Coherent Processor," *IEEE Trans. on Aerospace and Electronic Systems,* Vol. AES-17, No. 1, January 1981. Discusses the correction of gain and phase errors in coherent receivers that use quadrature mixers.
14. Harris, F., "On the Use of Windows for Harmonic Analysis with the Discrete Fourier Transform," *Proceedings of the IEEE,* January 1978. Provides a detailed examination and comparison of numerous window functions.

15. Newell, A., *Planar Near-field Measurements,* Lecture notes, NIST, Boulder, CO, 1985. Discusses planar near-field measurements in general. Describes one approach to cable length compensation.

16. Thompson, A.R., *et al.,* "Phase Stabilization of Widely Separated Oscillators," *IRE Trans. Antennas Propag.,* Vol. AP-16, pp. 683–688, 1968. Paper discusses both microwave and optical phase stabilization systems.

17. Tuovinen, J., *et al.,* "Antenna Phase Measurements at 105–190 GHz," *AMTA Conference Proceedings,* Philadelphia, PA, 1990. Discusses electrical cable length measurements using an S_{11} measurement with a directional coupler base discontinuity.

18. Slater, D., "Inverse Synthetic Aperture Imaging Radar," *AMTA Conference Proceedings,* Melbourne, Fl, 1985. Paper covers swept frequency pulse compression receivers which derive phase information through the use of the Hilbert transform.

Chapter 5
COORDINATE MEASUREMENTS AND MACHINING

Near-field antenna measurement systems incorporate a robotic subsystem capable of performing tasks other than RF near-field measurements. An example is the extensive use of the CMM-based near-field scanners, discussed in Chapter 7, that performs mechanical coordinate measurements. This section discusses the subsystem applications and the related payloads that can be carried by the near-field robots. The applications of a near-field robotic system generally are in three areas: machining operations, coordinate measurements, and RF performance measurements.

In machining operations, the shape of a surface such as a reflector, subreflector, lens, or beam waveguide can be machined precisely by tools carried by the robot. Also, a repetitive surface texture, such as a dichroic surface or a slotted phase array structure, can be machined by the robot.

In coordinate measurements, a mechanical contact probe can be used to precisely measure the overall antenna geometry, reflector, and subreflector surface shape, lens surfaces, beam waveguide assemblies, and alignment target positions. Optical techniques can be used to measure the surface of a reflector, subreflector, phased array, or lens surface. Holographic processing of the RF phasefront measurements can be used to assess reflector, subreflector phased array, and lens surface errors. RF measurements also can be used to assist in the correct placement and alignment of components in multibeam antennas and beam waveguide systems.

In RF performance measurements, the overall antenna performance can be determined from near-field measurements, such as the far-field pattern, gain and axial ratio, sidelobe levels, beam pointing, defocusing, and autotrack parameters. RF measurement can be used to test antenna subassembly performance, measuring feed pattern, feed phase center, feed interaction, dichroic element performance, and mesh losses.

In the future a near-field robot may perform the entire assembly, tuning, and testing of some antennas. This chapter will concentrate on the coordinate measurement and machining capabilities of near-field robotic systems.

Table 5.1 compares different coordinate measurement techniques that can be used by near-field robots. The gain of an antenna is directly affected by the surface roughness of the reflector. The gain loss due to an rms surface deviation error (e) at a wavelength (λ) was determined by Ruze to be

$$\text{Gain loss (dB)} = 10 \log \{\exp [-(4\pi \, e/\lambda)^2]\} \qquad (5.1)$$

Losses due to surface roughness are shown in Table 5.2.

Table 5.1
Coordinate Measurement Sensors

Parameter	Mechanical	Optical	Microwave
Physical contact	yes	no	no
Stand off	none	medium	large
Safety	poor	good	good
Speed	slow	fast (100X)	fast (100X)
Attitude stabilization	required	required	not needed
Measure tooling balls	yes	limited	no
Measure RF surface	no	no	yes
Lateral (X, Y) resolution	0.001″	0.1″	1 λ
Depth (Z) accuracy	0.0005″	0.005″	0.01 λ
Shape error measurement	indirect	indirect	yes
Mirror-black surfaces	limited	no	yes
Mesh measurements	no	limited	yes
Multipath problems	no	possible	yes
Deformation problems	yes	no	no
Phase problems	no	yes	no

Table 5.2
Representative Surface Roughness Losses

rms Surface Error	Wavelengths (λ)	Gain loss (dB)
0.2	1/5	27.4
0.1	1/10	6.8
0.05	1/20	1.7
0.02	1/50	0.27
0.01	1/100	0.069
0.005	1/200	0.017

5.1 MECHANICAL COORDINATE MEASUREMENTS

The near-field robot can be fitted with a mechanical probe that measures the physical dimensions of antenna assemblies, including

1. Overall alignment between antenna and scanner,
2. Overall geometry between different antenna elements,
3. Beam waveguide alignment,
4. Alignment target positions,
5. Reflector surface shape,
6. Subreflector surface shape,
7. Lens surface shape.

Mechanical coordinate measurements are made by touching a mechanical sensor to the coordinate positions and recording the robot joint positions. These joint measurements are then transformed into a reference coordinate system. A machinist's dial indicator is a simple sensor often used in smaller systems to determine the alignment between the AUT and scanner or to make other limited coordinate measurements. Electronic depth sensors such as LVDT probes and precision contact switches allow the measurement process to be automated. A representative contact switch touch probe developed specifically for coordinate measurement applications is the Renishaw PH9 probe (see Figure 5.1). This probe includes several internal motor axes to control the probe tip orientation in difficult measuring situations.

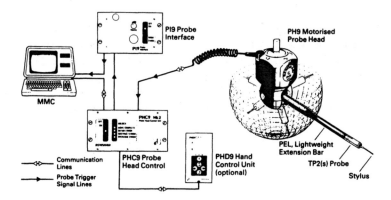

Figure 5.1 PH9 coordinate measurement probe.

The PH9 or similar probe is often used on a near-field measurement system as a primary alignment tool. The probe measures reflector shape and feed placement, and aligns the scanning plane relative to the AUT. The probe precisely measures slot location and dimensions for phased array antennas.

5.2 OPTICAL COORDINATE MEASUREMENTS

The shape of a microwave reflector or lens surface can be measured optically, which means fast measurement and safety enhanced by a long stand-off distance. An optical ranging sensor aligned along the scanner z-axis can measure the antenna surface shape as the scanner moves. The distance from the near-field scanner to the antenna surface can be acquired simultaneously with the RF measurements.

Optical ranging sensors generally use either triangulation or time-of-flight techniques. The triangulation systems typically provide an accuracy of 0.0005 to 0.05 inch rms depending on stand-off and antenna optical surface properties. Errors, however, can exceed 1 inch for antennas with poor optical surface properties. The time-of-flight units provide an accuracy of 0.05 to 1 inch rms. This technology is advancing rapidly: developmental optical pulse compression ranging systems provide range resolutions near 0.001 inch.

A representative laser ranging unit is manufactured by Coe engineering. The unit has an accuracy of 0.005 inch rms with a usable standoff between 15 and 35 inches. The unit operates by projecting a laser beam to a target location and triangulating with a linear array camera.

The *laser ranging probe* (LRP) is a robotic vision system that provides electro-optical range measurements. The LRP is intended to provide higher accuracy, longer stand off, and better surface tolerance than existing ranging systems. The LRP uses a pair of CCD television cameras mounted on the robot as the sensors viewing a laser projected target. The CCD camera images may be viewed on monitors at the control station.

The picture taken by the CCD camera may be viewed in real time by the operator, and the images may be used to assist the operator in maneuvering near the AUT and to support its close inspection. A videotape recorder can make permanent records if desired. The near-field ranges use a computer model of the AUT to prevent probe collisions. To simplify operation, the operator may "fly" the camera with joystick commands in the camera body coordinate system or slew to previously marked positions. The camera also may be used in a target track mode, where the moving camera is kept pointed at a fixed target location.

The LRP can measure the range to a target or the surface of a reflector. The range measurement is accomplished by triangulating on a point projected onto the surface of the AUT by a laser. The triangulation angle is measured by the CCD camera using pixel interpolation for high accuracy. Surface irregularities can shift the position of the centroid causing a significant ranging error. A second camera is used in a differential mode to suppress this error. The CCD camera orientation and optics errors are corrected by the method of least square adjustment.

The LRP processes a target by acquiring a pair of video frames from two cameras. The target is a point image of the intersection of the LRP laser beam with the AUT surface. The LRP uses a set of algorithms to identify the target image and perform a pixel interpolation. The pixel interpolation results in the effective resolution of the target position to a few hundredths of a pixel. The following sequence of steps is used to obtain a range measurement:

1. Acquire a pair of video frames from both CCD cameras.
2. Search for a candidate target based on a brightness threshold. Move the candidate target into a 5×5 pixel array, called the *subframe buffer.*
3. Determine if the candidate target is valid and adequately centered by comparing the candidate target against other pixels in a 5×5 region. If any other pixel is brighter than the center pixel, reject the candidate target and start a new search.
4. Determine if the candidate target is correctly formed. Check that the energy in each of the two outer rings decreases monotonically. Reject any candidate target that fails this test.
5. Apply a gamma correction to compensate for the nonlinear brightness response of the CCD camera.
6. Suppress the background illumination by subtracting the minimum brightness value from all pixels in the 5×5 pixel subframe buffer.
7. Compute the centroid of energy for the 5×5 pixel array. The centroid position, X_p, is the first moment of the intensity values in the subframe buffer:

$$X_p = \frac{\sum_{j=1}^{n} I(j) \cdot X(j)}{\sum_{j=1}^{n} I(j)} \tag{5.2}$$

where

$I(j)$ = intensity of jth pixel,
(j) = jth pixel position,
n = number of pixels.

8. Perform a centroid validity test by verifying that the computed centroid is within ½ pixel of the candidate target location.
9. Determine the target range from the pixel location and the LRP geometry.
10. Combine the measured ranges from both sensors to suppress any target centroid shift. A centroid shift can be produced by an optically nonuniform AUT surface such as a mesh reflector.

5.3 MICROWAVE HOLOGRAPHIC METROLOGY

High-quality measurements can be made of antenna surfaces using *microwave holographic metrology* (MHM), a specialized form of bistatic CW *inverse synthetic aperture radar* (ISAR) imaging that can be readily implemented on both near- and far-field ranges. In most near- and far-field ranges, no additional hardware is required, as the MHM technique is compatible with all types of antennas. In reflector antennas, MHM can provide detailed maps of reflector surface currents, aperture illumination, and surface shape errors. In phased-array antennas, MHM can provide maps of aperture illumination, element weights, and geometric errors.

As an example, a small x-band phased-array weather radar antenna has a defective element. Figure 5.2 shows the measured near-field phasefront acquired at a 3 in. separation between the AUT and probe antenna. Figure 5.3 shows the result of a back projection to the aperture plane. Figure 5.4 shows the result of a 90° rotation of the imaging plane.

The use of microwave holographic metrology has been well proven in the shape measurement of large ground-based antennas. MHM has provided a depth resolution on the order of 0.01 wavelength and lateral resolutions on the order of a few wavelengths for many test configurations. Table 5.3 lists some MHM measurements.

Surface distortions in both parabolic reflectors and phased-array antennas result in distortions to a planar phase front. If the antenna is properly focused and no significant diffraction is present, an unprocessed plot of the measured near-field phase will graphically show any reflector surface errors. This is the simplest form of microwave holography. It is similar to shadow photography. Some defocusing of the image will occur because the energy leaving the antenna is diverging and the

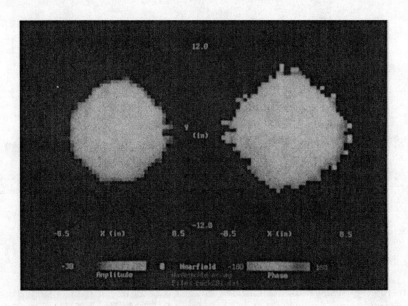

Figure 5.2 Unfocused weather radar antenna phase front.

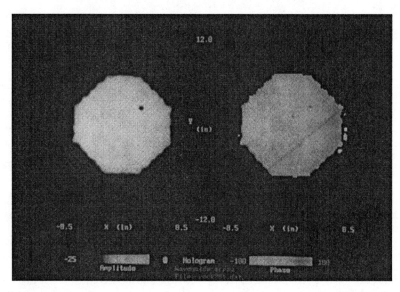

(a) Near-field amplitude   (b) Near-field phase

Figure 5.3 Focused weather radar antenna phase front.

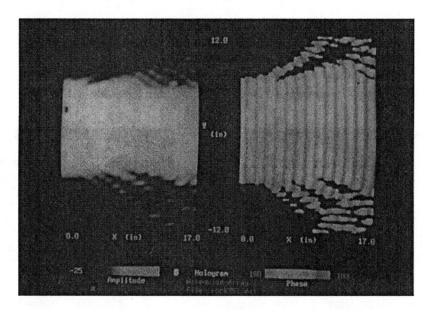

Figure 5.4 A 90° rotation of the imaging plane shows the energy leaving the weather radar antenna.

Table 5.3
Representative MHM Measurements

Antenna	Size (ft)	Frequency (GHz)	Grid	Resolution (in.)	RF Source	Notes
DSN	210	2.28	11×11		radio star	1
DSN	210	11.45	189×189	36	satellite	1
JPL	5	11.30	127×127		NFTF	1
Offset cass	18	11.70	21×21		tower	3
Chilbolton	75	11.50	100×100		satellite	4
Parabolic	12	8.15	90×90		tower	5
NASA NTTF	30	12.00	33×33	12	satellite	6

Notes:
1. Reference [1].
2. Reference [2].
3. Reference [3], the source is a tower 2 km away, scan was ± 2°.
4. Data from reference [4], 30° spacecraft to horizon angle, 3.5 hr acquisition time. An accompanying brochure indicated that surface error measurements on the order of 0.001 wavelength were thought possible.
5. Data from reference [5]; the source was mounted on a tower in the near-field ($0.23 \, D^2/\lambda$) of the AUT. The antenna was scanned ±5°.
6. Data from reference [6]; the source was a geosynchronous satellite. Measurements were performed both in the day and night. Thermal expansion effects were observed. A spiral scan pattern was used.

probe antenna is some distance away from the reflector surface. Holographic transforms, as discussed later in this chapter, can back project the energy to the aperture or reflector surface, resulting in a focused image.

As an example, Figure 5.5 shows the near-field phasefront of an offset Cassegrain antenna operating at 28.75 GHz as sampled with a high-gain probe

(a) Near-field amplitude

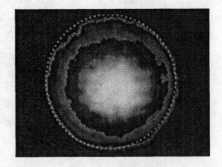

(b) Near-field phase

Figure 5.5 Offset Cassegrain antenna phase front images.

antenna. The primary reflector was 10 ft in diameter. The test produced a 128×
128 element raster scan phase image of the antenna. This image clearly showed a
30 mil taco-shaped distortion caused by a shim. No other technique has shown the
reflector distortions as clearly. Note that no determination has been made of the
actual shape of the reflector, only the error in its shape.

5.3.1 Microwave Holography Theory

The theory behind microwave holographic measurement is related very closely to
several other fields, including antenna near-field measurements, seismology, and
aperture synthesis in radioastronomy. All of these techniques use the concept of
transforming a phasefront into an angular spectrum. The microwave holographic
transform essentially is the inverse operation with a "phase correction." The microwave holographic transform is related even more closely to the focused CW bistatic
ISAR transforms [7, 8], which perform the inverse transformation of a doppler
(angular) spectrum into a phasefront. The input to an MHM transform is far-field
E or H field measurements. The far-field input may be directly from far-field measurements or calculated from near-field measurements. The output of an MHM
transform is E or H field measurements in the aperture plane or at another desired
position in space. Certain MHM transforms can directly compute the reflector surface currents on a parabolic surface.

The basic MHM transform in essence is the inverse of the near- to far-field
transform described in Chapter 2 with the addition of a focusing (phase compensation) operation. The microwave holographic concept can be explained from six
viewpoints:

1. Fourier optics (most common),
2. Doppler processing,
3. Aperture synthesis,
4. Correlation with a reference beam,
5. Angular matched filtering,
6. Doppler dechirp.

Each viewpoint leads to different insights about the capabilities of the holographic transformation. For example, using concept 2 (doppler processing), the various regions of the antenna can be sorted by sorting the doppler signal components
from the various parts of the reflector. These viewpoints are explained in more
detail in Chapter 2 and [9].

5.3.2 MHM Transform

A map of the aperture field or reflector surface currents with the associated phase
information is the output of the MHM transform. This information can be con-

verted to a map of surface deviations by unwrapping the phase and dividing by the wavenumber. Additional processing using pulse compression techniques can resolve the image in the delay domain. This is useful in observing multipath signals and increasing their resolution.

Several different MHM methods can be used:

1. Use the near-field phase front (no transform),
2. Transform to the far-field phase front, focus, and perform an inverse transform,
3. Use aplantic wave functions.

The near-field phase front normally is measured some distance away from the focal surface because of instrumental requirements, obstructions and the desire to minimize evanescent coupling. The measurement distance results in a loss of resolution due to spreading. The resolution loss can be recovered by a focusing operation in which the measured phase front is back projected onto a region near or on the aperture surface. The resultant phase error relative to a plane wave can be related to the reflector surface shape error.

Most MHM transformations are performed using method 2; the approach is described in the following section. Several of the steps listed below are optional. The MHM transformation inputs are coherent E or H field measurements and other measurements that define the system geometry.

1. If the measurements initially were acquired in the near-field domain, transform the measurements into the far-field domain, using any far-field transform technique. This step is not required if measurements were taken on a far-field range or compact range.
2. Apply filtering, if required, to minimize multipath and other error sources. This is equivalent to changing the properties of the near-field probe.
3. Interpolate the measurements onto a uniform grid in the K space. This step generally is not required for planar near-field measurements sampled in a raster format or for far-field measurements sampled at a uniform K spacing.
4. Apply a phase correction to the far-field data. The phase correction is used to shift the phase front to a plane near the aperture surface of the antenna, resulting in a focused near-field phase image. The MHM phase correction is analogous to the focusing operation performed in a SAR radar.

   The phase correction concept is based on the Fourier transform shift theorem (discussed in Appendix D). A sine wave can be shifted in time by changing the phase in the Fourier transform domain. For example, changing the phase of a sine wave in the transform domain delays a sine wave by 90° cycle. The concept is similar to that for a two-dimensional plane wave. The plane wave position can be translated in two dimensions by changing the phase of the azimuth and elevation components in the far field. As energy leaves an aperture in different directions, the plane waves no longer overlap. The idea is to focus the plane waves leaving in different directions into a common region.

Each component of the *plane wave spectrum* (PWS) is back propagated along its direction of travel from the measurement plane to the plane of focus, usually the aperture plane. This simply means multiplying each component in the far field by the following equation. The second form in the equation can be derived by applying the cosine law of right spherical triangles to the first form (see also equation (3.16) and (3.19)):

$$e^{-iz \cos\theta} = e^{iz \cos(\text{el}) \cos(\text{az})} = e^{-izKz} \tag{5.3}$$

where

K = constant,
z = probe to aperture distance (wavelengths),
θ = angle of the plane wave spectral component relative to the boresight axis.

In measurements performed on far-field measurement systems, a more complex focusing may be required due to the positioner geometry.

5. Perform a two-dimensional inverse fast Fourier transform to convert the K space spectrum into the aperture field. The output of the Fourier transform is the near-field phase front near the focal surface of the AUT. The phase front can be positioned on either side of the reflector using the previously described focusing procedure.
6. Clean up the aperture field distribution (to compensate for Gibbs's ripple due to truncation) by an iterative application of the FFT [1]. This step is optional and in many cases does not significantly affect the result. The operation primarily affects the aperture edge when the reflector edge illumination is not tapered.
7. Apply a phase unwrap to obtain the relative aperture phase distribution. Scale the unwrapped phase by the wavenumber $(2\pi/\lambda)$ to obtain a surface error map.
8. Use a least squares technique to solve for defocus and feed placement errors, if desired.

The reconstruction plane can be rotated in yaw, pitch, and roll to provide additional insights. Figure 5.6 shows an example when the output is rotated 90° in yaw. A picture of the path of energy leaving an antenna often can provide useful insight into the operation of an antenna.

5.3.3 MHM Sampling Criteria

The MHM transform usually is implemented in a discrete form on a general purpose digital computer. As such, the sampling of the far-field energy needs to meet the Nyquist sampling requirements. The sampling constraints outlined here are defined in the far-field domain and use the TDRSS satellite KSA antenna as an example.

1. The far-field scan angle should be large enough to sample all significant energy from the AUT. Larger scan angles result in higher lateral resolutions. The achievable resolution (r) for focused processing is approximately equal to the lateral distance over which a 1 wavelength differential path length for the peak-to-peak antenna tilt excursion (θ) occurs.

$$r = \lambda/\sin(\theta/2) \tag{5.4}$$

   For example, if the TDRSS KSA antenna operating at 15.003 GHz were scanned over $\pm 2°$, the approximate lateral resolution would be 11.2 in.

2. The sampling density should be high enough to ensure that none of the energy is aliased. The Nyquist sampling theorem is satisfied when the highest doppler component is sampled at phase intervals of less than 180°. The highest doppler frequency component usually is produced by the rim of the reflector antenna; however, reflections from other parts of the spacecraft could induce higher doppler frequencies. The sampling interval can be determined easily from the geometry. For an antenna of a diameter D with no multipath, the angular samples should be spaced by less than

$$\theta = \arctan(\lambda/D) \tag{5.5}$$

   For example, the Nyquist sampling interval for the 15 ft diameter TDRSS single access antenna operating at K-band (15.003 GHz) would be 0.2347°.

In many cases, when testing radially symmetric antennas, a lower sampling density can be achieved by using a polar or spiral scan. This is because the circular spatial frequency components decay rapidly with harmonic number. The required circular sampling density can be derived directly from the Nyquist theorem, which states that the highest circular spatial frequency in the transformed domain must be represented by more than two samples per cycle. In antennas with significant gore lobes, such as the TDRSS SA antenna, the number of *full*-width radial cuts should be greater than the number of gores.

Many different far-field sampling patterns are possible. Patterns that have been used or suggested for use include

1. Raster (uniform spacing in angle domain),
2. Raster (uniform spacing in K space),

3. Polar,
4. Spiral,
5. Cycloids,
6. Random,
7. Sparse random (main beam and sidelobes only).

All of these should produce identical results if the sampling theorem has been correctly satisfied and all significant energy is collected. In far-field measurements, uniform K-space raster sampling has been most popular because the measurements are easy to process in this form.

Closely related yet subtly different from the reflector surface error measurements is the precise determination of the position of the reflector surface relative to the near-field scanner. This measurement is useful in AUT alignment and in establishing the geometric relationship between the AUT and the near-field scanner. The obvious solution is to use a form of bistatic SAR to image the surface of the reflector. The doppler histories required by the SAR are contained in the sampled near-field phase front. The SAR transmitter is the antenna feed, and the SAR receiver is the probe antenna.

The probe antenna can be "focused" onto the antenna focal surface by SAR techniques. This results in the sorting of energy by doppler frequency corresponding to different regions of the focal surface. A point scatterer on the surface of the parabolic reflector can be treated as a new source point as a consequence of Huygen's principle. A doppler frequency-shifted signal is generated for any scatterer on the parabolic dish surface by moving the probe relative to the AUT test. The doppler frequency history is unique for each point on the aperture. With appropriate computer sorting of the doppler signals, the time delay to each point on the surface of the antenna can be determined. If the motion of the probe is along the normal scan plane the near-field range is synthesizing a set of phased array antennas focused on the AUT surface.

The only problem is that, whereas normal SAR techniques will accurately image diffuse scatterers, they will not accurately image highly specular reflections from mirror surfaces. A well-designed reflector acts like a mirror and therefore does not scatter the illumination except at the edges. The specular reflections result in a loss of the SAR doppler signal at all positions except when the receiver is in a specular reflection. This reduces the cross-range resolution to an unusable level.

The problem of imaging the surface of a nonscattering reflector has been studied extensively by the oil industry in the interpretation of seismic data. Many of the underground layers detected by reflection seismology act like mirrors. The processing of seismic information to form corrected images of the mirrorlike surfaces is called *migration*.

The path length from the transmitter (antenna feed) to the reflector surface to the receiver (probe antenna) can be measured by radar techniques. Under these conditions the reflecting surface must be tangent to a position on an ellipsoid with the foci at the transmitter and receiver phase centers. The size of the ellipse is directly related to the propagation time delay. If we construct a set of ellipsoids for different receiver positions, the ellipsoids will make osculatory contact with the reflector surface. Several techniques can be used to determine the points of osculatory contact.

One method involves the generation of *aplanatic wave functions* (AWF) [10]. A summation of the AWFs produce the complex cross correlation between a frequency-swept back-projected antenna aperture phase front and forward-projected reflector illumination phase front. The AWF is a three-dimensional function that will reach a maximum value at the reflector surface where the back- and forward-projected phase fronts are equal. The complex product between the two wavefronts is integrated over a set probe positions and microwave frequencies. The varying probe positions provide primarily cross-range information. The cross-range processing is similar to SAR processing modified by the additional processing of the reference phase front transmitted by the antenna feed. The varying RF frequencies provide the down-range resolution. The process is similar to down-range pulse compression in a chirp radar, modified by the additional processing of the reference phase front transmitted by the antenna feed.

5.4 ON-ORBIT HOLOGRAPHIC METROLOGY OF SPACECRAFT ANTENNAS

This section discusses the use of MHM techniques for the measurement of the on-orbit shape deformations of spacecraft antenna surfaces. The MHM technique measures the satellite reflector shape by processing the doppler signal components induced by angularly moving the spacecraft antenna relative to a ground station or other RF source. Minimal modifications are required at the ground station. The TDRSS spacecraft (Figure 5.6) is an example for an MHM test design [11, 12]. Reasons for on-orbit reflector surface measurements include

1. Measurement of on-orbit thermal distortions,
2. Assessment of antenna launch and deployment damages,
3. Validation of zero G models,
4. Validation of on-orbit aperture illumination,
5. Study of aperture blockage or scattering by feed or other parts of the spacecraft,
6. Measurement of feed position errors (defocus and lateral shifts),
7. Measurement of feed interaction and spacecraft-induced multipath signals,
8. Development of a real-time shape control sensing technique.

The general capabilities of the MHM technique applied to on-orbit spacecraft can be projected to be similar to the ground-based tests that used satellites as RF

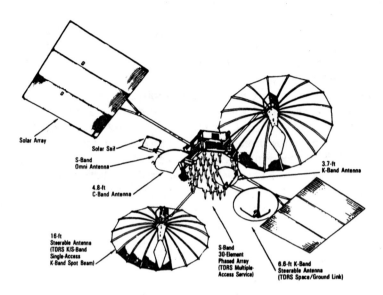

Figure 5.6 TDRSS satellite.

sources. Typical ground-based measurements provide an axial resolution of 0.01 wavelengths and a lateral resolution of 10 wavelengths, as outlined earlier. Several extensions to the MHM technique are proposed that significantly enhance conventional MHM capabilities. These extensions are primarily in the form of a new multilook test technique, a new transform algorithm, and multipath imaging by pulse compression. The new test technique may provide near real-time surface measurements and, in certain cases, eliminate the requirement for physical motion of the test antenna. An MHM test focuses on the following problems:

1. Aperture or reflector phase (surface) error,
2. Errors in aperture or reflector surface illumination function,
3. Feed position errors (lateral, defocus, interaction),
4. RF multipath images at different delay times.

Not all spacecraft can be tested by MHM techniques. For an on-orbit MHM test to be possible, as outlined here, the following spacecraft characteristics are required:

1. To establish a pair of mutually coherent unidirectional links (test and reference signal) from the RF source to the spacecraft.
2. To measure the relative amplitude and phase angle between the test and reference signal. This usually implies that the spacecraft must have a coherent transponder. In some satellites, the required phase coherence can be obtained through the digital transponder, although amplitude information must be

derived independently from the spacecraft receiver AGC signal telemetry. There may be problems maintaining receiver lock in the sidelobes. In other spacecraft, the phase reference signal can be alternately provided by a coherent command uplink.

3. To determine phase errors induced by motion of the reference antenna. The reference antenna may either be another communication antenna (such as a TDRSS SA or MA antenna) or the command uplink antenna (if coherent).
4. The precise pointing direction of the spacecraft antenna relative to the RF source at the measurement time must be known.
5. Sufficient spacecraft time must be available. Note that a modified MHM technique may provide the capability to perform the antenna surface measurements in near real time without any significant impact on the primary mission.

5.4.1 Signal-to-Noise Ratio Requirements

The resolution achievable with MHM techniques is heavily driven by the system SNR. High lateral resolutions of the aperture require measurements at a large angle relative to the antenna boresight where link margins are low. Process gain in the holographic transform can reduce the link margin requirements.

The RF source antenna should have sufficient gain to ensure an adequate signal-to-noise ratio in the AUT sidelobes. A 24 dB SNR at the *transform output* will allow surface error measurements with an rms uncertainty around 0.01λ. Note that the transform can provide a substantial increase in SNR due to the process gain.

Atmospheric propagation can cause a significant decrease in the measurement SNR due to phase dispersion. The primary cause of phase dispersion is the Faraday effect, which describes the rotation of the plane of polarization of a radio wave passing through an ionized medium under the influence of a magnetic field [13]. The Faraday rotation decreases with increasing test frequency.

The decrease in SNR due to phase dispersion can be minimized by reducing the magnitude of the Faraday effect and suppressing the differential path delays. The following techniques accomplish this:

1. Use a single RF source for both the test and reference signals, because otherwise paths are uncorrelated and therefore noncoherent.
2. Use the same frequencies for both the test and reference signals to minimize differential chromatic dispersion.
3. Transmit both the test and reference signals in the same direction, because the path is nonreciprocal and time varying, therefore noncoherent.
4. Use an exoatmospheric RF source to eliminate the Faraday effects in the ionosphere.

5. Use higher frequencies to minimize the magnitude of the Faraday rotation.
6. Use multiple test frequencies for direct measurement of the differential chromatic dispersion.

5.4.2 Test Configuration

The MHM test requires that the spacecraft be configured as a two-arm interferometer. One arm contains the AUT. This concept is explained in more detail in Chapter 4. The microwave energy is transmitted over two adjacent paths to the spacecraft. Test and reference antennas on the spacecraft receive the two signals. Note that the two paths need not be at the same frequency, although this would be desirable to minimize Faraday rotation. As in all interferometers, the two signals must be combined into an interference pattern. In the MHM measurements, the two signals received by the spacecraft are transmitted to the ground and converted into an amplitude ratio and a phase difference. These measurements are processed by a computer using holographic transformation techniques to arrive at a surface image.

5.4.3 Phase Reference

The MHM transform requires as input the far-field measurements of the E or H field intensity and phase. The phase is measured relative to an arbitrary reference angle. The selection of the phase reference method often is driven by the available spacecraft hardware. We have several different options in choosing a phase reference:

1. In a communications satellite such as the TDRSS spacecraft, a second stationary communications antenna on the same vehicle can provide the phase reference. This technique is used in the TDRSS test example. The reason is that the same frequency can be used for both the test and reference antennas (minimizing atmospheric effects) and the electronics for both antennas will tend to track closely.
2. Many spacecraft already receive a coherent timing reference on the command uplink. This signal can provide the MHM phase reference. The advantage of this approach is simplicity and minimal disruption of other spacecraft services. The main disadvantages are additional errors introduced in the ground station, uncorrected atmospheric effects if the test and reference frequencies are greatly different, and mismatched spacecraft electronic assemblies.
3. Closely related to the command link is the ranging link, which is of particular interest because it almost always is phase coherent and has been optimized for phase stability. This link may be used to provide additional information

about the atmospheric effects by comparing the ranging data at the ranging frequency with ranging data derived from the MHM measurements at the test frequency.

5.4.4 MHM Test Set

The additional hardware required at the ground station to support MHM measurements generally is minimal; some ground stations would require no additional hardware. The MHM test set requires relative amplitude and phase measurements between the output of the two spacecraft antennas. These measurements are then processed by an IBM PC or similar computer using the MHM transform. The ground station already may have the amplitude-phase measuring hardware and most likely will have sufficient computational power. A typical ground station calibration antenna or another satellite can be used as the RF source for the test.

5.4.5 Advanced On-Orbit MHM Test Concepts

The MHM concept although powerful has certain drawbacks: long data acquisition time, the requirement to physically scan the test antenna aperture, and long processing time. Some modifications to the MHM measurement technique that might eliminate these problems are described in the following text.

The test and reference signals can come from a ground station or from another earth-based or exoatmospheric source. If the source were exoatmospheric, many of the propagation path errors would disappear. In TDRSS spacecraft, both KSA antennas would be pointed at another spacecraft. The reference KSA antenna would both downlink the spacecraft data (as part of the normal mission) and provide a phase reference for the MHM measurements. The test KSA antenna would be scanned in azimuth and elevation. Measurements of the relative amplitude and phase between the test and reference antennas provide the necessary information for the MHM transform.

A further extension is to consider using a multiplicity of RF sources as randomly distributed over some angular extent. The sources could be a combination of satellites and ground-based transmitters. If the sources can be separated by frequency, time, or coding, the mechanical scan requirements can be significantly reduced. If frequency separation methods are used, images can be formed at certain time delays.

Some improvement in the signal-to-noise ratio can be achieved by selecting RF sources with power outputs that vary according to the inverse of the test antenna far-field pattern. A simple low-amplitude conscan motion of the test antenna or the associated feed would be sufficient to produce the differential doppler signal required for MHM imaging.

If a new spacecraft antenna were being designed, the conscan feed motion could be adequately simulated by switching among three separate feed elements. In a phased array antenna, the MHM differential doppler signal can be produced by perturbing the element weights. The latter case has many similarities with the theory of self-adaptive array antennas. An appropriately designed phase array also can provide the necessary MHM reference signal. There are some constraints on the reflector feed and phased array element spacing to meet the Nyquist criteria. At this point it would be possible to perform MHM measurements without requiring any motion of the AUT.

The partially factored DFT described in Chapter 3 can provide immediate results, even when the measurement sequence is not complete. This characteristic is analogous to optical holograms in which a complete image at lower resolution can be seen even if part of the hologram is removed. This concept, when combined with Kalman filtering techniques leads to a so-called *model reference adaptive* (MRA) system. As the partially factored near-field transform algorithm is compatible with multiple frequency, randomly distributed beam steering angles, a quasi-real-time determination of the reflector may be possible. This MRA-based MHM technique would have minimal impact on the primary mission. In the future, MHM techniques could be used to provide very high quality on orbit shape measurements of large antennas (both parabolic reflector and phased array) as part of an active shape control system.

MHM imaging can be additionally expanded by using stepped or random frequency pulse compression techniques to further resolve the image in the delay domain. This results in the development of a 3-D bistatic ISAR transformation with two cross-range dimensions and one down-range dimension. This technique was described in Chapter 4. The output of the transform can be displayed as a series of two-dimensional images at various delay times. This type of display would clearly show multipath effects in the spacecraft antennas. The stepped frequency techniques in combination with the Hilbert transform also allows the identification and minimization of some error sources such as certain propagation effects and receiver errors. Note that any combination of one, two, or three dimensions can be acquired and processed as needed.

5.4.6 Transformation Algorithms

The previously described FDFT algorithm provides several advantages in on-orbit holographic imaging:

1. Real-time imaging providing compatibility with MRA and Kalman filtering techniques,
2. Speed,
3. Capability of imaging onto nonplanar surfaces,

4. Capability of processing unusual scan patterns including multifrequency data sets,
5. Configuration that is short, simple, and intuitive.

Other algorithms for processing randomly sampled data are described in [14, 15].

5.4.7 MHM Measurement Uncertainty

The reflector surface measurement uncertainty can be defined in terms of three basic error mechanisms:

1. Uncertainty of the relative amplitude and phase of the received signal.
2. The uncertainty as to the spacecraft antenna attitude relative to the ground station.
3. Uncertainty as to the positions of the spacecraft test and reference antennas relative to the ground station.

The surface measurement uncertainty is derived by generating three separate error budgets for the three classes of error and then combining the budgets into a total error budget.

5.5 MACHINING OPERATIONS

Near-field robots with coordinated multiaxis servo systems are quite similar to high-precision *computerized numerical control* (CNC) milling machines. *Coordinate measurement machine* (CMM) robots have been modified to perform ultra-precise machining operations to the precision required for visible light optics [16]. The near-field measurement robots can be fitted with various machining and surface buildup tools. These tools can be used to modify the shape of a surface to a very high precision. Some surfaces of interest include reflectors, subreflectors, beam waveguide optics, lenses, phased arrays, and the templates or molds used to make these items.

Near-field measurement robots used for machining operations generally require three or more axes of precisely coordinated multiaxis continuous path control. Methods of achieving this type of motion control are described in Chapter 7. Most near-field robots do not currently have this capability.

A significant problem in the construction of large spacecraft antennas is producing an antenna surface that matches the desired shape. Antenna reflectors often are molded. An obvious extension is to use robotic systems for a final trim of the reflector high points by using a milling cutter or by building up the reflector low points with a conductive paint. Dust from the machining operation can be removed by a vacuum system. A variation of this technique has been used to produce 30 foot submillimeterwave antennas for radioastronomy with an rms surface accuracy of 15 μm (0.0005 inch) [17]. Material also can be removed by impacting the surface with a jet of small glass beads. This approach has been used by JPL in the production of a millimeter-wave antenna for the *millimeter-wave limb sounder* (MLS) satellite payload.

Phased array antennas often require precision slots to form the beam. The slots must be at the right positions and of the right dimensions for correct antenna operation. Typical accuracy requirements are on the order of a 0.002 inch. A suitable high-speed cutter carried by the CMM could precisely cut the slots. A similar problem exists in the generation of dichroic subreflector surfaces. Currently the surfaces are produced by a process similar to printed circuit manufacturing. Difficulties arise, however, because the dichroic surfaces often are curved. A precise robot could be used to solve both problems. The application of robotics to antenna manufacturing can be expected to increase significantly in the future.

The application of CNC and CMM technology to near-field antenna testing is evident with the conversion of several CMM machines into near-field antenna measurement systems (discussed in Chapter 7). The modifications include a very precise, multiaxis, continuous path, servo control system allowing plane polar scanning and a new software control program. The software supports the original CMM capabilities while adding the specialized processing needed for near-field measurements [8].

When suitably designed, the near-field robot can provide a highly integrated machining, coordinate measurement, and near-field measurement capability. All operations are performed in a common coordinate system without moving the AUT. An example of the integrated test and assembly of a spacecraft cassegrain antenna using this type of near-field system is described in Chapter 9.

REFERENCES

1. Rahmat-Samii, Y., "Microwave Holographic Metrology for Antenna Diagnosis," *IEEE Antennas and Propagation Society Newsletter,* June 1987. Covers the basics of microwave holography as used by JPL. Shows several examples of holographic images of the NASA/JPL 64 m DSN antenna at the Goldstone Deep Space Tracking Station. Initial studies were performed at 2.28 GHz using a radio star as a source. More recently, a geosynchronous satellite beacon operating at 11.45 GHz has been used to produce reflector surface maps that achieve a 1 m lateral resolution.

2. Slater, D., "Large Area Precision Inspection System (LAPIS)," TRW Internal Rep. B211.83-TR-4, 1986. A detailed technical description of the proposed LAPIS near-field range. The LAPIS is designed to test large spacecraft antennas with dimensions approaching 400 ft. Report discusses some theory and several experiments with microwave holographic metrology.

3. Anderson, A., "Developments in Microwave Holographic Imaging," Ninth European Microwave Conf., Brighton, England, 1979. A history of some experiments in microwave holography.

4. Godwin, M., *et al.,* "Microwave Diagnostics of the Chilbolton 25 m Antenna Using the OTS Satellite" Describes surface measurements of the Chilbolton 25 m antenna in England. The

microwave source used in the test was the OTS satellite. An accompanying brochure indicated that depth accuracies on the order of 0.001 wavelength were possible.

5. Bennett, J., *et al.*, "Microwave Holographic Metrology of Large Reflector Antennas," *IEEE Trans. on Antennas and Propagation*, Vol AP-24, No. 3, May 1976. A detailed mathematical description of the process of antenna surface measurements using far- to near-field transformations.

6. Freedman, D., *et al.*, "Measure Antenna Surface with Microwave Holograms," *Microwaves and RF Magazine*, February 1986. Describes a portable microwave holography test system.

7. Mensa, D., *High Resolution Radar Cross-Section Imaging*, Artech House, Norwood, MA, 1990. Describes ISAR, pulse compression, CW imaging, and the related processing algorithms. A classic in the field.

8. Slater, D., "Inverse Synthetic Aperture Imaging Radar," AMTA Conf. Proceedings, Melbourne, FL, 1985. Discusses ISAR imaging, a concept closely related to MHM imaging. A simple, yet powerful ISAR radar is described. The ISAR radar uses a swept frequency pulse compression receiver that derives phase information through the use of Hilbert transformers. These techniques can be used to both increase the capabilities and decrease the cost of MHM measurements.

9. Ulaby, F., A. Fung, and R.K. Moore, *Microwave Remote Sensing*, Vol. 2, Artech House, Norwood, MA, 1982. Discusses SAR transformations from several different viewpoints. The focused SAR transformation is very similar to the MHM transformation.

10. Walter, W., *et al.*, *Seismic Imaging Atlas 1976*, United Geophysical Corporation, Pasadena, CA. A description of seismic techniques used to determine the position of underground seismic reflectors. Covers the theory of aplanatic wave functions.

11. NASA, *Tracking and Data Relay Satellite System (TDRSS) User's Guide*, Goddard Space Flight Center, Greenbelt, MD, 1984. Describes the interface to the TDRSS satellite system.

12. Yuen, J., *Deep Space Telecommunications Systems Engineering*, JPL publication 82-76, California Institute of Technology, Pasadena, CA, July 1982. Describes various details of spacecraft ranging systems and the associated error budgets. The design of the ranging system is similar to the design of the MHM system in that both are forms of interferometers. The main difference is that the MHM operates in a differential mode to obtain highly accurate ranging estimates among different parts of the spacecraft rather than measuring the spacecraft-to-ground station range. This book also contains a chapter on the TDRSS spacecraft interface.

13. Krassner, G., and J. Michaels, *Introduction to Space Communications Systems*, McGraw-Hill, New York, 1964. Describes propagation errors present in a space-ground link.

14. Rahmat-Samii, Y., "Nonuniform Sampling of Radiation from Antennas," *NASA Tech. Brief*, Vol. 12, No. 11, Item 67. Discussion of nonuniform sampling and transform methods suitable for use with on-orbit antenna tests.

15. Thompson, A.R., and J.W. Moran, *Interferometry and Synthesis in Radio Astronomy*, John Wiley and Sons, New York, 1986. Discusses a variety of subjects relevant to near-field and holographic measurements, including interferometry, phase coherent receivers, atmospheric effects, aperture synthesis, and geodetic measurements. Highly recommended.

16. Davidson, W., *et al.*, "Microns, Microns Everywhere and All of Them out of Line," Optical Alignment 3, *SPIE*, Vol. 608, 1986. Discusses the problems associated with grinding optics 8 m in diameter to an accuracy of a few microns. The large optics generator is a modification of a commercial precision vertical grinder.

17. Leighton, R., "A 10-Meter Telescope for Millimeter and Submillimeter Astronomy," Final report NFS Grant AST 73-04908, California Institute of Technology, 1978. Describes the problems associated with the testing of large, highly accurate antennas. This report has many novel ideas and is highly recommended.

Chapter 6
SMALL, NEAR-FIELD RANGE
MEASUREMENT SYSTEMS

6.1 SIMPLE, LOW-COST, NEAR-FIELD RANGE MEASUREMENT SYSTEMS

A better understanding of the near-field measurement process can be obtained by building a simple, low-cost, near-field antenna measurement system. For example, much of the data shown in this book was acquired and processed on the author's home-built near-field antenna measurement system (see Figure 6.1).

A simple, low-cost near-field measurement system requires three subsystems:

1. Interferometer (RF or acoustic),
2. Scanner (*xy* plotter or scanner),
3. Computer (IBM PC compatible, Apple, *et cetera*).

In the author's system, shown in Figure 6.1, the scanner mechanism was part of a microfilm camera system purchased in a surplus yard for $50. The scanner has a travel range of 18×36 in. and uses a stepper motor drive system for x and y positioning. The system has been used for both raster and plane polar scan patterns. A future extension is to add spherical and cylindrical scanning capabilities by using an additional pair of rotary axes.

The steppers form an interface to the computer (A Compaq 386/20) by a parallel port driving a translator box. The computer transmits a pulse for each motor step; no separate stepper controller is used. Several advantages result from driving the steppers in this manner:

1. The receiver timing can be synchronized very tightly,
2. The motor control algorithms can be modified readily,
3. The hardware costs little.

The pulse trains are generated in the computer by using a *numerically controlled oscillator* (NCO) algorithm. The NCO algorithm in essence is a digital fre-

Figure 6.1 Home-built near-field measurement system.

quency synthesizer using a coherent phase adder concept. The commanded NCO frequency corresponds to the motor velocity. The use of an NCO allows the motor to be accelerated smoothly, minimizing scanner vibrations. Multiple axes motion can be produced by software extensions similar to those used in vector graphics systems.

The RF system is extremely simple, as is shown in Figure 6.2. The components were purchased in various surplus stores, and the design was based on what RF components were available. For example, the test frequency was 12.725 GHz because that was the frequency of the available source. Two measurement passes are required, one each for the I and Q channel measurements. The line stretcher is set for a ¼ wavelength difference between the two passes. This is a simple form of a homodyne interferometer. We used the following components to build a 12.725 GHz near-field interferometer:

RF source: 12.725 GHz phase-lock oscillator

Power splitter: 1-to-16 GHz power splitter

Probe antenna: Feed for a dish antenna (OEWG)

(2) Isolator: Ku-band isolator

Mixer: TRW double-balanced mixer

Line stretcher: Weinschel 1504 precision phase shifter

Reference cable: Goretex

Microwave absorber: AN-73

Preamplifier: Tektronix AM-502 amplifier

Computer interface: Metrabyte 12-bit ADC

Several improvements could be made to this design. The need for two passes is not desirable and, as this receiver is a homodyne design, it has excessive mixer

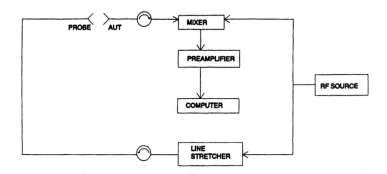

Figure 6.2 Home-built near-field RF interferometer block diagram.

leakage and $1/f$ noise. One solution to the two-pass problem is to use a quadrature mixer to produce the I and Q signals simultaneously. The leakage and $1/f$ noise can be minimized by amplitude modulating the RF signal.

A second approach is to use the system shown in Figure 6.2 with the line stretcher (phase shifter) computer controlled. The resultant phase modulation can directly provide the quadrature component. The phase modulation is equivalent to a frequency shift. The frequency shift developed by the phase modulator corresponds to an IF. As the receiver is now a superheterodyne design, $1/f$ noise and leakage are greatly reduced. This technique, called *phase modulation interferometry,* is discussed further in Chapter 4. Self-calibrating phase modulated interferometers can provide excellent performance at a very low cost. The system has since been upgraded with this type of interferometer. The dynamic range of the PMI design is approximately 70 to 80 dB as compared to 35 to 40 dB for the two-pass homodyne system.

A third approach is to use a swept frequency source in conjunction with a Hilbert transformer, as explained in Chapter 4. This converts the system into a superheterodyne design, which minimizes $1/f$ noise and suppresses mixer leakage. The phase can be extracted to a high accuracy using the Hilbert transform. The modification to Figure 6.2 is to remove the line stretcher and replace the fixed frequency RF source with a computer-tuned RF source.

Even lower cost near-field scanner designs are possible if we are willing to work with crystal detector RF receivers (as described in Chapter 4) or in the acoustic domain. A loudspeaker can be used to simulate the antenna under test (AUT) and a small microphone simulates the probe antenna. A computer pen plotter can be used to position the microphone if it is light enough. The source is an audio oscillator. The receiver consists of a pair of analog multipliers driven by the received signal and the audio oscillator output in quadrature.

The software for the low-cost near-field range is straightforward. Data acquisition is performed by moving the probe to the desired position (compute the desired raster or plane polar position and command the scanner to transmit the output), measuring the complex gain through the AUT-probe path (digitize the receiver reading), saving the measurements on disk storage, and returning to the starting position until all points have been measured. Data transformation is performed by transforming the measurements to the far field and plotting the results.

The home-built system has been expanded into a commercial product (Figure 6.3), currently manufactured by Nearfield Systems, Inc. [3]. The commercial version uses a higher quality scanner mechanism and a Hewlett Packard 8510B or Wiltron 360 vector network analyzer or, alternatively, a PMI (Chapter 4).

Commercial systems require much more software and documentation than our home-built system. The data acquisition software needs to support other operations, such as indexing axes and running linearity and swept frequency tests. A

Figure 6.3 Low-cost near-field measurement system (5×5 ft scan area).

more sophisticated scan generator is required to support multifrequency and multibeam antenna testing. Better motor drive algorithms are required.

The data reduction software has been upgraded to provide more complete system capability. Its data processing functions include:

1. Data storage and retrieval (file management, raw data display, extraction of measurement subsets).
2. Transformations (pulse compression, near- to far-field transformation, probe correction, holographic transformation).
3. Processed data displays (gray scale and pseudocolor amplitude and phase images, cuts, contour plots, 3-D plots, radiation distribution plots, listings, disk file outputs).
4. Other (gain and directivity computation, error analysis).

6.2 PORTABLE NEAR-FIELD RANGE MEASUREMENT SYSTEMS

Relatively few small portable near-field measurement systems exist. With the ability to move rapidly to a new site, applications for such a system are being found (examples of output from such systems are shown in Figure 6.4):

1. A small near-field measurement system can determine the equivalent far-field antenna performance. One application, for example, is on-site measurement of vehicle antenna-radome performance. As the measurement system is quite portable, the antenna-radome assembly need not be removed from the vehicle during the test. Another use is to test antenna-spacecraft or antenna-antenna interaction in a high bay assembly area. Results of near-field antenna measurements can include far-field pattern; X and Y cuts; directivity; axial ratio; beam width; beam pointing; phase center position; defocusing; auto-track bias, scale factor, and linearity; reflector surface distortion; feed position errors; microwave holographic measurements.

   In some cases, the probe may be scanned while in direct contact with a phased array antenna surface, eliminating the need for a back projection and reduce crosstalk between measurement positions. For the best measurement quality, mutual coupling between the probe and AUT must be minimized. As is discussed in Chapter 9, mutual coupling can be greatly reduced by using a very well matched probe antenna.

2. A near-field measurement system can provide focused microwave images of antenna and radome defects. With appropriate holographic processing, the microwave energy can be back projected onto curved radome and antenna surfaces, allowing the direct imaging of reflector surface currents and radome anomalies. With additional processing, phased array element excitation problems can be identified.

3. A near-field measurement system, with modification, can measure the near-field RCS of antennas, radomes, and other structures. Although somewhat less desirable than far-field RCS measurements, the near-field measurements still can be quite useful in a go–no go situation. Very little additional hardware is required. This capability can be easily integrated into a near-field measurement system and will become increasingly important as low observable aircraft come into use. By using pulse compression techniques, high-resolution range measurements can be made, which allows a precise identification of the scattering locations. Cross-range (SAR) imaging in one, two, or three dimensions also is possible.

4. Coherent microwave leakage from avionics boxes, cables, *et cetera* can be imaged directly by near-field techniques. The leakage sources can be considered elements of a phased array antenna. This new technique may provide a

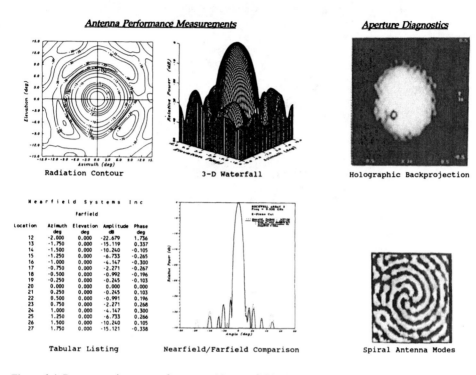

Figure 6.4 Representative output from portable near-field measurement systems.

powerful and rapid method for identifying RF leakage sources within low observable and other aircraft.

5. A near-field measurement system can be used to locate electromagnetic interference on printed circuit boards [1, 2]. A commercial system, shown in Figure 6.5, uses an electronically switched diode system to raster scan through a 40 × 32 array of 1280 antenna elements. The basic switching circuit is shown in Figure 6.6. Similar probing methods have been used in conventional antenna near-field measurement systems. As this system is used to measure energy emitted from the circuit board, the RF system consists of a tunable amplitude only receiver with a dynamic range of 30 dB. The measured data is plotted on an IBM PC or compatible computer. No near-to-far-field transformations are performed. An example of an RF circuit board image is shown in Figure 6.7.

The system has several interesting features: Low resolution scans are performed by enabling clusters of diode switches so that 1, 4, 9, or 12 probes are active at a given time. As a secondary mode, a frequency spectrum of 10 to

Figure 6.5 PC board near-field scanner. (Photo courtesy of Marubeni International.)

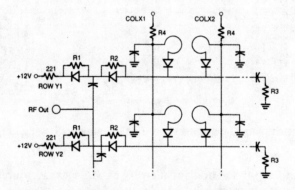

Figure 6.6 Diode antenna multiplexing circuit (courtesy of Marubeni International).

Figure 6.7 Typical circuit board RF field intensity image. (Photo courtesy of Marubeni International.)

750 MHz may be plotted for any given point. To detect both polarizations, alternate antenna rows are polarization rotated by 90°.

6. A portable near-field measurement system can be used to image and locate multipath interference within far-field ranges, compact ranges, and anechoic chambers. The near-field scanner measures the phase front of the quiet zone. A Fourier transform of the measured phase front is a K space image of the arriving energy. A Kaiser-Bessel or similar window function is required to suppress sidelobes. When the transform output is remapped into angle space, the image is very similar to a conventional photographic image, with the image intensity corresponding to the energy arriving from a given direction.

7. A near-field measurement system requires a capability to precisely determine the position of the microwave probe antenna. As such, the near-field scanner can be modified to determine the precise position of other payloads. For example, a touch probe could be used to rapidly make dimensional measurements in the field. Ultrasonic detectors likewise could be used to precisely map radome voids.

There are four operational requirements for a flight line or highly portable near-field measurement system:

1. The system must allow for rapid setup in a flight line or similar environment. As such, the system must be highly portable and rugged. Conventional high-accuracy near-field scanner technology cannot be used due to weight and fragility. The issue of multipath and stray EMI needs to be addressed specifically, because the use of anechoic chambers is not practical on the flight line. Staggered Z scan techniques (Chapter 4) can help substantially reduce axial multipath errors. Additionally, spatial filtering and swept frequency pulse compression techniques can be used to further reduce multipath problems. Noncoherent EMI can be suppressed by the receiver design and the transform process.

2. The portable near-field measurement system must be rugged and easily used by flight-line or spacecraft technicians with minimal RF experience. Additional holographic processing, contour plots, and similar functions can be performed on- or off-line using IBM PC–type computers.

3. The system must be low in cost. Most existing near-field scanners are both very costly and impractical to move. Portable systems can achieve significant cost reductions in the following ways: through low-cost near-field scanner designs, low-cost phase-coherent receivers, simple FDFT far-field transform algorithms, or effective use of low-cost computer technology.

4. The portable near-field measurement system must be accurate. A minimum of absorber is required as the systems are quite small. Even higher accuracy can be achieved by using staggered Z scan multipath suppression.

REFERENCES

1. Ettles, S., *A Cost Effective Path to Electromagnetic Compatibility*, EMC90 Conference Proceedings, ERA Report 90-0089, Leatherhead, U.K. (1990). Paper describes a novel near-field EMI measuring system.
2. Previti, J., *EMSCAN: A Tool to Measure EMI Emissions from Printed Circuit Boards*, EMC Testing, Nov–Dec 1989. Article describes a novel near-field EMI measuring system.
3. Slater, D.G., and G. Hindman, *A Low-Cost Near-Field Antenna Measurement System*, AMTA Conference Proceedings, Antenna Measurement Techniques Association, Monterey, CA (1989).

Chapter 7
ROBOTIC SYSTEM DESIGN

7.1 OVERVIEW

This chapter discusses the design of large, very high-precision robots as used in near-field measurement applications. These scanner mechanisms are actually complete robotic systems capable of much more than RF field probing. The emphasis is on two basic types of robots: very precise systems based on modified granite coordinate measurement machines and portable robots using high-precision optical and fluid measurement skeletons. Smaller systems were described in the previous chapter. This chapter also includes detailed discussions of high-precision position sensors and servo control systems.

The near-field measurement system measures the phase front of an antenna under test and converts the measured phase front into an equivalent angular energy distribution. The near-field range system requires a precise robotic system to position an electromagnetic field probe at various positions on the measurement surface enclosing the phase front of the AUT. The robot performs the following sequence of operations when making near-field measurements:

1. Determine the desired RF probe position,
2. Move the RF probe to the desired position,
3. Measure the complex gain through the AUT-probe path,
4. Save the measurements in the computer memory,
5. Check that everything is in correct working order,
6. If measurement sequence is not complete, return to step 1,
7. Transform the measurements to the far field.

The robot also can be used to carry other payloads, including coordinate measurement sensors and various machining cutters. The command sequence is similar.

The design of high-accuracy robotic systems for near-field measurements is similar to the design of other programmable robots. The basic design goals for a high-accuracy near-field robot are accuracy, speed, adaptability, simplicity, maintainability, user friendliness, and safety.

Accuracy

High accuracy can be achieved by a variety of techniques:

1. Separate reaction and measurement skeletons can be used to provide higher quality position measurements.
2. Position measurements should be made directly, relative to a clearly defined reference. An example of this approach is the Itek Surfitek system that tracks a single cat's eye reflector with four solid-mounted lasers [1].
3. Active suppression of structural resonances minimizes payload position uncertainty.
4. Smooth servo motion minimizes structural disturbances.
5. Payload position measurement systems that are inherently accurate and self-aligning will minimize alignment drift with time. The Itek Surfitek system is an example of this concept.
6. Decreased measurement time resulting from continuous path motion will minimize mechanical and thermal drift.

Speed

To remain competitive, the robots will have to become even faster. The throughput of the robots can be increased by the following methods:

1. *Continuous path control* (CPC) servos are used to eliminate starts and stops. In many applications CPC will increase the throughput by an order of magnitude.
2. Higher accelerations reduce the time to move to a new location.
3. Higher velocities allow a job to be completed sooner.
4. Noncontact laser and microwave surface sensors eliminate the need to dwell at a coordinate measurement location.
5. The trajectory path length should be as short as possible. As an example, a raster pattern is scanned with the alternate scan lines in opposite directions.
6. Multiple frequencies, beams, polarizations, *et cetera,* can be acquired simultaneously in a single scan. This increases the RF subsystem and computational requirements.

Adaptability

The robot design must be easily adaptable to new applications and requirements. This implies a modular design:

1. All servo axes should use a simple, consistent interface philosophy. The number of axes that may be added is limited only by computer speed.

2. Special purpose payloads should be easy to add. Standard payload mounts allow the straightforward installation of specialized payloads. Spare cable trays allow additional payload cabling to be easily added.
3. Robot control software consists of a set of common primitive functions with an application-specific control layer on top. Software module intercommunication can be handled by state space techniques resulting in a high level of modularity [2].
4. The robot should include a network communications capability so that the robot can be easily configured into a *flexible manufacturing system* (FMS). In this case, the robot is simply a module in a much larger system.

Simplicity

A simple robot is easy to build and maintain, but some level of complexity is required to meet the performance requirements. The complexity often can be shifted into the computer software, leaving the hardware simple. The techniques used to simplify the robot design, construction, and installation include the following:

1. Modular design concepts require clearly designed, simple module interfaces for both the hardware and software.
2. The servo system should be based largely on software, using a minimal amount of hardware.
3. The direct and friction drive power transmission designs tend to be simple compared to other transmission designs.
4. Numerous interacting adjustments can be eliminated by using fluid and optical skeleton concepts.

Maintainability

Robots must be reliable, easily repaired, and easily calibrated. These techniques improve the maintainability of the robot:

1. In multiaxis coordinated systems, self-tuning adaptive servo control minimizes the need for skilled technicians.
2. Modular design concepts require carefully thought out and consistent interfaces. Additional servo axes should be easily added, deleted, or replaced.
3. Built-in test equipment, primarily in the form of software, can eliminate the need for such test equipment as oscilloscopes and meters.
4. Inherently accurate skeletal references (such as a beam of light or level of a fluid) eliminate the need for time consuming rail straightness measurements and adjustments.

5. Fault stabilization, analysis, and recovery are natural applications for expert systems. A simple expert system can identify, analyze, and correct many common faults.
6. The servos should use sophisticated, highly reliable servo amplifiers.

User Friendliness

The robot must be usable with minimum training of personnel. Techniques and methods which improve the robot "friendliness" include the following:

1. Menu-driven software provides a means to help the user structure and organize the measurement process.
2. The menu system can be configured for both basic and advanced users. The basic menus prevent the user from becoming overwhelmed during the learning phase. One menu design allows a menu option to be easily redefined as a basic or advanced option at running time.
3. Tests are set up automatically by using rule-based expert systems.
4. On-line help and users manuals eliminate searching for lost technical documentation. The on-line help can be easily searched by the computer for the relevant information.
5. Self-tuning adaptive control systems keep the machine operating at peak performance. No operator interaction is required.
6. Most faults are stabilized, analyzed, and recovered by using expert systems concepts. This minimizes damage and operator frustration.

Safety

This will be discussed in detail later in this chapter.

Other Considerations

A few other robotic design considerations specific to near-field applications are the following:

1. The robot should have a low microwave cross section to minimize RF scattering.
2. A special phase reference cable feed to the RF payload is generally required.
3. The robot should be compatible with the optical tooling techniques used in antenna alignment. This means that some thought is required to ensure that likely sight lines are accessible.
4. Special security requirements often exist. The security constraints are associated mostly with the computational system; for example, RF interferometer

emissions, nonvolatile memory restrictions, tempest-shielding requirements, communication system requirements, operating system requirements, or maintenance restrictions.

7.1.1 Representative Large Near-Field Measurement Robot Designs

NASA-Lewis Vertical Scanner

The NASA-Lewis near-field test facility is an example of a moderately large near-field measurement system (Figure 7.1). The scanner consists of a *y*-axis tower mounted on a set of tracks defining the *x*-axis. The scan plane is vertically oriented.

Figure 7.1 NASA Lewis vertical near-field scanner (courtesy of NASA-Lewis Research Center).

Texas Instruments CMM-Based Scanner

A number of near-field scanners have been built by using modified *coordinate measurement machines* (CMM). These extremely accurate scanners use granite structures and are capable of a precision better than 0.001 inch over the entire travel volume. These systems also retain a comprehensive coordinate measurement capability. Figure 7.2 shows a $8 \times 8 \times 3$-foot scan volume CMM-based scanner built by LK Tool for Texas Instruments.

Figure 7.2 A CMM-based near-field scanner (courtesy of Texas Instruments).

Precision Near-Field Scanner

This scanner is an extremely sophisticated unit that uses granite horizontal rails, a carbon fiber y-axis tower and a laser interferometer-based probe position tracking system. This system is capable of scanning a 23×30-foot region to a planar precision of 0.001 inch over the primary central region. This system was built by LK Tool as a modification of a mechanical coordinate measurement system. The mechanical design is completely kinematic in that all structures use three-point instead of four-point mounts. The independently mounted laser tracking system uses a multilateration technique to monitor the probe XYZ position in space.

NSI Plane Polar Scanner

A plane polar scanner built by Nearfield Systems, Inc. uses a polar scanning technique to sweep a 12-foot diameter planar measurement surface. This highly portable millimeter-wave near-field system is based on a relatively simple and low-cost mechanical structure with a precise optical skeleton. Optical skeletons, which measure structural deformation, are described in more detail later in this chapter.

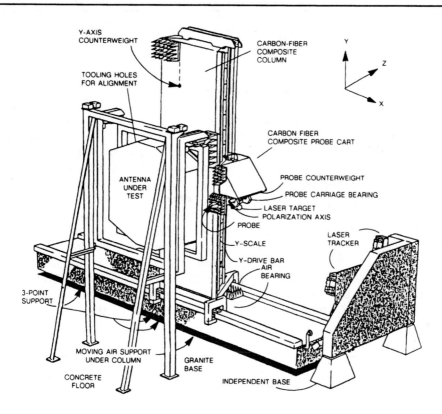

Figure 7.3 Precision near-field scanner.

Figure 7.4 NSI 12-foot diameter, optically augmented, portable near-field scanner.

Very Large Scanners

The largest currently operational near-field scanner, to the author's knowledge, is located at Martin Marietta [25]. This scanner will cover a 78×78-foot area, using an array of four probes with suitable accuracy for measurements up to 18 GHz.

Larger near-field scanners with dimensions of hundreds of feet have been proposed. One design is based on a probe suspended by a series of cables attached to computer-driven winches [14]. Similar cable-suspension systems have been used for precisely positioning cameras within the volume of a sports stadium [3], positioning an RCS probe [4], and supporting antenna feed elements in the Arecibo radio telescope [5]. The precise probe position would be determined by a dispersion-compensated, inertially smoothed optical interferometer. The RF phase reference is transmitted to the probe by an optical fiber embedded in the suspension line. Alignment and calibration of the geometry and correction for fiber stretching in the phase reference system are handled through least-squares techniques in a manner analogous to that used in photogrammetric systems. Because of the large area that must be covered, the scan speed is quite high, on the order of 20 miles per hour.

Other design concepts for very large scanners have included systems that use patch scans (segment of a plane polar scan) produced by an optically augmented tower crane and robotic vehicles that traverse the floor below an antenna. Many of these very large systems can be designed to be quite portable.

A representative level of performance for a high-accuracy near field robotic system is as follows:

X travel: 30 ft
Maximum speed: 30 ips
Maximum acceleration: 10 ips^2
Static accuracy (uncorrected): 0.005″ (peak)
Static accuracy (corrected): 0.001″ (rms)
Repeatability: 0.0002″ (peak)
Dynamic servo error: 0.005″ (10 ips)

Y travel: 23′
Maximum speed: 30 ips
Maximum acceleration: 10 ips^2
Static accuracy (uncorrected): 0.002″ (peak)
Static accuracy (corrected): 0.001″ (rms)
Repeatability: 0.0002″ (peak)
Dynamic servo error: 0.005″ (10 ips)

Z travel: 1′
Maximum speed: 30 ips
Maximum acceleration: 10 ips^2

Static accuracy (uncorrected): 0.005″ (peak)
Static accuracy (corrected): 0.001″ (rms)
Repeatability: 0.0002″ (peak)
Dynamic servo error: 0.005″ (10 ips)

XY orthogonality: 3 arcsec
YZ orthogonality: 3 arcsec
XZ orthogonality: 3 arcsec

Yaw axis: 0° (no servo)
Static accuracy: 3 arcsec
Pitch axis: 0° (no servo)
Static accuracy: 3 arcsec
Roll axis: 360°
Maximum speed: 5°/s
Maximum acceleration: 5°/s^2
Static accuracy: 30 arcsec
Repeatability: 10 arcsec
Dynamic servo error: 60 arcsec

7.1.2   Environmental Considerations

The design of extreme precision robots requires a careful evaluation of the environment in which the robot will be placed. Environmental factors can cause a significant loss of accuracy in a high-precision robot. *Thermal effects* cause scanner dimensions to change, resulting in scale errors, loss of orthogonality, and other distortions. Thermal effects also cause a refractive index change, affecting RF and laser interferometer measurements. *Humidity* causes a refractive index change, affecting RF and laser interferometer measurements. *Atmospheric pressure* also causes a refractive index change affecting RF and laser interferometer measurements. *Ground tilt* can cause the robot axes to become distorted with time. *Ground vibration* can cause the robot payload to vibrate, resulting in positional errors. Ground vibration can corrupt fluid skeleton sensor outputs.

Thermal Effects

Thermal effects usually are the single largest environmental source of error. High-precision near-field facilities, almost without exception, are thermally stabilized to within a few degrees Fahrenheit. Airlocks are commonly used to prevent large temperature changes when antennas are brought into or out of the facility.

Even more important is the deleterious effect of thermal gradients. Destratification fans and ducting are commonly used to minimize thermal gradients. Small thermal gradients can result in large position errors. A large, high-precision scanner may easily distort by 0.001 inch with a few degrees of temperature change. A large scanner can take a week to fully stabilize after a 20° F temperature change.

Refractive Index Variations

The air temperature, like humidity and barometric pressure, is a term in both the optical and microwave indices of refraction. These terms may need to be considered in very large and high-accuracy systems.

A major factor limiting the accuracy of laser interferometers in very large near-field measurement systems is the uncertainty of the refractive index or dielectric constant of the atmosphere over the intervening turbulent path. In interferometers using electromagnetic waves, the atmospheric index of refraction is a function of pressure, temperature, humidity, and the operating wavelength.

For an optical frequency with a wavelength of λ (μm), the group refractive index (n_0) for dry air under *standard temperature and pressure* (STP) conditions ($T = 0°C, P = 760$ mm Hg) is

$$n_0 = 1.0002876 + (4.887 \times 10^{-6}/\lambda^2) + (6.80 \times 10^{-8}/\lambda^4) \tag{7.1}$$

The actual optical refractive index n is a modification of (n_0) by pressure P (mm Hg), water vapor partial pressure (e) mm Hg, temperature T (C), and compressibility ($\alpha = 0.000367$):

$$n = 1 + \frac{n_0 - 1}{1 + \alpha T}\frac{P}{760} - \frac{5.5 \times 10^{-8}e}{1 + \alpha T} \tag{7.2}$$

At microwave frequencies the refractive index n is

$$n = 1 + \frac{3.8 \times 10^{-7}(P - e)}{1 + \alpha T} + \frac{3.2 \times 10^{-7}(1 + 21e/1 + \alpha T)}{1 + \alpha T} \tag{7.3}$$

Table 7.1 shows the extent of some environmental errors.

A near-field range operating over a 20-foot (240-inch) aperture with a 0.001-inch accuracy requires a proportional accuracy of

$$0.001/240 = 4.16 \text{ ppm}$$

For small near-field measurement systems, these error sources are not of much concern. In large systems, the errors can become significant. In general, tem-

Table 7.1
Refractive Index Sensitivity to Meteorological Elements

Parameter	Meteorological Error	Optical Error	Microwave Error
Temperature	2° C	2.0 ppm	2.6 ppm
Pressure	1 mm Hg	0.4 ppm	0.4 ppm
H_2O partial pressure	1.5 mm Hg	0.08 ppm	8.7 ppm
Total error		2.0 ppm	9.1 ppm

perature gradients are a dominant error source in large near-field measurement systems. The temperature gradients may severely affect the measurement structure.

Seismic Considerations

Ground motion disturbances can affect near-field measurements in several ways:

1. Long-term differential settling of the foundation can significantly distort the scanner mechanism. Differential motions can be quite large, as evidenced by the cracks often seen in concrete.
2. Vibration of the electromagnetic field sensing probe relative to the AUT will result in an increase in phase noise. The probe vibration changes the RF path length and, therefore, the received phase. An unwanted probe deflection of 0.001 in. corresponds to a phase error of 3° at 100 GHz.

Past experience has indicated that the ground motion of a correctly designed foundation has four significant components:

1. Microseismic motion (0.1–20 Hz, 0.05–0.5 arcsecond) caused by ocean waves, the wind, or cultural elements.
2. Diurnal variations (0.5–22 arcseconds per 24-hour period) due to solar or cultural effects.
3. Secular variations (1–90 arcsec per year) due to seasonal temperature variations, rain, or ground settling.
4. Earthquakes.

The magnitude of the ground tilt and vibration can vary significantly as a function of the geophysical environment and foundation design [6, 7]. Literature [8] has reported tilt rates as high as 90 arcseconds per year, 22 arcseconds per day, and 11 arcseconds per 6 hours. Cultural effects are often clearly observable. Diurnal tilts typically varied from 1 to 10 arcseconds, peak-to-peak. Some of the measurements reported in the literature were not performed on good foundations.

The microseismic motion has never been found to cause problems with near-field measurements in a properly designed system, even a large system located several hundred yards from a train track. If necessary, a scan could be halted automatically during excessive seismic activity as sensed by a geophone. The basic requirements for minimizing seismic effects within a near-field facility are

1. Install the scanner on a ground floor. Floor motion is generally much greater on upper floors,
2. Use a building with a good foundation,
3. Have no compressors, shake tables, or other machinery that causes high vibration levels within 50 feet of the scanner.

The magnitude of the diurnal motion is usually quite low, on the order of a few arcseconds if the foundation design is correct. Furthermore, the scanner and antenna probably follow the same trajectory as they share a common foundation. The diurnal motion generally causes no problems.

Long-term tilts of the entire near-field scanner structure and floor generally cause no problems other than a slight complication to optical alignment operations. Long-term foundation settling, ground settling, and scanner structural deformations can cause significant scanner distortion problems. Structural deformation of the scanner can be minimized by doing the following:

1. Design the scanner so that it can be realigned easily. Minimize the use of interacting alignment adjustments.
2. Use a kinematic scanner design to minimize coupling of the foundation forces into the scanner. This design technique uses a separate substructure with a three-point isolation mount to minimize coupling differential ground motion into the scanner. Some very high-precision millimeter-wave near-field measurement systems have used pneumatic suspension and isolation systems.
3. Use an optical skeleton. The optical skeleton converts the problem of maintaining high accuracy in the large scanner into a problem of maintaining high accuracy in a small assembly (i.e., the optical skeleton). Long-term motion of the optical skeleton reference can be measured readily by using precision levels and autocollimation techniques.

Earthquakes, if severe, can cause significant alignment problems. The scanner alignment, therefore, should be rechecked after any significant earthquake.

A seismic survey can be performed prior to the installation of the near-field measurement system. A representative survey could include the following tests:

1. Visual inspection to identify potential vibration sources,
2. Ground velocity measured by a short period seismometer,
3. Long-term ground tilt measured by a tiltmeter,
4. Differential floor motion measured optically.

At a minimum, visually inspect the region surrounding the proposed facility to a radius of 100 ft. Check particularly for large compressors, punch presses, and similar items. Unless the system is very small or well isolated, verify that the proposed facility is on the ground floor.

Vibration and stability can be tested simply by setting up a sight level or theodolite and viewing a target 10 or 20 feet away. No relative motion should be visible. This test looks at relative motion between two points and gives an indication of potential relative motion between the antenna and near-field scanner or even between parts of the scanner itself. This test has only moderate sensitivity with a noise floor of 0.001 inch. More detailed tests can be performed using seismometers and tiltmeters if necessary. A representative equipment list is in Table 7.2.

Table 7.2
Equipment for Testing Vibration and Stability

Item	Vendor	Model
Short period seismometer	Teledyne Geotech	S-13
Calibration kit	Teledyne Geotech	21323
Interconnect cable and load	Nearfield Systems, Inc.	None
Preamplifier	Tektronix	AM502
Oscilloscope	Tektronix	SC503
Digital voltmeter	Tektronix	DM501
Tiltmeter	Rockwell	None
Alignment base	Rockwell	None
Chart recorder	Soltec	6723
Precision optical level	Hilger & Watts	TB95/3
Precision sight level	Wild	N3
Target scale	Brunson	564-10
Trivet assembly	K&E	9099-70

Some examples of seismic site survey measurements are listed in Table 7.3. All measurements were made at various locations within the Los Angeles basin. Sites A, B, and C are located within a large building at a large aerospace company. These sites were all located below a parking structure. Site D is in a small industrial park. Site E is in a rural residential location.

The ground vibration tests were performed by monitoring the velocity output of a Teledyne Geotech S-13 short period seismometer on an oscilloscope. A Tektronix AM502 preamplifier was used to provide the necessary signal conditioning. The seismometer is sensitive to the vertical component of seismic energy in the 1–20 Hz region [7]. Values are indicated in units of mils, which are equivalent to units of 0.001 inch.

The quiescent seismic noise at all locations except for site E was predominantly low frequency with a level around 0.15 mil/s. At 1 Hz, this is equivalent to a ground displacement of 0.04 mil, peak-to-peak.

Table 7.3
Seismic Survey Measurements

Location	Peak Velocity
Site A (quiescent)	0.15 mil/sec
(car traffic)	0.88 mil/sec
Site B (quiescent)	0.11 mil/sec
(car traffic)	0.37 mil/sec
Site C (quiescent)	0.15 mil/sec
(car traffic)	0.59 mil/sec
Site D (quiescent)	0.15 mil/sec
(truck traffic)	0.59 mil/sec
Site E (quiescent)	0.01 mil sec
(truck at 100')	0.29 mil/sec

Car traffic in the overhead parking structure (sites A, B, and C) was clearly observable. The ground velocity levels increased by up to six times the quiescent level. A structural resonance is evident with an energy peak near 15 Hz. Because the ground displacement is the integral of the measured velocity, a 6 dB/octave roll-off in the measured data is required to determine ground displacement. The ground displacement due to the traffic in the parking structure is approximately 0.01 mil. The observed ground vibration at all sites would pose no problems to conventional small- to medium-sized near-field measurement systems.

An example of a tiltmeter recording in Site A is shown in Figure 7.5. The tiltmeter was set up to monitor long-term ground motion. The measurements were made with a modified Rockwell bubble tiltmeter and recorded on a small two-channel chart recorder. The tiltmeter measurements resulted in the following observations.

1. A diurnal east-west tilt of 2 arcsec peak-to-peak amplitude is clearly observable on workdays only. The tilt starts at 7 AM, builds up to a maximum at 12

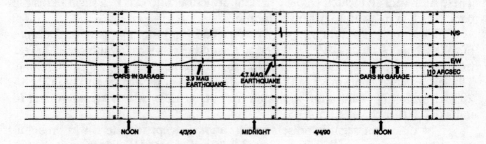

Figure 7.5 Example of ground tilt history (site A).

noon, decreases slightly (0.5 arcsecond) until 1 PM, and then increases to the maximum value again until 4 PM, where it gradually tapers to the starting value around 6 PM. This phenomena clearly is the cars entering and leaving the parking lot. The noon lunch break also is quite visible. The peak tilt rate is generally quite slow, on the order of 1.5 arcsec per hr.

2. The observed long-term tilts (after tiltmeter thermal stabilization) are quite low. The NS tilt was approximately 1 arcsec over five days or a slope of 0.2 arcsec per day. The EW tilt was essentially zero. No diurnal tilts were observed other than the previously described culturally induced structural loading. Thermally induced diurnal tilts often are observed in structures as they are differentially heated by the sun.

3. Several small earthquakes can be seen in the tiltmeter record. The earthquakes have a characteristic signature in terms of an exponentially decaying envelope or coda. The largest observed earthquake occurred on April 4, 1990, at 2 AM with an 11-arcsecond peak-to-peak tilt observed on both the N–S and E–W channels. The coda was observable for a duration of 6 minutes. A simple, empirically derived approximation of earthquake magnitude for a local event within California is $M = -1.7 + 2.6 \log T$, where $T =$ the duration of the coda in seconds. The 6-minute coda duration translates into a magnitude 4.9 (Richter scale) earthquake. This event correlates well with a magnitude 4.7 earthquake located 28 miles offshore of Oceanside at 1:54 AM on April 4, as reported by the Caltech Seismological Observatory. A smaller earthquake was observed Wednesday, April 3, 1990, at 7:10 PM. The EW peak-to-peak ground tilt was 2 arcseconds; the NS ground tilt was 1 arcsecond. With a duration of 2 minutes, this corresponds to a magnitude 3.7 earthquake. This event correlates well with a magnitude 3.9 earthquake at 7:13 PM located 7 miles northeast of Lake Arrowhead (CalTech data).

7.1.3 Robot Design

The design of a robot can be simplified by using analogies to a living organism. The robot, like a living organism, is a closed-loop system that responds to external stimuli using an internal world model and a set of rules. An organism senses some event and transmits the sensory data to the brain. The brain responds to the stimuli using a world model and a set of rules. The response is through the muscular system. The robotic and biological equivalents in the order of signal flow are shown in Table 7.4. The high-accuracy robot includes the following subsystems:

1. Skeletal subsystem,
2. Position measurement subsystem,
3. Servo system,
4. Computational system,

Table 7.4
Equivalent Systems in Robots and Organisms

Robot	*Organism*
Skeletal system	skeleton
Sensory group	senses
Communications system	neural system
Computational system	brain
Effector group	muscles
Power distribution	circulatory system

   5. Communications system,
   6. Fault protection.

These subsystems will be described in detail in the order just given. The software requirements will be described in a later section. Closely related to the robot, but not technically a part of it, is the payload. The typical payloads (microwave interferometer, optical surface sensor, and high-speed cutter) were discussed in earlier sections of this book.

7.2 ROBOT SKELETON

The robot skeleton provides two basic functions: a means of reacting against the payload forces and a means to reference the payload position and orientation to the world coordinate system. Most near-field robots use a single mechanical skeleton for both purposes. Performance can be increased substantially by using two separate skeletons individually optimized for each application. The two skeletons are called the *reaction* and *measurement skeletons.*

7.2.1 Reaction Skeleton

The payload carried by the robot is subjected to forces created by gravity, payload acceleration, aerodynamics, and, in certain cases, forces created by physical contact with the work. The mechanical structure provides a reaction mass for the payload.

Reaction skeleton techniques used by mechanical structures include the following:

   1. Cartesian (NBS, NSI scanners),
   2. Polar (JPL, NSI plane polar scanners),
   3. Cylindrical (IBM robot, cylindrical near fields),
   4. Spherical (Puma robot, spherical near fields),
   5. Cable suspension systems (LAPIS, Arecibo, Skycam).

Reaction skeleton techniques used by nonmechanical structures include these:

1. Reaction mass (satellites),
2. Fluid (aerial, undersea RPV),
3. Magnetic (MagLev trains),
4. Electrostatic (LDR antennas, gyros).

The near-field scanners discussed in this chapter all use some form of a mechanical structure. A careful selection of the structure type and orientation can improve the near-field measurement quality. Planar scanner designs of particular interest are compared in Table 7.5.

Table 7.5
Planar Scanner Designs

	Scanner type				
	XYZ Cup H	XYZ Cup Up	XYZ Cup Down	Polar	Cable Suspension
AUT relative to NFTF	side	below	above	side	below
Gravity simulation	poor	good	good	good	good
Synthetic coordinates	yes	yes	yes	limited	yes
Thermal gradients	poor	good	good	good	excellent
AUT protection	good	poor	good	poor	poor
Portability	poor	poor	good	good	excellent
AUT alignment ease	average	good	good	poor	good
Multiple AUTs	yes	yes	yes	limited	yes

Gravity Simulation

The antenna orientation relative to gravity currently is the most important design driver for near-field range scanners used to test spacecraft antennas. Most spacecraft antenna reflectors become distorted in a 1 G gravity field. The distortions are analyzed most easily if the antenna is pointing either directly up or down. Note that some near-field measurement systems use a synthetic coordinate system, allowing continuous rotation of the scan plane to any arbitrary orientation [9]. This can minimize sampling densities in plane polar scans.

Thermal Gradients

The atmosphere tends to stratify thermally. Therefore, a scanner with a horizontal scan plane will have a somewhat higher accuracy. This is because the entire scanner mechanism can be held within a constant temperature stratum.

AUT Protection

A required or preferred orientation of the antenna under test drives the scanner design. In the case of parabolic antennas, the orientation of the antenna concave surface is often described as having a cup up, down, or sideways orientation.

Certain design configurations, such as the cup down and cup sideways designs, provide better protection to the AUT, because a part that falls off the scanner will not hit the AUT. In one case, problems occurred when small particles of microwave absorber fell into the throat of a millimeterwave horn antenna. This problem was solved by placing a Mylar film across the horn aperture.

Portability

The floor-mounted cup down scanner, when properly designed, is reasonably portable.

Ease of AUT Alignment

Near-field scanners with horizontal scan planes are the easiest to align optically with respect to the AUT reference frame. This is because the AUT alignment can be performed with a sight level. Note that the CMM-based scanners are vibration isolated and float on a cushion of air, so that the gravity vector is not stable relative to the scan plane. The CMM-based scanners are aligned relative to the AUT using mechanical sensors.

Scanners using a polar format are more difficult to align. The rotational axis must remain normal to the scan axis to within a tolerance of 2 arcseconds to maintain a 0.001-inch scan plane accuracy for a 20-foot aperture. Antenna coning will also cause problems and may be difficult to adjust if not considered early in the design phase. An advantage of the polar format scanners is that the control system does not need multiaxis coordination for plane polar scans. Other advantages are simplicity, portability, and low cost.

Reflection Control

The cup down scanner designs are often considered to be more susceptible to reflection problems, because the AUT is aimed directly at the floor, which may be reflective. Past experience however, indicates that this is not a problem, because absorber can be placed readily on the floor. Equivalent far-field reflection levels for a typical near-field scanner are less than -40 dB relative to the main-beam peak. Ceiling reflections in the spacecraft high-bay area are higher in level.

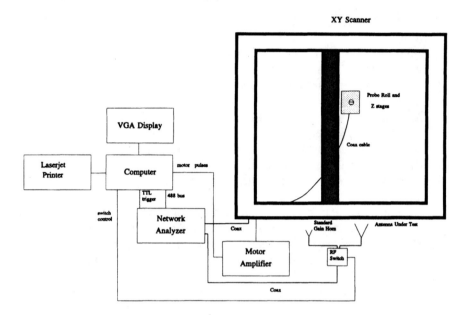

Figure 7.6 Typical NFTR robot block diagram.

Multiple AUTs

The Cartesian near-field scanners using synthetic coordinate systems easily support multiple AUTs. This capability is important in gain comparison measurements. Testing multiple antennas is not as easily supported on the polar near-field designs. In one case (NSI plane polar), the small reference antenna was scanned with a sector portion of a plane polar scan.

Bridge versus Overhead Gantry Designs

CMM-based bridge designs (Figure 7.3) are less likely than overhead gantry designs to cause reflections or block the view of optical alignment instruments. The design trade-offs between different skeletal configurations include

1. Ease of installation and alignment,
2. Cost,
3. Modularity,
4. Portability,
5. Payload maneuverability,

6. Payload capacity,
7. Motor size,
8. Safety,
9. Environmental compatibility,
10. Position measurement sensor compatibility,
11. Payload cabling,
12. Compatibility with additional axes,
13. Structural mode frequencies and damping ratios,
14. Lighting system compatibility and thermal effects,
15. Microwave cross-sectional area,
16. Compatibility with optical tooling instruments.

A representative very high-precision scanner design based on coordinate measurement machine (CMM) technology is described along with the rationale for the design. The correct design of the skeletal subsystem is critical to the overall performance of the near-field measurement system. A variety of technologies are used in this example.

The x-axis (30 feet of horizontal travel) is a carriage traveling on a pair of precision-lapped, natural close-grained granite rails. This design allows very stable, smooth, and repeatable x-axis positioning. The granite surface remains quite stable with time due to the natural formation and machining processes and has a third of the thermal expansion coefficient of steel. The large mass of the granite damps seismic vibrations. Granite surfaces can be lapped to a high-precision scanner without imposing any stresses into the material and, therefore, will remain accurate over long periods of time. Granite will not corrode nor will it adhere to the bearings when not in use for a long time.

Accidental damage to the guideways is not normally detrimental because pieces tend to break out rather than raise burrs on the surface. The air bearings have a large surface area and will glide over any such damage with no effect. Such bearings and rails have been used for high-precision dimensional inspection robots for many years. Overtravel protection is provided electrically by limit switches and mechanically by pneumatic shock absorbers.

The x-axis carriage rides on a kinematic configuration of three self-aligning air bearings. The choice of air bearings in this application is well proven and provides higher accuracy than conventional roller bearings, as the air bearings tend to ignore local surface variations or damage to the rails. The air bearings ride 0.0004 inch above the granite surface. Precise spacing is maintained continually by an air pressure regulation subsystem. The air bearings have virtually no hysteresis and eliminate the stick-slip problems common to other bearings.

The granite rails are tied to the foundation by using a three-point suspension at the Airy points. The Airy points are the optimum points at which a bar must be supported horizontally to minimize bending. The separation between support points, s, given the length of the bar, l, and number of supports, n, is

$$s = \frac{l}{\sqrt{n^2 - 1}}$$

A carriage mass unloading system is also installed below the granite rails. This system uses a series of air cylinders to dynamically counteract the weight of the moving carriage.

The y-axis (23 feet of vertical travel) uses a stress-relieved steel or carbon composite structure to support a set of steel rails. This concept is used because the weight of the granite would become excessive. The structure uses a trusswork to maintain high rigidity with minimum mass. The geometry of the steel structure may drift slightly with time. These effects are minimized by using a solid foundation (i.e., the granite x-axis), by relieving stress to the steel structure, and by an optional structural deformation monitoring subsystem. The z-axis again uses a steel structure for reasons similar to those for the y-axis.

This design provides extreme accuracy and may be used when antenna surface machining operations are contemplated. The system is quite costly and is suited only to permanent locations, however. Near-field robotic systems are now evolving toward portable, lower accuracy structures, augmented with structural deflection sensors.

7.3 PAYLOAD POSITION MEASUREMENT SYSTEM

The payload position measurement system measures the payload position relative to a reference coordinate system. The probe position measurement system consists of three basic sensor types combined into an integrated system:

1. Distance measuring sensors (distance along line of sight),
2. Angle measuring sensors,
3. Straightness measuring sensors (displacement perpendicular to line of sight).

The sensors are combined into a position measurement system by adding a computer interface, related software, and a series of mechanical structures. The mechanical structure, called the *measurement skeleton,* is used to reference the various sensors to the world coordinate system.

A variety of systems can provide high-accuracy position measurements. Several of the systems listed in Table 7.6 lack any real-time capability, but are useful

Table 7.6
High-Accuracy Position Measurement Systems

Measurement System	Proportional rms Accuracy (ppm)	Random Fixed rms Error (in.)	Notes
*CCD star tracker (Ball)	106.0	0.12	
Kern Mecometer	10.0	0.12	
*Theodolites	10.0	0.001	
*NBS interferometer	4.2	0.005	
Photogrammetry	4.0	0.0003	
*Granite-encoder (LK)	3.1	0.0003	1
*Leighton system	1.6	0.0003	2
*Granite-encoder (OSC)	0.44	0.00001	3
*Surfitek (Itek)	0.32	0.000007	4
*Dual interferometer	0.1	0.03	5
*Triple interferometer	0.01		5
VLBI	0.006	0.3	6

Notes:

1. Based on an 8-foot measurement to an rms accuracy of 0.0003 inch.
2. Based on measured rms accuracy of 15 μm over a 30-ft diameter area. Note that the accuracy spec-ification is for the machining accuracy of this unit. The machine itself is actually more accurate if used only for noncontact measurements [10].
3. The unit was a precision vertical grinder manufactured by Campbell Grinder Co. and heavily mod-ified by the Optical Sciences Center at the University of Arizona. It achieved a machining accuracy of 3 μm on a 6-ft size optical mirror segment. The coordinate measurement accuracy was 1 μm rms over 6 feet [11].
4. Surfitek measured a 24-inch diameter optical mirror surface with an accuracy of 0.27 μm rms [1, 12].
5. The dual and triple wavelength interferometers have been used in earthquake and geodetic studies measuring small distance changes (1 mm) over path lengths of many miles [13]. The use of multiple wavelengths suppresses atmospheric effects. The random fixed error in the comparison table is based on the geodetic application. This concept, when applied to short-range (500 feet) measurements, should provide virtually unmatched performance and accuracy. The method is used by the proposed LAPIS near-field system [14].
6. *Very long baseline interferometry* (VLBI) techniques can measure intercontinental distances with an accuracy of 1 cm. The VLBI technique is mentioned because of its similarities to short-range, high-accuracy interferometers.

for calibration and validation. The systems are listed in order of increasing propor-tional accuracy. Asterisks indicate that the sensor is suitable for real-time positional feedback.

Note that the highest accuracy position measurement sensors are all varia-tions of interferometers. The highest accuracy interferometers all compensate for atmospheric propagation effects by using multiple wavelengths.

7.3.1 Position Sensors

The position sensor measures the payload position relative to a reference coordinate system. Important position sensor requirements are as follows:

1. The position sensor must provide real-time position measurements with minimum (5 ms or less) latency, because the sensor is part of a control loop and excessive lag will destabilize the control loop.
2. The actual time of a position measurement must be known with high precision, typically a few μs, because the position often is changing rapidly. Without accurate time tagging, the position measurement cannot be correlated to other payload sensors, and the control loop will produce noisy, incorrect servo commands. For example, an axis moving at 12 inches per second will have a 0.012-inch position uncertainty for each millisecond of timing error.
3. The sensor ideally should measure the payload position relative to the reference coordinate system with no intervening structures, because intervening structures are a major, often unpredictable, error source.
4. The position sensor should provide a real-time estimate of the position measurement uncertainty to verify correct operation of the sensor system.

Different near-field ranges use a variety of techniques to determine the probe position.

7.3.2 Distance Measuring Sensors

Most near-field robots use three basic types of distance measuring sensors: resolvers and inductosyns, incremental encoders, and laser inferometers. Incremental encoders include the Heidenhain optical encoder, the rotary optical encoder, and the Sony magnescale. Laser interferometers include the HP-5501 interferometer and inertially smoothed, dispersion-compensated interferometer. Table 7.7 compares these three types of sensors.

Table 7.7
Distance Measuring Sensors

Comparison	Laser Interferometer	Encoder
Accuracy	higher	lower
Stability	higher	lower
Resolution	higher	lower
Noise	higher	lower
Complexity	higher	lower
Misalignment tolerance	better (0.1 in.)	worse (0.005 in.)
Reliability	lower	higher
Cost	higher (3×)	lower (1×)

The main reasons for using optical encoders is their lower cost and simplicity. The laser interferometers mainly are used for their less-demanding axis straightness requirements and higher accuracy. The HP laser interferometer will allow up to 0.1 inch of lateral misalignment as compared to the 0.006-inch misalignment for the Heidenhain optical sensors.

In all cases, the distance measuring sensors used in the near-field robots should measure the payload positions as directly as possible. This is in contrast to systems that use optical encoders mounted on the motor drive shaft.

Incremental Encoders

An incremental encoder is an electromechanical device used to measure a change in the linear or angular position of a robot joint. Virtually all incremental encoders measure the passage of some type of a grating past a sensor head. The grating pattern may be sensed optically, magnetically, capacitively, or by electrical contact. Optical sensors are most common.

Typically, a high-resolution optical encoder consists of five components (see Figure 7.7):

1. Light source (LED or incandescent),
2. Moving grating,
3. Stationary grating,
4. Light sensor,
5. Conditioning circuitry.

The light illuminates the moving grating. A moire pattern is formed between the moving and stationary gratings. The moire pattern causes a periodic fluctuation in the intensity of the light passing through the pair of gratings. A pair of photo-detectors measures the intensity fluctuations. Two photodetectors are required to resolve the direction of travel. The detector output is amplified and processed in a signal conditioner.

The output of an incremental encoder is a pair of sine or square waves in quadrature (see Figure 7.8). The pair of sine or square waves is often called a *quadrature signal* or simply an I and Q signal. The frequency of the sine waves are proportional to the velocity of the axis. The phase relationship between the I and Q signals indicates the direction of travel.

The output of the encoder is converted to a position by integrating (counting the edges of the I and Q signals) the encoder signals. Interfacing an incremental encoder to a computer requires the following elements:

1. Line receiver,
2. Quadrature to count and direction conversion,

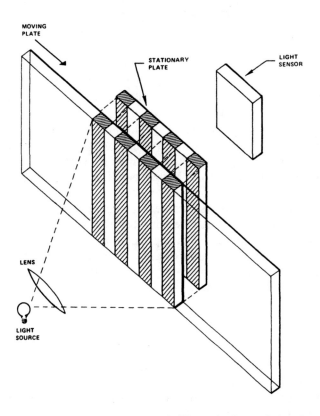

Figure 7.7 High-resolution optical encoder (courtesy of Dynamics Research Corp.).

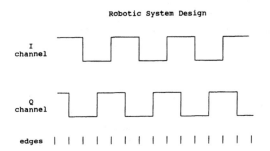

Figure 7.8 Encoder quadrature signals.

3. Counter,
4. Double buffer and time tag.

The line receiver accepts a noisy *I-Q* signal from the encoder and converts it into a high-quality digital *I-Q* signal. The quadrature converter translates the *I-Q* signal into a count and direction signal.

The quadrature decoder drives a digital up-down counter. The counter contains the definite integral of the encoder output pulses. A constant of integration must be defined before using the position counter. This operation, known as *indexing,* consists of searching for a single known position. When the known position is identified, the counter is preset to a known value.

High-performance servo systems need precise knowledge of the time that a position measurement was made. One approach that works well is to both double buffer the counter and interrupt it at a periodic rate (100 Hz). This approach is used by the QIC-486 encoder interface card, in the previously described near-field range scanners. Positions are available at a 100 Hz rate within the computer with a timing accuracy of approximately 1 μs.

Laser Interferometer

A number of near-field scanners use laser interferometers to sense the *x* and *y* axes positions. The laser interferometer can achieve a very high accuracy and often is used as a primary distance measuring standard. The laser interferometer has another significant advantage in that the straightness of the axis is less critical than many of the other sensors. This was the main reason for using a laser interferometer in one near-field measurement system.

In most interferometers, including both the near-field microwave measurement interferometer and laser position sensing interferometer, the wavefront interference is formed directly by the radiation field. The laser interferometer (shown in Figure 7.9) measures range by determining the phase difference between two interferometer paths. One path includes the unknown distance, the other path contains only a fixed delay. A phase meter measures the phase difference between the two interferometer paths. Both the ranging and reference paths start at the laser.

A signal will experience a phase delay equal to 2π rad per wavelength of path length difference. One cycle of phase shift corresponds to a distance of 0.0000249 inch at the HeNe laser line (632.8 nm) used by the interferometer.

The operation of the laser interferometer is similar to that of the microwave interferometer, except the operating frequency is much higher. Most laser interferometers operate at a frequency of 473755 GHz (473 THz). This corresponds to a

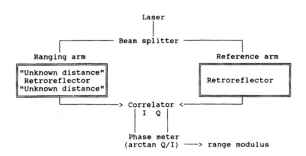

Figure 7.9 Laser interferometer.

wavelength of 632.8 nm or 0.0000249 inch. The wavelength varies slightly with atmospheric changes, as described earlier. The laser interferometer measures distances in terms of wavelengths.

Conventional fringe counting interferometers cannot determine the direction of motion, yet the servo system requires this information. Two basic variations of the laser and correlator solve this problem by developing a quadrature signal. With the quadrature signal, direction can be extracted in a manner similar to the previously described optical encoders.

The less common design is actually simpler and provides excellent high-speed capabilities. One variation of this concept uses a linearly polarized single-frequency laser and the optical equivalent of a quadrature mixer. The quadrature mixer is formed by a pair of photodiodes and a quarter-wave plate similar to a 90° hybrid. The laser sends out a linearly polarized beam at a 45° orientation relative to the vertical. The beam is split into two paths by an optical cube beam splitter. The reference and measurement paths are established by a pair of retroreflectors, only one of which may move. The quarter-wave plate is placed in series with one arm resulting in that beam becoming circularly polarized. After recombining the two beams in the beam splitter, the vertically and horizontally polarized interference fringe components are split in a Wollaston prism and transferred to two photodetectors. The output from the photodetector corresponds to an I and a Q signal.

A common laser interferometer design, used by HP, Marktek, and others, uses a dual-frequency, dual-polarization laser (see Figure 7.10). The laser uses magnetically induced Zeeman line splitting to produce two frequencies separated by approximately 2 MHz. The two frequencies are cross-polarized. The two beams are separated by a polarization beam splitter and used as the measurement and reference beams. The two beams are then recombined in the same beam splitter and sent to a single PIN photodetector. The fringes detected by the photodetector are formed through additive interference. A second detector mounted in the laser mea-

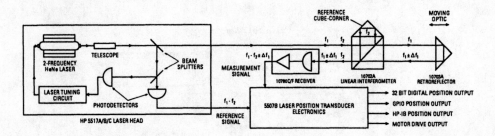

Figure 7.10 Hewlett-Packard laser interferometer block diagram (courtesy of Hewlett-Packard).

sures the Zeeman difference frequency. A digital quadrature mixer is used to combine the two signals and to derive the I and Q signals.

7.3.3 Angle Measuring Sensors

Angular sensors often are used in secondary roles to provide measurements of robot and AUT twist, seismic disturbances, and polarization axis angles.

Rotary Encoder

Rotary optical encoders frequently are used to measure the angle of the polarization axis. The rotary optical encoder operates on the same principle as the previously described linear optical encoders. Synchros, resolvers, and "inductosyns" can be used in a similar manner.

Accelerometer

Accelerometers may be used as precise electronic levels to monitor the pointing of the AUT or parts of the NFTR robot. A secondary role is to monitor for earthquakes or other seismic disturbances. Accelerometers generally are not capable of measuring dynamic tilt. Most of the accelerometers either use a variation of a fluid level or a force rebalance pendulum. Fluid sensors will be described later.

The force rebalance accelerometer (Figure 7.11) has a small proof mass suspended on the end of a pendulum. A sensor measures the proof mass position, and a small electromagnet applies a force to the proof mass. The accelerometer contains a servo loop that tries to hold the proof mass at a given position by using the electromagnet. The amount of current in the electromagnet is a direct measure of the acceleration force present.

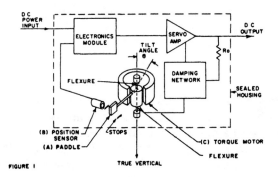

Figure 7.11 Force rebalance accelerometer (courtesy of Schavitz Engineering).

The accelerometer scale factor and linearity may be calibrated by using a precision rotary table to align the sensitive axis at various angles relative to gravity. The acceleration is equal to

$$A = g \sin\theta \qquad (7.4)$$

where

$g = 980.665 \text{ cm/s}^2,$
$\theta = \text{tilt angle.}$

Autocollimator

Angular tilt of a mirror can be remotely monitored by an autocollimator. An advantage of the autocollimator is that angular tilt measurements can be made of a moving object. The autocollimator can measure angles to a small fraction of an arcsec. As a representative application, the NSI plane polar scanner (Figure 7.5) uses an electronic autocollimator to monitor wobble of the ϕ axis bearing and general motion of the support structure.

7.3.4 Straightness Measuring Sensors

Straightness sensors are used to measure the displacement of a target at right angles to the line of sight. The straightness sensors are used within the robot to monitor errors in the straightness of the rails and correspondingly errors in the position of the payload. Basically, two types of straightness sensors are of interest: optical and fluid. Both types of sensor will be discussed, followed by the integration of the sensors into complete systems.

Optical Straightness Sensors

Deflections of the skeletal rails can be measured by optical straightness sensors, which measure motion at right angles to a laser beam. Hewlett-Packard, Marktek, and others manufacture straightness interferometers. Marktek, K&E, UDT, and others manufacture dual-axis alignment sensors that use lateral effect photodiodes. The lateral displacement detectors usually are preferred for their simplicity, lower cost, and ability to sense two axes. The primary disadvantages of lateral effect detectors is a 1% linearity error and some sensitivity to stray light. *Change coupled device* (CCD) sensors can be used instead of the lateral effect photodiodes to improve linearity at the expense of higher cost, complexity, and reduced bandwidth.

This section will concentrate on optical straightness sensor designs that use a laser with a lateral effect photodiode. Other designs are quite similar. Most straightness sensor systems consist of a combination of three basic elements:

1. Laser head

    HeNe laser (light source),

    Spatial filter (improves beam quality),

    Quarter wave plate (reduces beam-pointing instability),

    Collimator (reduces beam wandering),

    Invar housing (reduces beam wandering).

2. Reference angle generator

    Pentaprism (Rotates laser beam 90°),

    Pentaprism servo (establishes a plane reference).

3. Detector

    6328 Å filter (suppresses stray light),

    Lateral effect photodiode (senses laser beam centroid),

    Signal conditioner (computes centroid position),

    Analog-to-digital converter (computer interface).

The laser head generally includes a *helium neon* (HeNe) laser operating at 6328 Å. The output power normally is a few milliwatts or less. The laser output passes through a collimator consisting of a quarter-wave plate, a focusing lens, a spatial filter, and a collimating lens, as shown in Figure 7.12. The quarter-wave plate is used to circularly polarize the light. The circular polarization suppresses laser cavity instabilities created by external reflections into the cavity, as these now would be cross polarized. The collimator reduces laser beam wandering by the magnification ratio (approximately 10). The spatial filter consists of a pinhole at the focal plane of the focusing lens. The spatial filter eliminates off-axis energy due to diffraction and high-order modes. The output of the collimator is typically a 10 mm diameter beam with a Gaussian profile.

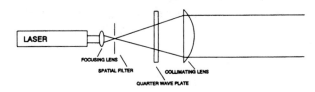

Figure 7.12 Laser head for straightness measurements.

Right-angle turns of the laser beam can be accomplished with very high accuracy (1–3 arcseconds) by using an optical square or pentaprism. This capability is useful in measuring the orthogonality between two axes. A plane can be swept out by rotating the pentaprism. If the input beam is not centered along the axis of rotation, the height of the output beam will vary in a cyclic manner. This can be measured easily by a beam splitter and lateral effect detector at the pentaprism output. Other errors occur if the pentaprism is tilted relative to the incident laser beam. These errors can be readily measured and suppressed. Changing incidence angles on the detector (causing optical filter problems) can be suppressed by using a retroreflector.

Straightness is measured when a detector measures the relative motion of the laser-beam centroid. A lateral-effect photodiode is a common sensor providing an accuracy of 1% of full scale. This type of sensor is used on several systems, including the NSI plane polar near-field measurement systems. Higher linearities, better than 0.05%, can be obtained with CCD television sensors at the expense of more complexity and cost. Both types of sensors are upset by stray light. A shroud and an optical bandpass filter tuned to the laser wavelength of 6328 Å effectively eliminates this problem.

One problem with the optical straightness sensors is the noisy output of the detector. The noise is caused by local variations in the atmospheric index of refraction. Noise levels are typically around 0.001 inch rms per 20 feet. The noise can be eliminated by sufficient filtering (0.1 Hz bandwidth). This is adequate for on-line calibration purposes but may not be suitable for real-time continuous path measurements.

Experiments have indicated that the sensor noise can be reduced by an order of magnitude by careful control of the atmospheric path. One approach is to enclose the laser beam in a tube and blow air through the tube with a small fan.

Another approach is to use *model reference adaptive* (MRA) technique, which is closely related to the Kalman filter. In this method, a computer model of the structural deformations is slowly updated. This approach works with structures that remain relatively stable with time. The MRA technique is also used in CPC servo control systems, as will be described later.

Another approach uses inertial smoothing techniques to filter out the atmospheric noise. This approach is used in the LAPIS near-field range [14]. Inertial smoothing, unfortunately, is an expensive, specialized, complex approach and is not further discussed in this book.

Fluid Straightness Sensors

Fluid sensors and skeletons are extremely rare but are quite accurate and cost effective. One popular application has been in earthquake and volcano ground-motion studies. A small tiltmeter commercially available from Autonetics, a division of Rockwell International, has a noise level in the vicinity of 0.0001 arcsec. Another example of particular interest is a fluid skeleton that was developed as part of a very high accuracy CMM-machining system [10]. This system was used to manufacture large, high-accuracy, millimeter-wave radio telescope reflectors. This very elegant and simple CMM-machining system, developed by Leighton of CalTech, has been used in the manufacture of parabolic antennas for millimeter-wave radioastronomy applications. The system has achieved an accuracy of 10 μm rms over a 30-foot diameter. The fluid leveling portion of the system had an accuracy of 2 μm rms.

Leighton's fluid level reference consists of an aluminum trough 200 inches long, 2 inches wide, and 1 inch deep. The trough is filled with a light oil to a depth of 8–10 mm. The height of the oil surface is measured by a modified monocular microscope. The microscope images a point source (produced by a laser) onto the surface of the oil. A beam splitter allows the user to view the image of the point source on the oil surface. The point source will be sharply defined only at a certain separation between the microscope and oil surface. The position of the microscope is measured by a small linear transducer. The direction of travel required to null the microscope is easily determined by adding a cylindrical lens into the system.

Leighton's system could be automated by using a different optical system. The optical system, similar to an autocollimator but focused at a finite distance, consists of a low-cost laser diode light source, an anamorphic objective lens, a beam splitter, and a four-quadrant photodetector. Fluid height sensors using other than optical pickoffs have been used. Another popular technique used in earthquake research is based on capacitive sensing of the fluid surface. This principle is used in the previously mentioned Autonetics tilt sensor.

The advantage of fluid skeletons include their low cost and very high-accuracy, referenced directly to gravity. The problems with fluid skeletons include their sensitivity to thermal effects, dirt, vibrations, and surface tension effects; the need for fluids to be stationary; and the undetected errors due to trapped bubbles in the fluid static reference line.

Measurement Skeletons

The position and attitude of the payload must be accurately related to the world coordinate system, and the measurement skeleton performs this task. The actual measurements are performed by the position sensors.

Three types of measurement skeletons will be discussed: mechanical, beams of light, and levels of fluids. All of the skeletons establish some form of a line or plane in space. For example, the CMM-based scanners use purely mechanical measurement skeletons. The CMM-based accuracy is dependent on the dimensional stability of the granite rails that establish the straight-line geometry for the CMM-based position sensors.

During the installation process, the granite rail straightness is compared against a beam of light, which is assumed to be straight. If the position sensor measurements always were related to the beam of light instead of the granite rails, then the robot would be using an optical skeleton. In a similar manner, a fluid surface can be used to establish a planar reference. As an example, the horizontal straightness of a scanner could be measured by measuring the fluid height in a trough.

Optical measurement skeletons can be either optically augmented mechanical skeletons, like the NSI plane polar, or pure optical skeletons, like the LAPIS, Surfitek, NBS, MTS. Optically augmented mechanical skeletons operate by determining the geometric errors for low-precision mechanical measurement skeletons. The errors are determined by optically sensing the deflections and twists of the mechanical skeleton.

An example is the NSI 12-foot plane polar scanner. It uses an optical skeleton to monitor structural deformations and bearing wobble in a relatively low-precision mechanical scanner. The NSI plane polar scanner (see Figure 7.13) uses a two-axis straightness sensor to measure straightness deviations of the radial axis and a two-axis autocollimator to measure ϕ bearing wobble and support structure flexure.

In this system, both near-field scanners may be moved easily to new locations. For example, the NSI plane polar system has been airlifted across the country, then set up and operational in less than one day after arrival. Also, the optical skeleton greatly reduces the accuracy requirements of the mechanical gantry. This corre-

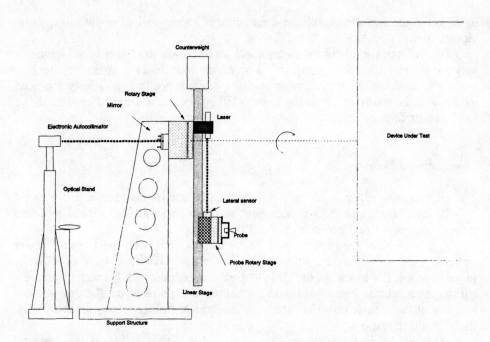

Figure 7.13 Optical diagram of the NSI 12-ft plane polar scanner.

spondingly reduces the weight of the gantry and enhances the portability of the near-field scanner. Aligning the mechanical structure to an equivalent tolerance is substantially more difficult and time consuming than optical alignment. The newer NSI 12 ft plane polar system is relatively easy to align. Another problem is that optical skeletons do not measure secondary errors such as probe tilt or position errors between the probe optical sensor and probe antenna.

In Cartesian designs (see Figure 7.14), a single laser is used with three pentaprisms to establish the x, y, and z deviations of the mechanical structure. The x and y error are established by a laser and pentaprism beam splitter. The z error is determined by sweeping a laser beam through a horizontal plane. The z-plane accuracy is established by a pentaprism assembly. A linear position photodiode sensor mounted on the probe antenna measures the intersection of the laser plane with the probe antenna. The optical skeleton consists of a laser, a pentaprism to form the vertical plane, a vertical reference system, and several probe antenna height error sensors.

The optical skeleton can be described in terms of four basic subsystems: the *laser reference assembly* (LRA), the x prism, the detector assembly, and the computer interface.

The LRA, mounted on a stable pillar at one side of the near-field scanner (see Figure 7.14), generates three separate laser beams. Two of these beams are horizontal and define the scanner x- and z-axes. The third beam sweeps out a plan that is at a constant z position. This beam can be moved by a tracking servo system. Yaw and roll stability of the LRA is monitored in real time by a biaxial tiltmeter.

One subsystem determines z-axis deformation errors, the other subsystem determines x- and y-axis deformation errors. All deformations are measured as near as possible to the payload. Both subsystems measure deflections at right angles to a reference laser beam. These deflections are measured with a simple lateral effect photodiode instead of using the more complex laser interferometer techniques. Advantages include two-axis sensing, lower cost, higher reliability, and a lack of beam-polarization restrictions. The only disadvantages are some secondary y-axis measurement errors and the need to suppress stray light and compensate for detector nonlinearities.

The z component of the structural deflection is measured very near to the payload so that the payload azimuth and elevation need not be monitored. A set of tiltmeters can be installed to characterize the static payload pitch and roll errors. The z-axis subsystem operates as follows:

1. A laser is mounted on a stable pillar near one corner of the robot. The beam exiting the laser defines the direction of the z-axis and is available for laser

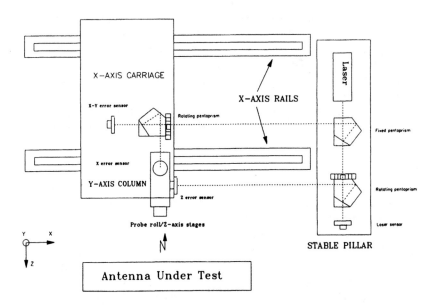

Figure 7.14 Optical skeleton for Cartesian planar robots.

beam-pointing stability monitoring and as a reference for AUT alignment, if needed.

2. A pentaprism beam-splitter assembly is mounted in a servoed rotational mount adjacent to the laser. One beam exits at precisely 90° relative to the input beam. Rotation of the prism results in the beam sweeping a surface that defines a plane.

3. A lateral effect sensor mounted near the probe detects the intersection between the laser beam and the probe. The value measured by the sensor is the z-plane error. A tracking servo loop keeps the laser beam pointed at the detector. Alternately, a retroreflector can be mounted at the probe position with the beam returned to the pentaprism region. A detector mounted at this point always will be normal to the incident beam, simplifying the design of the optical bandpass filter used to reject stray light.

Travel of the z-axis can be accommodated by using a stationary sensor, a longer or more complex sensor, or by adding a z-axis servo to the pentaprism.

The x and y components are monitored in a similar manner:

1. A laser is aligned along the nominal x-axis of travel.

2. A pentaprism, mounted on the traveling carriage, splits the beam into two separate beams, one of which is directed at a sensor mounted near the payload.

3. One lateral effect photodiode is mounted at the output of the pentaprism. The bottom of the y-axis position also is referenced to this point. This photodiode measures y-axis deflections at the bottom of the y-axis position sensor. The assumption is that the position sensor does not distort and that the probe y position clearly can be related to the position sensor. These assumptions are clearly valid when no z-axis motion is present. Some degradation of the y-axis accuracy will occur if z-axis motion is used.

4. A second lateral effect photodiode mounted near the probe measures x-axis deflections of the robot. A tracking servo keeps the laser beam pointed at the detector.

Local variations in the refractive index of the atmosphere cause errors with an approximate standard deviation of 0.001 inch per 20 feet of path length (measured in a typical laboratory environment). The technique can be used to suppress the atmospheric effects by an order of magnitude to approximately 0.0001 inch per 20 feet. The MRA technique is based on adaptively updating a structural deformation model in the computer memory. This results in the formation of a low-pass spatial filter that effectively eliminates the high-frequency atmospheric noise.

The assumption used by the MRA technique is that structural deformations tend to vary slowly with time. Rapid vibrations, if present, are ignored. In near-field measurements, vibrations, if unbiased, are effectively suppressed in slower systems by narrowing the receiver IF filter. Vibration of the probe will raise the apparent sidelobe levels as indicated by the Ruze's equation. In high-performance systems, vibration-free motion is essential. High-performance servo systems, as described later, will provide the smoothest motion.

The effects of large thermal gradients within the facility are minimized by the MRA technique. Small destratification fans are strategically placed, and temperature measurements are incorporated by using a mount near the probe antenna. The temperature measurements are used by the MRA algorithm. A summary of potential error sources and the associated control techniques are in Table 7.8.

This example will use a combination of mechanical, optical, and fluid skeletons as applied to a CMM-based near-field scanner. Not all mechanical errors will be measured; the errors of primary importance are those affected most by ground settling. The emphasis will be on the fluid reference technique, which provides very high accuracy measurement, referenced to gravity, for a low cost. The fluid measurement skeletons are fluid and optically augmented mechanical structure, like the Leighton. The more costly optical skeleton monitors less significant errors and may not be required for a given performance level.

The fluid skeleton measures the tilts of the bridge structure. The skeleton consists of two oil-filled troughs along both *x*-axes. A set of three optical surface-height sensors mounted at the three kinematic points of the bridge structure will measure the bridge height relative to the oil level. The troughs are interconnected to maintain a constant height reference between both rails. A third trough is installed on the *y*-axis to measure *y* height errors and carriage rotation around the *x*-axis. An additional oil height sensor is located in each trough to monitor seismic and thermal effects.

Optical straightness sensing systems using lasers, lateral effect detectors, and optical squares can monitor additional secondary error sources. The baseline skeleton sensor is summarized in Table 7.9.

Note that the table does not include all error terms. This shows the advantages of pure optical skeletons that have fewer error terms and often can be made entirely self-calibrating. For many applications, however, just adding the fluid skeleton can provide a significant improvement in CMM robot accuracy or allow a significant reduction in the size and weight of the skeletal system.

One possible implementation of a fluid skeleton would be the installation of a pair of troughs along the *x* and *x'* granite rails of CMM-based near-field scanner. The troughs are interconnected by tubes to provide a common height reference. Optical fluid height sensors are mounted near the three kinematic bridge-mounting points. These sensors will provide a readout of the relative heights of the *x* and *x'* rails and both tilts of the bridge structure. This system can be used despite CMM motion because the fluid reference is stationary.

Table 7.8
Laser Displacement Sensor Errors

Error Source	Control Technique
1. Laser beam wandering	*stable laser design
	*collimating optics
2. Laser mount instability	*correct mount design
	*monitoring detector (tiltmeter)
	*thermally stable environment
3. Atmospheric noise	*adaptive spatial filter (MRA)
	*temporal filter
	*destratification fans
	*temperature probe
	*environmental control
	elimination of atmosphere
	inertial smoothing
	possibly use of noncoherent light
4. Stray light	*optical filter
	*optical filter and retroreflector
	*optical shroud
	*modulated laser
	*nonreflective surfaces
5. Detector nonlinearity	correction by look-up table
	*central portion of detector
	*nulling one axis with a tracking loop
	bias of the lateral effect photodiode
	CCD detector
	straightness interferometer
6. Pentaprism wedge	*initial calibration
	*corrected by computer model
7. Pentaprism tilt	*initial calibration
	autoreflection to a second detector
8. Pentaprism decentering	*initial calibration
	decentration detector
9. Scan bearing wobble	*careful bearing selection
	wobble sensors
10. Sensor lag	*wideband width sensors
	*minimization of short-period errors
	*geometry
11. Tracking servo lag	*servo design
	*geometry
12. Probing azimuth-elevation errors	*minimization of sensor-payload distance
	attitude sensors

Note:
*This technique is used in the example system.

Table 7.9
Baseline Skeleton Sensor Summary

Parameter	Sensor	Mode
x rail straightness and level	fluid	real time
x' rail straightness and level	fluid	real time
y rail straightness and level	fluid	fast cal
	optical	real time
z rail straightness	optical	real time
Oil level in trough, *x* rail	fluid	real time
Oil level in trough, *x'* rail	fluid	real time
Oil level in trough, *y* rail	fluid	real time
x to world height	fluid	real time
x to *x'* height differential	fluid	real time
Bridge rotation around *x*-axis	fluid	real time
Bridge rotation around *y*-axis	fluid	real time
Bridge rotation around *z*-axis	encoder	real time
y carriage rotation around *x*-axis	fluid	fast cal
	optical	real time
x-y orthogonality	optical	real time
y-z orthogonality	optical	real time
z-x orthogonality		

Notes:
Modes: real time = information is available in real time; some filtering may be required.
fast cal = axis can be calibrated automatically without work removal in a few minutes.
The expected accuracy of fluid sensors is 2 μm rms if previously described fluid error sources are carefully controlled [10]. The expected accuracy of the optical sensors is 10 μm if error sources are carefully controlled.

An additional trough can be placed in the *y*-axis to measure its deflections. This sensor, however, can be used only while the *x*-axis is stationary. The sensor could be used for the rapid determination of *y*-axis errors that are corrected by a computer look-up table.

Many errors disappear if the payload position and attitude are measured directly relative to an earth-fixed station. Because of this, the direct sensing systems will become the dominant measurement system in the future. In these systems, several sensors are mounted as directly to the world reference system as possible. The previously mentioned NSI plane polar upgraded optical skeleton tends to this direction. The sensors measure line-of-sight distance to the payload or payload line-of-sight angles.

Examples of this approach include the NBS range-angle system [15], the MTI system [16], the proposed LAPIS near-field range system [14], and the Surfitek multilateration interferometer [1, 12]. The Surfitek system is used to precisely measure the shape of large optical reflectors. The accuracy is 0.2 μm for a 24-inch diameter test object.

These systems are expected to become quite popular in the future, due to their very high accuracy and the elimination of massive skeletal hardware. These robots easily can be made portable. The main disadvantages are the requirements for the more complex target tracking systems and maintaining a line of sight to the payload. For many applications, such as antenna and optics manufacturing, the latter restriction generally would cause no major problem.

7.4 SERVO CONTROL SYSTEM

The servo control system is the muscular part of the robot. It accepts, as input, the desired robot motion and the sensed joint positions. It physically moves the joints by using motors according to control laws. Ideally, this results in the correct positioning of the near-field probe antenna. Three types of probe positioning systems currently are in use:

1. Most near-field measurement systems scan the probe along a single axis. The positioning requirements are very simple. A motor moves the probe along the axis at a somewhat arbitrary and unstable speed. A laser interferometer or optical encoder determines the instantaneous position. The receiver is triggered when the instantaneous position passes through a trigger position. This is simple, fast, stable, reliable, and low in cost. However, it is limited to a single-axis scan; random data smear in certain designs; it cannot be used easily for plane polar scans on Cartesian scanners; and it does not support tilted scan planes.

2. If multiple axis control is required, conventional positioning servos and stepper motors can be used. This allows starburst scans and supports tilted scan planes.

3. The more advanced near-field range systems use coordinated multiaxis *continuous path control* (CPC) techniques. All axes are moved simultaneously along a predefined trajectory and the receiver is triggered precisely at the desired sampling points. This allows very precise multiaxis positioning, speed, and can support scan plane rotations and plane polar scans on Cartesian scanners. The cost is in complexity, a need for careful construction, and some servo tuning.

The CPC servo controller consists physically of three parts: the previously described joint position sensor, a control law, and a velocity servo loop. The velocity servo loop, also known as a *rate loop,* can be further broken down into a velocity sensor, a motor drive amplifier, a motor, and power transmission. The velocity servo loop ideally turns the motor at the commanded rate.

Virtually all servo systems operate by comparing a desired position or velocity with the commanded position or velocity. The difference in position or velocity is an error signal, which is amplified and sent to the motor to correct its speed or position. The positioning errors in this CPC servo system are minimized by a unique combination of techniques:

1. The servo commands are modified to inherently minimize errors. The basic concept is feed-forward processing, however, in this case, the feed-forward signal has been modified to simultaneously minimize several different error sources.
2. An additional position sensor (tachometer) and supervisory loop provide an independent measure of the motor position, irrespective of the load position. Errors in the power transmission can be identified and corrected by this technique, which can result in a very wide control bandwidth [17].
3. A position loop is used to determine the amount of error. Unlike conventional servos, this system does not use classical integral and derivative terms. Integral processing is instead achieved by adaptively tuning the feed-forward processor using Kalman filter-like techniques. Derivative control is handled by the supervisory loop.

Each of the primary control laws corrects disturbances in different parts of the frequency spectrum: velocity feed forward at >20 Hz, a position loop at 0.1 to 20 Hz, and a Kalman filter at <0.1 Hz.

The high-accuracy CPC servo system comprises a system-dependent combination of the following components (see Figure 7.15):

1. Trajectory generator (computer software), which includes the scan endpoint generator, path interpolator, homogeneous coordinate transformer, nonlinear motion filter, and resampling filter.
2. Velocity loop (hardware), which includes the tachometer, motor drive amplifier, motor, power transmission, and computer interface.
3. Feed-forward processor (computer software), which includes servo lag compensation, the tachometer nonlinearity corrector (for the dc tachometer only), a flutter suppressor (optional), a structural resonance suppressor (optional), a gravitational-coriolis effect suppressor (optional), and a coupling inertia suppressor (optional).
4. Position loop (computer software), which includes the position sensor, loop filter, slew controller, adaptive parameter estimator, and performance analyzer.

The subsystems of the CPC servo system, as used in several near-field systems, will be described in this order. The position sensors have been described previously.

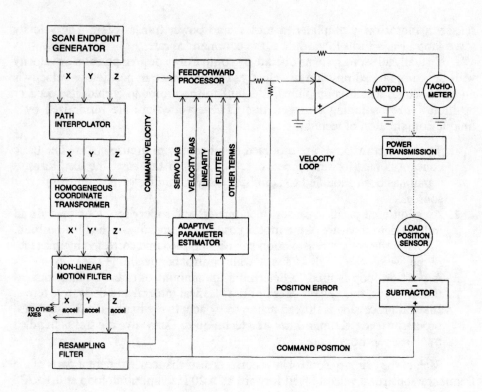

Figure 7.15 CPC servo system block diagram.

7.4.1 Trajectory Generator

The trajectory generator produces a trajectory that describes the desired instantaneous probe path in a fixed Cartesian coordinate system. The trajectory generator is a software module residing within the control computer and sends two signals at a 128 Hz rate for each of the servo axes. The outputs are instantaneously commanded position and velocity. The design goals of the trajectory generator depend on its intended application but a representative set might be as follows:

1. Produce interpolated position, velocity, and acceleration state vectors that define the desired motion trajectory.
2. Produce command position, velocity, and acceleration state vectors, corresponding to the exact time a position sensor measurement was performed. The position sensor measurements may have significant timing jitter.

3. Filter trajectory commands to avoid exciting structural resonances.
4. Filter trajectory commands by using position, velocity, and acceleration limits to avoid driving the servo rate loop with unrealizable commands, which would saturate the control loop.

Many designs are possible for a trajectory generator. A design suitable for use in near field measurement robots consists of the following software modules:

1. Endpoint generator,
2. Path interpolator,
3. Homogeneous coordinate transformer,
4. Motion filter,
5. Resampling filter.

Endpoint Generator

The desired scan pattern in three degrees of freedom is generated by a software-based scan endpoint generator. The scan generator produces points in a raster, starburst, or arbitrary format. The starburst scan mode is most often used. The arbitrary scan format uses a disk file playback. For planar scans, the scan generator z-axis is set to zero. For cylindrical, spherical and parabolic scans, the z-axis is computed as a function of the x and y positions of the probe. The scan generator output for each scan point is the desired x, y, and z locations of the probe phase center.

Path Interpolator

The path interpolator computes intermediate way points between the motion endpoints. Various designs are possible, depending on user requirements. Popular interpolation algorithms include linear, spline fits, and conic sections. The near-field scanners generally use linear interpolation because of the natural compatibility with raster and starburst scans.

The path is linearly interpolated at a 16 Hz rate to produce intermediate positions during continuous path motion. During point-to-point motion, the path need not be interpolated as the motion filter (described later) generates a suitable trajectory.

Homogeneous Coordinate Transformer

The homogeneous coordinate transformer converts the desired path command in the antenna reference frame into the robot reference frame. The transformations may include arbitrary compound rotations, translations, scaling, and shear operations. The concepts behind the homogeneous coordinate transform are covered in many computer graphics and robotics books [18].

The output points from the scan generator are converted to a homogeneous coordinate representation by augmenting the x, y, and z positions with a scale factor W, resulting in four vectors (Wx, Wy, Wz, W). The augmented vector is then transformed into the near-field scanner reference frame by a matrix multiplication:

$$\{W'x', W'y', W'z', W'\} = \{Wx, Wy, Wz, W\}\mathbf{M} \tag{7.5}$$

The $\mathbf{M}$ matrix establishes the geometric relationship between the scan trajectory generator and the near-field scanner reference frames. The homogeneous coordinate technique, which has been heavily used in three-dimensional computer graphic and robotic systems, supports arbitrary compound rotations, translations, scaling, shear, and perspective operations. The multiplication of the homogeneous transform by the input vector results in a new vector transformed into the physical coordinate system. Dividing by W' normalizes the transformed desired position vector.

The desired position vector is differentiated to determine the velocities of all axes. The differentiated values form the desired velocity vector.

Motion Filter

The motion filter, shown in Figure 7.16, uses nonlinear techniques to compute an output trajectory constrained by position, velocity, and acceleration limits, while simultaneously minimizing the group delay time relative to the input trajectory. The filter input is the desired position and velocity. The filter output is the commanded instantaneous servo acceleration.

The filter is used to prevent servo saturation, limit the servo dynamics to application-safe values, and minimize command energy at frequencies that will excite structural resonances. Its output displays the desired positions, desired velocities, and filter time delay; also the position, velocity, and acceleration limits. The output of the nonlinear motion filter (16 Hz) displays the filtered acceleration, velocity, and position.

The nonlinear motion filter begins its operation by linearly predicting the position at an arbitrary time offset and clipping the position to an acceptable value. It then computes the distance to go over the sample interval and the deceleration time in samples. If the deceleration time is longer than one sample, it computes the velocity error, converts that velocity error to the desired velocity, clips the velocity to an acceptable value, and converts to acceleration. If the deceleration time is shorter than one sample, it simply computes the desired acceleration. Finally, the filter applies an acceleration clip.

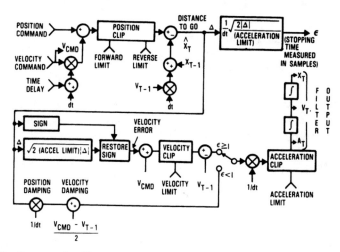

Figure 7.16 Nonlinear motion filter.

Resampling Filter

The resampling filter accepts the position, velocity, and acceleration output of the trajectory generator motion filter at a 16 Hz rate and produces interpolated position and velocity information at a nominal 128 Hz rate. The position information is used by the outer loop filter and parameter estimator. The velocity information is used by the feed-forward processor and parameter estimator.

The resampling filter operates by extrapolating the position and velocity command to a time in the future, based on a constant acceleration rate over the time interval. This results in a velocity ramp and a parabolic position profile. The position and velocity at a time t are

$$V(t) = V(0) + a\,t \qquad\qquad (7.6)$$
$$P(t) = P(0) + V(0)t + 0.5a\,t^2$$

where

$P(t)$ = position at time t,
$V(t)$ = velocity at time t,
$P(0)$ = position at time zero,
$V(0)$ = velocity at time zero,
$\quad a$ = acceleration during time interval,
$\quad t$ = time interval.

Both $V(t)$ and $P(t)$ are required by the servo system. $P(t)$ can be computed directly from $V(t)$ by using fewer operations:

$$P(t) = P(0) + \{V(0) + V(t)\}t/2 \tag{7.7}$$

The time interval need not be fixed. This allows the filter to match the timing of certain sensors that are operating in an asynchronous manner. If $V(t)$ is not required, $P(t)$ can be computed efficiently by

$$P(t) = P(0) + \{V(0) + [A(0) \, t/2]\} \, t \tag{7.8}$$

7.4.2 Velocity Loop

The velocity servo loop, also known as the *rate* or *inner loop,* is an important component of the CPC servo. It moves an axis at a rate directly proportional to a velocity control signal. The control signal in this case is the velocity command signal from the outer servo loop, which will be described later. The inner loop operates by comparing the commanded and measured motor velocities. Any difference (velocity error) is used to change the motor speed to null the velocity error.

The rate loop must perform in a predictable, accurate manner to support CPC applications. The performance of the rate loop is quantified by measuring the following parameters:

1. *Rate Loop Bandwidth.* The rate loop bandwidth is a measure of how rapidly the rate loop can respond to commands and disturbances. The bandwidth is measured by driving the rate loop with a sine wave signal generator and monitoring the tachometer output. The sine wave signal level should be low enough not to saturate the motor drive amplifier. A high-performance rate loop should have a bandwidth in excess of 1 kHz.
2. *Rate Loop Dynamic Response.* The dominant rate loop response can be conveniently modeled as a simple second-order system. The rate loop, in general, by itself, should deliver a critically dampened response. The transient response and associated damping ratio is easily measured by the computer.
3. *Dynamic Range.* The dynamic range is a measure of the speed range over which the rate loop can be commanded. The upper speed limit is set by saturation in the rate loop. The lower speed limit is set by loop gain and short-term dc drift. A dynamic range of 5000 to 1 or more is desirable for CPC servo applications.
4. *Linearity.* Linearity of the rate loop is a measure of how the velocity scale factor varies as a function of commanded velocity. Linearity is rarely specified for rate loops but is of considerable importance for high-accuracy CPC

servos. It can be measured by connecting an optical encoder to the servo motor shaft and measuring the encoder output frequency as a function of commanded velocity. Note that this information also can be obtained by comparing the derivative of the position sensor output with the velocity sensor output so that the CPC servo can measure linearity directly.

5. *Flutter.* Flutter is a periodic variation in the rate loop velocity assuming a constant input velocity command. Flutter is caused primarily by decentered rollers in the friction drive and tachometer ripple. The flutter caused by the friction drive is usually more significant than the tachometer ripple. Flutter is most easily measured directly in the robot by appropriate computer software.

6. *Velocity Scale Factor Stability.* The scale factor stability is a measure of how the motor velocity drifts with respect to a fixed command input with the velocity bias effect subtracted.

7. *Velocity Bias Stability.* The velocity bias stability is a measure of how the motor velocity drifts at zero velocity command.

Several different designs for the inner loop may be used. The inner servo loop, as currently used by several near-field measurement systems, consists of the following analog hardware elements (see Figure 7.17), in order of signal flow:

1. Tachometer,
2. Digital-to-analog converter,
3. Rate loop preamplifier,
4. Motor drive amplifier,
5. Motor,
6. Power transmission.

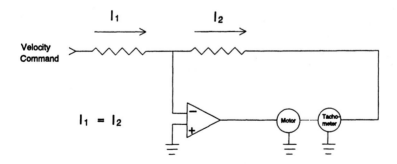

Figure 7.17 Velocity (rate) servo loop.

Tachometer

The tachometer senses the rotational speed of the servo motor shaft. The sensed velocity is compared with the commanded velocity, and the difference is used to correct the speed of the motor. The tachometer performance directly affects the overall servo performance. Several different types of rate sensors can be used: derived rate signal, dc tachometers, optical encoders, motor-back electromotive force sensors, or combinations of these.

One question that often arises is, as virtually all robotic servos have load position sensors, why not derive a rate signal by simply taking the derivative of the position sensor signal, thereby eliminating a second sensor. For low performance applications, this derived rate signal approach is fine. High-performance servo systems can significantly increase their performance by using separate axis position and motor velocity sensors [17]. This is because additional information is obtained by attaching the two sensors to different points in the control system. The position sensor should be coupled directly to the mechanical load. The tachometer should be tightly coupled to the motor. The position sensor provides accurate information relating to the instantaneous load position, but poor quality, low bandwidth information relating to the motor shaft velocity. There is a difference in the motor and load velocities because of mechanical errors, mechanical time constants, and propagation delays in the power transmission. For example, the rate loop bandwidth could fall from 1000 to 20 Hz if the derivative of the load position sensor were used instead of a tightly coupled tachometer. The derived rate signal tachometer offers low cost and simplicity, but it has poor performance due to its low loop bandwidth.

A commonly used motor speed sensor is the dc tachometer. The near-field robots, described earlier, use this as the motor velocity sensor. The dc tachometer is a form of a permanent magnet dc generator. The emphasis in tachometer design is on making the output voltage directly and accurately proportional to the shaft speed. The dominant tachometer errors of interest to a CPC servo design are its nonlinearity with speed, direction, and shaft angle (tach ripple); the drift of the tachometer scale factor with time and temperature; and its finite response time. These errors, if reasonable in magnitude, can be suppressed by using an error model in the CPC servo controller. The finite response time is not generally a problem if the motor and tachometer are tightly coupled, as measured by the *motor-tachometer torsional resonance* (MTTR) frequency. A good motor-tachometer assembly should have a MTTR above several kHz. In spite of the various error sources, the dc tachometer is a popular velocity sensor. Successful usage in a high-accuracy CPC application usually requires that the servo controller include at least a partial tachometer error model. The dc tachometer offers low cost and easy interfacing with the analog rate loop. However, it is nonlinear with speed, direction, and shaft angle (tach ripple), and must be checked for brush wear.

An optical shaft encoder can be connected directly to the motor shaft. The frequency produced by the optical encoder is a measure of the motor speed. The optical encoder, combined with motor back EMF damping, will probably be the velocity sensor of choice in the future. This is because it is highly linear if correctly installed and easily interfaced with digital rate loops. However, it is not easily interfaced with analog rate loops, has oscillation problems at low speeds due to quantization, and has complex electronics.

The motor itself can be used as a tachometer, if the effects of the motor current can be suppressed. Several methods have been used to derive the motor velocity. One method is to alternately pulse the motor power and then read the motor-back *electromotive force* (EMF). Because of the motor electrical time constant, this method does not work well. Another method is to place the motor in a bridge circuit to suppress the motor drive voltage. This method is equivalent to driving the motor from a source with a negative output impedance. This technique can perform quite well and will be discussed in more detail later. Motor-back EMF rate sensing offers low cost, wide bandwidth, and excellent high-frequency performance, but at the expense of sensitivity to ground loops and tuning.

Combinations of the previously described motor velocity sensing methods can provide the highest performance. The motor-back EMF rate sensing can be implemented by using a voltage or negative output impedance motor drive amplifier, providing excellent high-frequency damping. The primary sensor should be either the dc tachometer or optical encoder.

Note that the tachometer must provide a wide bandwidth rate signal to the motor drive amplifier. One measure of the performance of the motor-tachometer combination is the MTTR frequency. The MTTR frequency and damping ratio normally sets the upper limit on the rate loop gain bandwidth product. Care must be taken that capacitive coupling does not occur between the motor and tachometer windings. The effect is similar to a low MTTR frequency and easily suppressed by grounding the motor housing.

In many cases, high-frequency stability can be enhanced by using a low or even negative amplifier output impedance. Unfortunately most commercially available motor drive amplifiers have a fixed output impedance, normally infinity. The amplifier operates as a voltage controlled current source. The high-output impedance is used in an attempt to reduce the motor electrical time constant at the expense of back EMF damping.

Motor Drive Amplifier

The *motor drive amplifier* (MDA) is a straightforward but important part of the rate loop servo system. The MDA performs the rate loop processing and amplifies the error signal to a level sufficient to drive the motor. The MDA accepts as input the motor velocity command (differential voltage or digital), the tachometer signal, and the amplifier enable signal from the computer. Its output sends drive power data to the motor and fault status data to the computer. Desirable MDA features include the following:

1. The rate loop parameters should be easily adjustable using trimpot setting or computer download, because of its flexibility for adding additional servo axes and simplified maintenance.
2. If trimpots are used, settings should be measurable with an ohm meter connected to test points to simplify maintenance.
3. Overcurrent and ground fault protection is required to prevent amplifier destruction.
4. The amplifier should have visual fault indicators to simplify maintenance.
5. The computer should be able to read the MDA fault status to provide the axis condition to the computer.
6. The MDA should accept either an analog differential or digital binary command input to provide noise immunity.
7. The MDA should switch at a minimum of 15 kHz, to minimize acoustic noise.
8. The MDA should accept a remote amplifier enable input to allow the computer to control the MDA power and simplify emergency stop hardware.
9. An MDA variable output impedance capability is desirable to provide optimum rate loop performance.
10. The MDA should support a minimum of 5 kHz bandwidth to provide optimum rate loop performance.
11. The servo loop filters, if analog, should use capacitors with low dielectric retention, because high dielectric retention capacitors can adversely affect the servo system performance by causing short period velocity bias drift.

Servo Motor

The servo motor converts the current from the amplifier into mechanical torque. The motor is usually either a dc permanent magnet brush or brushless motor. The brushless motors are somewhat more reliable but require more complex support electronics (see Table 7.10).

The motor drive amplifier voltage (E_{max}) and current (I_{max}) requirements for a given motor can be computed from the following equation:

$$I_{max} = K_t T_m = 0.7394 K_v T_m$$
$$E_{max} = K_v V_m + I_{max} R$$

(7.9)

where

T_m = maximum required torque (oz./in.)
V_m = maximum required velocity (rev./min.)
K_t = motor torque constant (oz./in.)
K_v = motor velocity constant [V/(rev./min.)]
R = motor resistance at amplifier output.

Note that

$$K_t = 0.7394K_v$$

The torque requirements are established by the sum of drive friction and acceleration requirements. The maximum velocity is established by the maximum scan speed requirement. Some new planar near-field robotic systems have top speeds near 3 feet/s.

Table 7.10
Drive Motors Compared

Parameter	dc Brush	dc Brushless	Stepper
Accuracy	high	high	low
Torque	high	high	low
Vibration	low	low	high
Flutter	low	low	medium
Direct drive	yes	yes	limited
Friction drive	yes	yes	limited
Cost	medium	high	low
Complexity	medium	high	medium

Power Transmission

The power transmission couples the motor to the load. The transmission is used to improve the mechanical impedance match between the motor and load. Numerous types of power transmissions have been used in robotic systems including gears, pulleys, chains, ball screws, *et cetera*. Most of these transmissions cause significant problems in high-accuracy robots; therefore, the power transmission design will be discussed in some detail. The power transmission requirements for the high accuracy robots are as follows:

1. No backlash (transmission ratio remains constant during direction reversals).
2. Low flutter (transmission ratio remains constant for all shaft angles).

3. Smooth (no random bumps, *et cetera*).
4. No springiness (transmission ratio remains constant over a wide frequency bandwidth).

Very few power transmissions have low enough backlash and flutter to meet the requirements of high-accuracy CPC servos. The transmissions delivering acceptable performance, in order of desirability, are direct drive, friction drive, cable drive, and toothless belt drive.

Note that the cable and toothless belt drive transmissions are really variations of the friction drive. Types of transmissions *not* acceptable are listed in Table 7.11.

The highest performance transmission has a direct coupling between the motor and load. This approach is used on the highest performance servo systems with achievable accuracies in the 0.001 arcsecond region and lower rate limits below 1 rotation per year. Direct drive systems often require custom motor designs to meet the torque requirements. Linear axes can be driven directly by linear motors.

The cost and power consumption of the robot often can be reduced if a transmission is placed between the motor and load. The transmission improves the

Table 7.11
Unacceptable Transmissions

Power Transmission	Problems
Gears	flutter, backlash
Antibacklash gears	flutter
Worm gears	flutter, backlash, binding
Harmonic drives	flutter, backlash
Ball screw (rotating screw)	flutter, backlash, vibration
Ball screw (rotating nut)	flutter, backlash
Chain drives	flutter, backlash, vibration
Toothed belt	flutter, backlash
Shaft couplings	flutter, backlash, springiness

mechanical impedance match between the motor and load and can transform rotary motion into linear motion. The friction drive transmission provides excellent performance at a relatively low cost.

Few reports have been written on friction drive transmission technology [19, 20]. The Rohlex drive is one of the few high-performance friction drive units commercially available. The Rohlex drive is similar to a leadscrew drive, except that the shaft is unthreaded and the Rohlex nut uses cam followers to move along the shaft. Some of the best examples of low-flutter friction drive mechanisms are used in audio and instrumentation tape recorders [21] and in certain computer printers.

Some near-field measurement systems use friction drive transmissions. And, all of the linear friction drives used by the near-field robots use some variation of a tape recorder-like steel capstan-pinch roller design that clamps onto a long bar or tape. Rotational friction drives are configured as a pair of two different-sized, hardened, metal disks held in direct contact by powerful springs. Cam followers often are used to unload the primary bearings.

CMM-based near-field range scanners built by LK Tool of the United Kingdom use a friction power transmission. The drive uses a direct-drive dc torque motor with a tightly coupled tachometer to power the friction drive. The motor shaft is mounted with high-load capacity bearings, eliminating the need for backup cam followers. The drive roller is mounted directly to the motor shaft. The drive roller is a two-point contact V groove design intended to self-align relative to a two-inch diameter, hardened-steel, drive shaft rail. The rail is pinched between the drive roller and a idler roller mounted on a crossed roller bearing slide. The crossed roller bearing slide is tensioned by Bellville washers. This results in pinching the rail between the drive and idler rollers. An improvement would probably result if the V groove roller was replaced by a flat roller and flat drive bar. The flat roller and bar would allow a significantly smaller drive bar because of the increased surface contact area, which would still be self-aligning.

Another near-field scanner uses a friction drive system, based on a magnetic tape transport design (see Figure 7.18). The drive clamps onto a flexible steel tape,

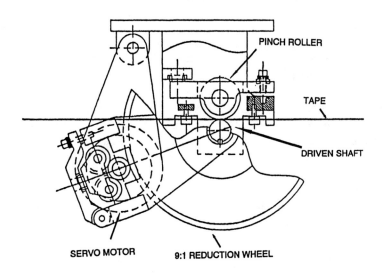

Figure 7.18 M4 scanner friction drive mechanism.

which are securely fastened at both ends of the tape. One end of the scanner is spring loaded. The tape is sandwiched between a flat steel capstan and a pair of steel cam followers. The cam followers are pressed against the steel capstan by a series of Belleville washers, pressing against a lever arm. Four additional cam followers are used at the entrance and exit of the capstan to provide lateral tape guiding. The capstan is driven by a dc servo motor through a 9:1 friction drive transmission. The transmission consists of two steel disks with a 9:1 diameter ratio. The smaller disk is connected directly to the motor shaft and pressed against the larger disk by a pair of self-aligning cam followers. The cam followers remove the tension load from the motor bearings, which could not directly handle the load.

Cable and toothless belt drives are really variations of friction drives. These can work quite well if carefully designed by using the guidelines to be described. The primary concerns with the cable and toothless belt drives is springiness and cable-belt vibration. Springiness can be minimized by using stiff enough cables and belts with adequate tension. Vibration can be eliminated by having the drive assembly move instead of the belt or cable. Advantages of the cable and belt drives include largely self-aligning operation and low cost. Notes on the design of friction drives:

1. The friction drive rollers and track should be hardened to a minimum of Rockwell 50 to minimize galling. The drive band or bar should be sufficiently hard so as to avoid permanently deforming or yielding.
2. The friction drive rollers when attached to the drive motor shaft should have a very low (0.0001 inch) run-out error as measured by a dial indicator. Run-out error translates into drive velocity fluctuations or flutter. Flutter alternately can be suppressed with sophisticated computer algorithms, as described later. Flutter can be identified easily in dynamic servo error plots as a sine wave error with a period equal to 2π times the drive roller radius.
3. The roller to drive bar alignment is critical. Misalignment results in the drive trying to climb up the drive bar. This problem is identified easily in the dynamic servo error plots as an exponentially decaying position error spike. If a band is used instead of a bar, lateral misalignment will result in the band wrapping up into a spiral shape. Cable drives are significantly less sensitive to misalignment.
4. Maximum power will be transferred into the load under the conditions of a mechanical impedance match. This occurs when the motor and reflected load moments of inertia are equal. Too low a transmission ratio will result in the drive stalling or a premature motor failure. Motor failures can result if the motor does not turn fast enough to clean the brushes.
5. It is preferred that the capstan assembly be in motion rather than the belt or rail to minimize mechanical vibration due to a moving, long, unsupported structure.

6. Carefully designed scrapers can be used to minimize dirt build-up.
7. Unless the motor bearings are specifically designed for high sideloads, one or more cam followers must be used to apply the clamping pressure on the drive rail.
8. A minimum number of transmission stages are desirable. The drive used on the LK CMM-based scanner is ideal from this standpoint. The drive uses a direct-drive dc torque motor to rotate the capstan directly. If an additional reduction stage is required, a friction drive transmission should be used instead of gears.
9. Protection should be provided to prevent inadvertent tightening of the idler tension roller to the point that the tensioning springs are fully compressed. Permanent damage can result to the friction drive if the springs are fully compressed.

7.4.3 Feed-Forward Processor

The feed-forward processor is a computer software module, operating at a rate of 128 Hz, that produces an estimate of the required velocity servo command by assuming that the servo is currently at the correct position. This is inherently a valid assumption for very high-accuracy systems. The input to the feed-forward processor is the velocity command signal produced by the trajectory generator. In most servos that use a feed-forward processor, the processor does nothing more than multiply the velocity input command by a scale factor to arrive at the velocity command for the rate loop hardware. The near-field measurement robots require a more sophisticated, unique approach.

High-accuracy continuous path control systems need accurate control of the servo velocity. Errors in the tachometer, power transmission, and structure must be actively suppressed. The CPC servo uses a computer model of the errors that must be suppressed to appropriately modify the velocity feed-forward signal. The feed-forward computer model used by the near-field scanners incorporates tachometer nonlinearity compensation and flutter suppression. Other possible error terms, such as inertial cross coupling, gravitational, and Coriolis forces are not required because all servo axes in the planar near-field robots are orthogonal. In summary, the CPC servo system incorporates the following terms in the error model:

1. Basic feed-forward processing,
2. Tachometer nonlinearity correction,
3. Flutter suppression,
4. Structural resonance suppression.

Basic Feed-Forward Processing

The velocity feed-forward signal will drive the rate loop directly. The baseline model of the significant errors in the rate loop requires eight parameters. The velocity feed-forward scale factor, therefore, must have eight degrees of freedom. Because the parameters vary over time, they are identified in real time through a variation of the Kalman filter. The eight degrees of freedom are

1. Tachometer scale factor,
2. Tachometer nonlinearity error,
3. Velocity bias error,
4. Flutter period,
5. Flutter magnitude,
6. Flutter phase angle,
7. Structural resonance frequency,
8. Structural resonance damping ratio.

Tachometer Nonlinearity Compensation

The CPC servo uses a unique method to compensate for tachometer nonlinearity: two separate velocity scale factors are used, one for each direction of motion. This method was used initially in a high-precision servo system developed for motion pictures [22]. This particular technique also nicely suppresses certain friction drive errors such as differential slipping due to a bias force.

Flutter Suppressor

An error source, often present in friction drives, is caused by an out-of-round friction drive roller. Experience with a CMM-based scanner indicates a dynamic error of ten times the drive roller's total indicated runout (TIR) when traveling at twelve inches per second. The highest possible accuracy requires the active suppression of cyclic drive flutter. The cyclic flutter can be actively suppressed by subtracting a computer derived model of the flutter from the feed-forward command signal. Continuous real-time tuning of the flutter suppressor is required due to the slow and continuous slip of the friction drive unit.

Structural Resonance Suppressor

Resonance in the structure can lead to a loss of accuracy, particularly during continuous path motion. Resonance effects are suppressed by a combination of command spectrum filtering and posicast processing. Command spectrum filtering is accomplished primarily by the motion filter, however, notch filters have been used in certain cases.

A particularly powerful, but little-known, technique for resonance suppression is the posicast method [23]. The posicast method obtains a deadbeat response by modifying the feed-forward command signal. The posicast algorithm for a second-order system operates by summing a delayed replica of the feed-forward signal with the normal feed-forward signal. The resulting feed-forward signal is scaled to provide the same steady state response as the original signal. The delayed signal component produces the deadbeat response.

The posicast technique was used successfully in the TDRS spacecraft to improve the pointing performance of the *single access* (SA) 15-foot diameter deployable antenna. The various structural resonance suppression techniques just described work best when the resonances are simple, stable, and low in amplitude.

Other error terms may be required for certain robot designs; for example, gravitational, centrifugal, and Coriolis forces. Another example is inertial cross coupling between axes. None of these error terms is required for Cartesian robot designs, because all axis motions are orthogonal and the gravitational loads essentially are constant.

7.4.4 Position Loop

The servo position loop uses a set of control laws to produce a motor speed command that dynamically positions the axis at the commanded position and velocity at the appropriate instant in time. The commanded position and velocity are provided by the previously described trajectory generator. The measured instantaneous position of the axis also is used by the control law and obtained from the previously described position sensor.

The servo position loop is implemented as software residing on the data acquisition computer. The position loop consists of a series of software modules: loop filter, slew controller, parameter estimator, and performance analyzer. These modules will be described briefly.

Loop Filter

The servo position loop continuously compares the commanded servo position with the actual measured position. The difference is the servo position error, computed at a rate of 128 Hz. The servo position error signal is processed by the servo loop filter and then added to the velocity feed-forward signal, producing the rate loop velocity command. The commanded position is supplied by the trajectory generator software module.

The loop filter used by the CPC servo system is greatly simplified as compared to a conventional proportional, integral, derivative (PID) servo position loop. The CPC filter normally uses only a linear gain term. Integral terms are not used in the loop filter because this function essentially is superseded by the parameter estimator (Kalman filter) described later. Derivative terms can be used but normally are not needed as they are effectively replaced by the tachometer in the rate loop. Unlike many servo systems, the tachometer-load small signal coupling bandwidth is relatively high because of the use of either a direct or friction drive transmission.

The position loop used by the CPC servo systems is relatively simple. The measured and commanded position at a given instant in time are subtracted. The difference is the instantaneous position error. The error is scaled by a parameter (K_p) to form a velocity error and summed with the velocity feed-forward signal. The sum is transmitted to a *digital-to-analog converter* (DAC), which then drives the rate loop.

Slew Controller

The slew controller reconfigures the servo controller to maintain control when large servo errors occur. The slew controller primarily serves a protective function.

Parameter Estimator

The parameter estimator (also called an *estimation filter*) adaptively tunes the control system for optimum performance. The tuning is accomplished in real time by a derivative of the Kalman filter. The filter estimates the values of the tuning parameters used by the model referenced feed-forward processor. The parameters need to be determined very accurately (0.1%) for high-performance CPC motion. Floating point arithmetic is used so that parameter quantization is not significant.

The currently used estimation filter is based on Kalman concepts (see Appendix B) but is not a true Kalman filter. The parameter estimator used by the CPC servos is simple and robust. The robustness is achieved by active divergence control. Currently, the parameter estimator is used to estimate the forward and reverse velocity scale factors, the velocity bias, and the axis misalignment.

Several interesting techniques are used in the simplified estimator to attain a high-quality estimate. Most important, the filter update occurs only when high CPC precision is required. In near-field measurements, the filter update occurs at the instant the microwave interferometer is triggered. The servo velocity bias estimate is computed by an *exponentially mapped past* (EMP) filter, which is approximated by subtracting 0.5% of the servo error at the last measurement from the current bias value. Divergence of the velocity bias is suppressed by clamping the velocity bias value to less than 0.005 inch per second. The pair of servo velocity scale factors are computed as follows.

If the current servo velocity is positive, then the forward velocity scale factor (K_{v+}) is

$$\hat{K}_{v+}(t) = \frac{EK_a}{V} + \hat{K}_{v+}(t-1) \tag{7.10}$$

where

E = servo error,
K_a = autotuning gain,
V = servo velocity.

If the current servo velocity is negative, then the reverse velocity scale factor (K_{v-}) is

$$\hat{K}_{v-}(t) = \frac{EK_a}{V} + \hat{K}_{v-}(t-1) \tag{7.11}$$

The flutter parameter estimator determines the amplitude and phase angle of the flutter error, assuming a fixed spatial flutter frequency. The flutter parameter estimator operates by performing an EMP cross-correlation between the computer model and servo error signal.

Under certain conditions the parameter estimator can diverge. For example, if a servo axis were to lock up mechanically for an instant, large servo errors would result. The large errors would cause the parameter estimator to adjust the model accordingly, resulting in highly inaccurate tuning parameters. The highly inaccurate tuning parameters may cause the servo to move violently or stall, further aggravating the tuning errors. Causes of filter divergence include the following:

1. Servo stall,
2. Servo saturation,
3. Excessive friction drive slippage,
4. Excessive autotuning gain,
5. Bad initial state vector,
6. Excessive tuning parameter error.

The CPC servo system must rapidly detect if a divergence has occurred and perform a recovery. Signs of divergence include the following:

1. Excessive servo error,
2. Excessive difference between the forward and reverse velocity scale factors,

3. Excessive velocity bias error,
4. Excessive flutter magnitude,
5. Overcurrent trip.

The recovery needs to be performed in a robust manner. As previously mentioned, velocity bias error divergence can be suppressed by a clamp. In a similar manner, the magnitude of the flutter model can be clamped. Divergence of the dual velocity scale factor is harder to prevent. To recover from divergence, reset the model, clamp the model (i.e., the velocity bias and flutter magnitude), clamp the servo error, and inhibit filter updates that increase the differential velocity scale factor error beyond a certain level.

The CPC servo system suppresses divergence by clamping the velocity bias to 0.005 inch per second and inhibiting any velocity scale factor updates that increase the forward-reverse scale factor differential when excessive servo error is present.

Performance Analyzer

The CPC servo system incorporates built-in test equipment to support development, testing, validation, and maintenance. These requirements are met through a series of graphic displays:

1. Plot servo error *versus* time,
2. Plot servo error *versus* position,
3. Plot servo error spectrum in the temporal frequency domain,
4. Plot servo error spectrum in the spatial frequency domain,
5. Plot the time history of any tuning parameter.

7.4.5 Servo Error Plot Interpretations

The analysis of the servo error and tuning parameter plots is an art; however, some guidelines are presented here (see Figures 7.19 to 7.21).

1. A well-tuned servo should have a servo error spectrum characteristic of uncorrelated Gaussian noise. This concept is similar to a whiteness test of a Kalman filter innovations sequence.
2. Cyclic errors that are phase stable as a function of position indicate drive runout problems.
3. Drive slippage is indicated by spikes in the servo error plot. If the spikes occur during reversals, then the drive system may have backlash. If the spikes occur at random positions, then the drive may be riding up the side of the drive bar or be otherwise misaligned. If the spikes occur repeatedly at certain random positions, then the drive has a dent or dirt particle.

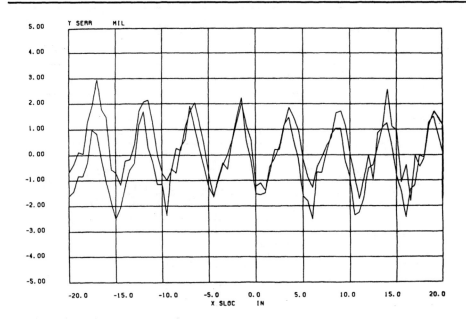

Figure 7.19 Example of a servo error plot with a decentered drive roller (*y*-axis).

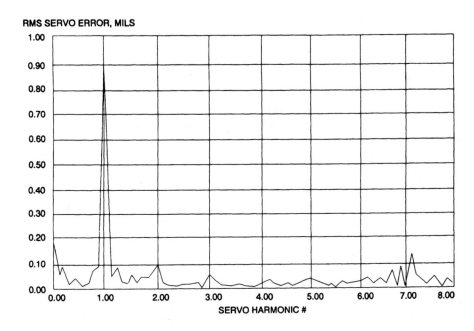

Figure 7.20 Example of the normalized servo error spectrum of a servo with a decentered drive roller.

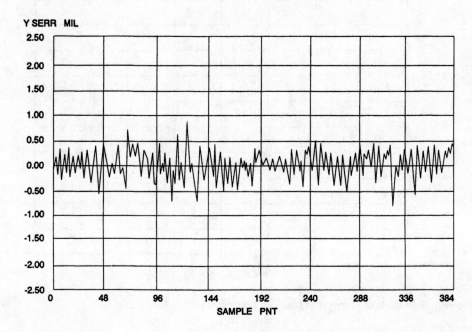

Figure 7.21 Example of the servo error for a correct servo axis (*y*-axis).

As an example, set up a full-travel, single-axis triangle, wave scan with a sample spacing of 0.2 inch. Record two complete cycles of the triangle wave scan. Plot the dynamic servo error as a function of the commanded position.

Ideally, the plot should have only random low-level servo errors. Any disturbance other than random noise should be removable.

Short period cyclic errors normally are caused by servo oscillations. Note that short period errors may alias into long period errors or random noise if the sampling interval is too large or the oscillation rate varies significantly.

Long (2–10 inches) period cyclic errors with a sine wave shape that overlays from scan to scan is caused by an out-of-round drive roller. The period is equal to 2π times the drive roller diameter.

There might be a low servo error in one direction only. A large servo error in a single direction indicates only that the drive is slipping in one direction. This usually is due to a mechanical bind.

Error spikes during reversals indicate that the velocity scale factor or velocity bias is incorrect. Running the servo for a while should allow it to retune itself and the problem should disappear. A second cause of error spikes during reversals is an unrealizable acceleration command. The acceleration is established by the computer using a model of the servo system. A menu option allows the user to change the acceleration limit. Error spikes at fixed positions usually are caused by dents, dirt, *et cetera*. Error spikes at random positions usually are caused by a misalignment between the friction drive and the drive bar. The spikes are produced as the friction drive reseats itself after riding up on the drive bar.

7.4.6 Servo Tuning

Tuning a CPC servo can be very difficult if alignment methods are not considered early in the design. Because all of the critical servo parameters are self-tuning, the manual tuning of the noncritical parameters (all servo parameters are given in Table 7.12) should be required only for the initial installation or after replacing servo hardware. The CPC servo used by the robots described in this chapter uses the following concepts to minimize tuning and maintenance time:

1. Loops can be reconfigured easily under computer control to allow straightforward fault isolation.
2. All critical parameters are self-tuning to greatly simplify servo tuning and hardware replacement and to track real-time hardware drifts.
3. A log of tuning values is recorded and monitored by the computer, so that the computer can watch for slow and subtle degradation of the control system.

Table 7.12
Servo Parameters

Parameter	Symbol	Function
Forward limit	FLIM	protection
Reverse limit	RLIM	protection
Velocity limit	VLIM	set top speed
Acceleration limit	ALIM	set acceleration
Timing corrector	COMP	receiver timing
Forward velocity scale	K_{v+}	command scale factor
Reverse velocity scale	K_{v-}	command scale factor
Velocity bias	K_b	dc drift correction
Flutter magnitude	F_m	flutter compensation
Flutter phase angle	F_p	flutter compensation
Flutter period	F_f	flutter compensation
Position loop gain	K_p	disturbance suppress
Autotune gain	K_a	long-term stability
Signal gain	—	maximum speed set
Tachometer gain	—	rate loop damping
Compensation	—	rate loop stability
Current limit	—	servo torque limit

4. The dynamic servo error can be plotted on calibrated scales for verification of performance and identification of certain hardware faults.
5. The servo error spectrum can be plotted in the spatial frequency domain to identify hardware problems.
6. Tuning parameters can be plotted to identify hardware problems.
7. Alignment procedure is on-line and available to the service technician and user to eliminate searching for manuals and because the alignment procedure is computer aided.

7.4.7 Tuning Stability

The day-to-day variations in the forward and reverse servo velocity scale factors (K_v and $-K_v$) can provide clues as to the cause of improper servo operation. Table 7.13 shows a representative forward and reverse velocity scale factor tuning history for the M4 scanner x, x', and y servo axes. Correct operation of the servos are indicated by good day-to-day stability and a small (less than 1%) differential between the forward and reverse scale factors for a given axis. A large differential indicates, in order of probability, one or more of the following problems:

1. Mechanical binding due to drive or gantry misalignment. Note that the higher K_v value corresponds to the direction of binding resistance.
2. An incorrectly defined servo model in the computer.
3. A defective tachometer, motor, or servo amplifier.

Table 7.13
Representative Tuning History for Self-Tuned Near-Field Scanner

Date	x^+	x^-	x'^+	x'^-	y^+	y^-	Notes
1/23/87	5985	5980	5364	5321	—	—	2 in./s
1/27/87	5975	5977	5345	5331	—	—	5 in./s
1/29/87	5983	5970	5349	5326	4779	4796	
1/29/87	5996	5968	5352	5328	4780	4795	
1/30/87	5988	5976	5347	5322	4783	4786	5 in./s
1/30/87	5986	5975	5342	5329	4786	4787	x belt adjusted
2/05/87	5979	5994	5357	5333	4791	4789	
2/05/87	5982	5990	5355	5337	4792	4788	
2/06/87	5977	5989	5362	5320	4767	4795	
2/06/87	5971	5991	5363	5331	4770	4792	y axis lubricated
2/06/87	6041	5998	5397	5371	4773	4791	
2/10/87	6013	5983	5348	5351	4789	4829	4 in./s
2/10/87	5994	5979	5340	5343	4775	4789	8 in./s
2/10/87	6086	5950	5334	5346	4786	4792	8 in./s
2/12/87	5951	5999	5355	5320	4762	4795	8 in./s
2/16/87	5970	5966	5341	5328	4776	4805	y belt adjusted
2/16/87	5958	5993	5350	5330	4766	4805	x belt adjusted

7.5 ROBOT COMPUTATIONAL SYSTEM

The near-field robot needs a powerful computational system to support the real-time and math-intensive operations required by the near-field measurement process. A good computer choice as of 1990 is one of the 32-bit 80486 and 80386 generation of IBM PC–compatible computers, such as the Compaq 33 MHz DeskPRO augmented with Intel 80387 and Weitek 1167 coprocessors. DSP processors can be readily added if required for very large systems. The use of the 80486 and 80386 IBM PC–compatible computers is recommended because of performance, readily available spare parts and maintenance, and the large body of low cost, yet very high-quality software that is available for it.

One computer is used to control the robot and data acquisition process. On larger systems, one or more additional computers are used to support the data transformation and analysis process. These computers provide a hardware back-up to the data acquisition computer. The data acquisition computer also can be used in the data analysis mode. The same software package is installed on all computers.

7.5.1 Robotic Control Software

The robotic control program consists of a series of software modules that perform the following basic functions:

1. Determine the current probe position.
2. Compute the desired probe motion trajectory.
3. Produce effector commands based on the desired effector velocity and the difference (error) between the desired and actual sensor probe position.
4. Acquire and correct for instrumental errors, the near field complex gain.
5. Acquire and correct for instrumental errors, the optical surface measurements.
6. Provide an operator interface.
7. Provide expert advice relating to the test setup.
8. Provide overall test control.
9. Data storage and retrieval.
10. Fault detection, analysis, and recovery.

7.5.2 Human Factors

The user can communicate with the software in three different ways: menus, directly interpreted command strings, and command files. The user can switch immediately and interactively between the three control methods as desired. The menu system can be interactively toggled between basic and advanced operational modes and the system includes context-sensitive help.

The software uses expert systems techniques to simplify the antenna test design, error budget determination, and system setup. The user describes the basic antenna properties to the software using menu options. The software then will provide a recommended test design. If desired, the software will then automatically set up substantial portions of the test. In a similar manner the production of antenna measurement uncertainty budgets can be automated. The expert system is also used to assist in the system fault recovery process.

The internal design of the robotic control software is heavily based on state space concepts [2]. The robotic control software is written in the Forth language, as it provides the speed, flexibility, and performance required by the data acquisition process. The robot software consists of a large number of independent programs operating as seven separate users that communicate through a common set of data vectors: the *state vector,* the *measurement vector,* and the *pseudovector.*

The state vector defines the system state, contains no redundant entries, and is contiguous in RAM. It is moved easily to and from disk storage. Examples of state vectors include the current position, velocity, scan radius, scan rotation, and position limits.

The measurement vector contains the sensor measurements and is updated only by device handlers. Examples of measurement vectors include the servo positions, servo errors, RF measurements, skeletal deflections, and surface measurements.

The pseudovector contains information redundant with the other vectors; for example, the current position in synthetic coordinates or the servo DAC command.

The use of state space methods leads to a highly modular and robust program with a simple to use checkpoint capability. The state space structure is compatible with the real-time, multitasking requirements of the robotic control application (see Table 7.14). The control program consists of seven real-time tasks with task syn-

Table 7.14
Real-Time Tasks

Task	Name	Rate	Function
1	—	128 Hz	servo interrupt
2	Servo	16 Hz	servo and receiver
3	Analog	0–16 Hz	receiver preprocessor
4	VAX	variable	communication and disk
5	Operator	variable	CRT 1 interface
6	Display	variable	CRT 2 interface
7	Printer	variable	printer or plotter

chronization by semaphores and intercommunications through the state, measurement and pseudo vectors. All program internal values are in MKS units.

7.5.3 Forth Computer Language

The robot control software is written in a combination of Forth and assembly languages. Forth has the advantage of being fast, providing access to all machine resources, unmatched interactiveness, and efficient real-time multitasking. Forth is an extensible language, allowing the straightforward addition of new data types, compilers, and structures.

The disadvantages of Forth include difficulty in linking to other languages, stand-alone operation (in older systems), and familiarity to fewer programmers. The first two disadvantages can be overcome with appropriate modifications to the language.

Forth achieves a high throughput while remaining interactive, because it efficiently combines both compiling and interpretive operations. The basic model of Forth includes two interpreters and one compiler. The outer interpreter processes operator commands. New subroutines are compiled incrementally and immediately and linked into a threaded list, called a *dictionary*. When a code is executed, a very fast inner interpreter (two machine language instructions in the LSI-11/73 computer) interprets the dictionary entry. Forth includes the ability to freely, easily, and interactively intermix assembly codes.

Subroutines, arrays, and other information are stored in the dictionary, which contains subroutine references, machine code, or data. Each dictionary entry additionally includes a name and an entry point.

7.5.4 Robot Control Program Modules

The robot control program consists of a series of independent modules that communicate through the state, measurement, and pseudo vectors. Some of the more important modules will be listed here. The state vector management module includes the following functions:

1. Pseudovector update, which regenerates the pseudo vector from the other data vectors.
2. State vector save, which copies the state vector to a disk, and can be used to checkpoint the system.
3. State vector restore, which copies the state vector on disk into the RAM then regenerates the pseudovector and can be used to initialize or change the robot to a different setup.

4. State vector editor, which allows the user to see and modify the state vector, can be implemented as a menu system, and is the primary user interface.

The utility module functions include the following:

1. Data recorder, which allows the user to record and display 14 channels of data, records and plots parameters in memory, stores data locally or sends them to another computer, and may be enabled or disabled at any time.
2. Command file processor, which allows the use of interpreted command files.

The AI program modules include the following functions:

1. Expert, which uses a test description in the state vector to provide a recommended test design using expert systems techniques.
2. SIM, which provides automated fault detection and recovery, by using expert systems concepts.

The I/O module includes the following handlers:

1. Servo handler, which generates trajectory, reads the optical and laser position sensors, implements the servo control law, and drives the servo rate loop.
2. Microwave interferometer handler, which controls the microwave receiver and source, as well as miscellaneous switches, attenuators, and so on.
3. Optical skeleton handler, which reads the optical skeleton sensors and computes the geometry errors.
4. PH9 handler, which supports coordinate and surface measurements.
5. Votan handler, which handles voice input-output.

7.6 FAULT PROTECTION

Many near-field robotic systems operate near human beings and expensive spacecraft hardware. Robots such as the large, 80-ton CMM type of scanner can generate significant destructive forces during fault conditions. The robot designer, therefore, carefully must consider the safety and fault protection systems. The safety systems must protect operators, bystanders, maintenance personnel, spacecraft hardware, and the facility from inadvertent contact. Isaac Asimov's three laws of robotics, written in 1950, provide an overall safety philosophy [24]:

1. A robot must never harm a human being or through inaction allow a human being to come to harm.
2. A robot must obey a human being unless this is in conflict with the first law.
3. A robot must not allow itself to come to harm unless this is in conflict with either the first or second law of robotics.

In the context of robots used for near-field applications, rule 3 should be modified to exclude the reference to the second law. The robotic safety systems design should consider the following points:

1. The safety system includes a simple and foolproof autonomous component independent of the computational system; for example, a separate and independent fault buss.
2. The chance of harming a user is minimized if the user is kept out of the work area; for example, moving parts of typical CMM-based scanners generally are out of reach of the user.
3. Long standoff sensory payloads can reduce the risk of inadvertent contact with the work; for example, the optical surface scanner or the microwave interferometer.
4. A loose part falling off of the robot will not damage the AUT if the AUT is suspended above the robot; for example, many near-field scanners are located to the side or below the AUT.
5. Expert systems methods can be used to keep fault conditions from degrading. A well-designed expert system can recover many faults better than a human. These methods are now being applied to aircraft and nuclear reactor safety problems; for example, the fault analysis in some near-field range systems.
6. Fault simulation capabilities are useful in validating the safety systems, training users, and developing software, such as the fault simulator in some near-field range systems.
7. Critical failures should be monitored redundantly by two separately developed safety systems. Separate designs reduce the possibility of a generic failure.
8. The use of a fault buss in the robot design can improve the modularity of the robot fault system. The user easily can add application-specific fault sensors and fault stabilization elements.
9. The fault system should actively minimize damage after a fault condition develops.

The robots incorporate four types of safety systems with increasing levels of protection. Safety is enhanced, first, by paying careful attention to human factors. The software should be menu driven or have an equivalent interface. The use of command files for repetitive tasks will reduce the probability of error. As another example, the operator should have a clear view of the scanner, AUT, and probe from control point. This can be further enhanced with clear real-time graphic or television displays showing the spatial relationship between the robot, work, and environment. A probe-mounted television camera can be quite useful.

Second, the robot should use a set of computer programs distributed throughout the robot computational system to monitor for and automatically recover from fault conditions. This set of programs, called the *system integrity monitor* (SIM), detects and corrects such faults as illegal position commands, operator errors, excessive probe velocity, and certain hardware failures. The SIM is discussed in detail later in this section.

Third, potentially very severe faults within the robot should be detected by an independent autonomic system. This system couples sensors directly to effectors, bypassing all computers in an attempt to minimize damage. Some faults detected by the autonomic system include payload impacts or servo amplifier overloads.

Fourth, very high-value work items, such as spacecraft, require an additional last resort positive safety back-up system. The philosophy of the last resort system is to use only simple mechanical protection techniques. An example of a last resort protection device is a fluid shock absorber that can be easily and reliably positioned along the drive rail. A chain mechanism is used on certain CMM-based scanners for positively preventing mechanical contact between the AUT and robot.

System Integrity Monitor

The SIM is a set of computer programs distributed throughout the computational system used to protect the robot and work from fault conditions and perform the appropriate recovery. The SIM is implemented using expert systems techniques and performs six basic functions:

1. Fault detection (determining the existence of a fault),
2. Severity assignment (determining fault priorities),
3. Fault stabilization (minimizing damage),
4. Fault analysis (determining the best recovery procedure),
5. Fault recovery (performing the fault recovery),
6. Fault simulation (supporting SIM verification and training).

The SIM monitors many of the robot sensors in real time to detect potential problems. The problems are assigned a severity level to set priorities in the fault analysis process. The severity priority levels are defined as follows:

5. Potential damage to the robot or work, no backup.
4. Potential damage to the robot or work, autonomic backup.
3. Potential loss of payload control or slow degradation.
2. Potential loss of measurement data.
1. Possible measurement data corruption.
0. Information only.

Immediately after the fault is identified and priorities are set, the SIM will attempt to stabilize the situation, which will prevent any further damage. Level 4 faults normally will be captured by the autonomic system first. Level 5 and 4 faults are stabilized by compiled code operating a 16 Hz cycle rate. Faults at or below priority level 3 do not require immediate stabilization. A simple fault stabilization analysis is performed to see if any of the following actions are desirable:

1. Apply brakes.
2. Inhibit the entire effector group.
3. Remove payload power.
4. Remove ac power.
5. Checkpoint the state and measurement vectors.
6. Start a recovery audit trail.
7. Alert operator.

Once the faults have been detected, priorities set, and the situation stabilized, the SIM starts a detailed analysis using expert systems techniques. After a thorough analysis, the SIM completes the fault recovery by performing the appropriate actions. The SIM also includes a detailed fault simulator to support SIM testing, user training, and software development.

Autonomic Communication System

Very severe faults within the robot are detected and responded to directly by the autonomic system. Very severe faults are those that can result in a direct contact between the robot and work environment, leading to catastrophic damage. The autonomic system will attempt to eliminate or reduce damage to the robot and work. The autonomic system couples sensors directly to the effectors, bypassing all computer control. It operates under the assumption that the computer system has lost control of the robot.

The autonomic system will transmit a message to the SIM computer software immediately upon the potential detection of a catastrophic fault. If the fault does not clear within 20 ms, the autonomic system will immediately perform the required fault stabilization. The computer may receive information from the autonomic system but not send anything to the autonomic system logic. The only autonomic override is a momentary key operated switch. Representative autonomic sensors include contact closures (panic buttons, payload fault sensors), crash sensors (breakwires, optical fences, ultrasonic sensors), and computer fault sensors (watchdog timers, processor halt signals).

REFERENCES

1. Egdall, M., "Large Surface Measuring Machine," Itek Optical Systems, Lexington, MA, 1983. Describes a self-calibrating three-dimensional laser interferometer-based coordinate measurement machine.

2. Slater, D., "A State Space Approach to Robotics," *J. Forth Application and Research,* Vol. 1, No. 1, 1983. Provides a brief overview of state space methods as applied to robotic control program structures.
3. Cone, L., "Skycam: An Aerial Robotic Camera System," *Byte Magazine,* October 1985. Describes the Skycam System, which is a large, cable-suspended, robotic camera positioner.
4. Wollny, W., "Quiet Zone Field and RCS Error Probe," Quick Reaction Corp, Report QRC-6042-88, Gilroy, CA, 1988. Describes a robotic cable-suspended target system.
5. "Arecibo Observatory Today," *Sky and Telescopes,* April 1972. A basic overview of the Arecibo (Puerto Rico) Ionospheric Observatory and the related cable-suspended feed assembly.
6. Gutenberg, B., "Microseisms," *Advances in Geophysics,* Vol. 5, Academic Press, New York, 1958, pp. 53–92. A detailed discussion of the measurement, causes, and spectrum of microseismic activity.
7. Willmore, P., *Manual of Seismological Observatory Practice,* NOAA, Boulder, CO, 1979. Discusses seismic sensors, measurement techniques, background noise, *et cetera.*
8. Weinstock, H., "Limitations on Inertial Sensor Testing Produced by Test Platform Vibrations," NASA Tech. Note TND-3683, 1966. Discusses the seismic noise background in the context of inertial sensor testing.
9. Slater, D., "Near Field Facility Design," *1985 AMTA Conf. Proc.,* Melbourne, FL, 1985. An overview of the basic theory and application of robotic systems as applied to the near-field measurement of spacecraft antennas.
10. Leighton, R., "A 10-meter Telescope for Millimeter and Submillimeter Astronomy," California Institute of Technology, Final Report, NSF Grant AST-73-04908, 1978. Describes the problems associated with manufacturing and testing large, high-accuracy antennas. Several novel techniques are used, including fluid plane references and direct parabolic shape generation by a nulled laser interferometer.
11. Davidson, W., *et al.,* "Microns, Microns Everywhere and All of Them out of Line," Optical Alignment 3, *SPIE,* Vol. 608, 1986. Discusses the problems associated with grinding optics 8 m in diameter to an accuracy of a few μm. The large optics generator is a modification of a commerical precision vertical grinder.
12. Greenleaf, A., "Self-Calibrating Surface Measuring Machine," *Optical Engineering,* Vol. 22, No. 2, 1983. Describes a self-calibrating, three-dimensional laser interferometer–based surface measuring machine.
13. Wood, L., "Progress in Electronic Surveying," *Trans. American Geophysical Union,* March 1977. Reviews current geodetic measuring techniques and systems. Includes a discussion of multifrequency ranging techniques that suppress atmospheric effects.
14. Slater, D., "Large Area Precision Inspection System (LAPIS)," TRW internal report, June 30, 1986. A detailed technical description of the proposed LAPIS near-field range. The LAPIS is designed to test large spacecraft antennas with dimensions approaching 400 ft. The LAPIS uses an unusual assortment of inertial and laser sensors to precisely determine the position of the payload.
15. Lau, K., "Robot End Point Sensing Using Laser Tracking System," Center for Manufacturing Engineering, NBS, Gaithersburg, MD, 1985. Describes a precision position measurement system that uses a laser interferometer and beam-steering system to precisely measure the position of a remotely located target.
16. Brown, L., *et al.,* "Coordinate Measurement with a Tracking Laser Interferometer," *Lasers and Applications,* October 1986. Describes a coordinate measurement system that uses a laser interferometer to track the payload.
17. Slater, D., *et al.,* "The Use of Precision DC Servo Systems in Motion Picture Special Effect Photography," *Drives and Controls International,* Vol. 1, No. 1, May 1981. Briefly describes a real-time servo control architecture that uses nonlinear minimum delay motion filters.

18. Nof, S.Y., *Handbook of Industrial Robotics,* John Wiley and Sons, New York, 1985. An extensive collection of articles on basic robot theory and applications. Good as an overview of basic robotics, however, many of the ideas are incomplete or wrong for high-accuracy applications.

19. Lowenthal, S., *Historical Perspective of Traction Drives and Related Technology,* NASA CP-2210, NASA/Lewis Research Center, Cleveland, 1981. A well written and detailed description of the technology and history of the friction drive power transmission, with numerous references. Other papers of interest are also in this volume.

20. Wernitz, W., "Friction Drives," in *Mechanical Design and Systems Handbook,* Sec. 14, McGraw-Hill, New York, 1964. Technical information related to friction drive power transmission design.

21. Athey, S., "Magnetic Tape Recording," NASA Special Report No. SP-5038, 1966. Describes low-flutter friction drive technology in the context of missile instrumentation recorders. Many of the design concepts are applicable to robotic friction drive systems.

22. Slater, D., "The Use of Computer Technology in Magicam Slave Camera System," *Proc. National Computer Conf.,* Vol. 49, 1980. Describes a proposed precision robotic system, using an aided inertial tracking system for position and attitude feedback.

23. Thaler, G., and M. Pastel, *Analysis and Design of Nonlinear Feedback Control Systems,* McGraw-Hill, New York, 1962. Has a brief discussion of the posicast technique.

24. Asimov, I., *I, Robot,* Doubleday, New York, 1950. A classic work of science-fiction that contains the three laws of robotics.

25. Hoover, J., *et al., Near-Field Testing of the 15 Meter Model of the Hoop Column Antenna,* Volume 1, Final Technical Report, Contract NAS1-18016, Martin Marietta Aerospace, Denver, CO (1986). This report describes the testing of a large spacecraft antenna using the large Martin Marietta near-field facility.

Chapter 8
OPERATIONS

This chapter discusses the general operational aspects of a near-field antenna measurement facility. The chapter is oriented toward larger near-field facilities, although many of the ideas are applicable to other systems. Note that the near-field facility can provide many useful capabilities other than RF antenna performance measurements. As shown in Chapters 5 and 7, the near-field scanners are general-purpose robots that can precisely measure surfaces and locations and perform precision machining operations. The machining, surface measurement, and RF measurement capabilities can be formed into a synergistic combination.

Near-field measurement systems generally require less facility space than competitive techniques. Small portable systems can fit in the corner of an office. Even the larger near-field measurement systems often can be installed directly in an antenna or spacecraft assembly area. In most cases, a minimal amount of microwave absorbing material is required due to the close proximity between the antenna under test and the probe antenna. Minimizing the use of absorbing material simplifies clean room requirements. The types of tests that can be performed by the near-field test facilities include

1. Far-field pattern,
2. Gain measurement,
3. Axial ratio measurement,
4. Beam width,
5. Beam pointing,
6. Autotrack performance,
7. Phase center determination,
8. Defocusing measurement,
9. Reflector surface distortion measurement,
10. Phased array weighting element tuning,
11. Mechanical coordinate measurement.

Near-field measurement systems are well suited to the development and flight qualification activities required by large and multiple element satellite antennas.

For example, near-field test methods are used to measure the performance of satellite antennas, such as multibeam antennas, high-gain autotrack downlink antennas, and telemetry, tracking, and command antennas. In spacecraft integration near-field methods measure antenna-satellite alignment and interaction and antenna-antenna interaction. They also are used to measure the characteristics of feed antennas, feed clusters, and beam waveguide subassemblies.

In satellite antennas, the most commonly required measurements are antenna gain, beam pointing, and axial ratio. Often measurements of very low sidelobes are not required, minimizing the need for microwave absorber material. Antenna characteristics beyond $\pm 9°$ generally are not needed, as many satellites operate at geosynchronous altitudes where the earth appears as a disk with an included angle of $18°$. As wide-angle data are not needed, a high-gain probe antenna or plane polar sampling can offer a substantial advantage in measurement speed (see Chapter 3).

The planar near-field measurement robot can be used for highly integrated machining, coordinate measurement, and RF near-field measurement. All operations can be performed in a common coordinate system without moving the AUT. Thus, errors in relating one coordinate system to another are eliminated, and no time is lost in realigning the antenna in various different systems. As an example, assume the following sequence of operations in the manufacture of a multibeam offset Cassegrain spacecraft antenna.

1. The main reflector surface is measured with a mechanical contact or an optical ranging probe. A least squares determination is made of the shaped parabola orientation and shape parameters.
2. If necessary, a high-speed cutter or other shaping tool carried by the near-field robot is used to correct minor surface shape errors. Step 1 is then repeated.
3. The subreflector is positioned at the desired position by using the coordinate measurement capability of the near-field robot to assist and verify the correct placement.
4. Feed horns are positioned at the desired positions by using the coordinate measurement capability of the robot.
5. The electrical performance of the antenna is measured using near-field techniques. The robot carries a probe antenna connected to a microwave interferometer or network analyzer. The measured electrical field values are mathematically transformed to the equivalent far-field measurements.
6. The electrical boresight can be related easily, accurately, and unambiguously to a mechanical reference frame because both the electrical and mechanical measurements are made in the same reference frame.
7. If any anomalies occur, mechanical, optical, and microwave probing techniques are immediately available in a known reference frame.

Spacecraft antennas are quite sensitive to gravitationally induced distortions. The planar near-field range system addresses this problem by allowing the AUT to remain stationary. In certain cases, a suspension system is used to counteract gravitational forces. In some planar near-field configurations, the AUT can be tested in horizontal orientation, which minimizes nonsymmetrical distortions.

8.1 TEST DESIGN

Near-field testing will be most successful when the test sequence is carefully planned. The following list describes a typical sequence of events in a near-field antenna test. Prior to entering the test facility,

1. Determine the test type (development test, manufacturing test, acceptance test),
2. Determine the accuracy requirements,
3. Set a preliminary error budget,
4. Design the test plan,
5. Build any special fixtures,
6. Determine the logistics of the test.

Upon entering the near-field test facility,

1. Install and align the antenna,
2. Measure the VSWR and so forth,
3. Perform a range checkout and final error budget,
4. Perform antenna near-field measurements,
5. Reduce the data,
6. Remove the antenna from the facility.

Upon leaving test facility, prepare the final report.

These steps will now be examined in more detail. Antenna tests normally are performed for one of three reasons, explained by Jones [1]: to make a better antenna design, to make a better product, or for customer acceptance. Understanding the distinctions among the differing test requirements will assist in the design of a test plan that is both efficient and successful.

1. *Development Test* The development test is used to make a better antenna design. Therefore, the design of a development test emphasizes the test anomalies and maximizes the gathering of numerical data. The analysis of the test anomalies often lead to new engineering insights. The error budget will define a lower bound on the measurement uncertainty due to lack of knowledge of all relevant error mechanisms. Measurement errors probably are worse than the error budget specifies. The value of a development test is the value of the design changes times the probability of finding those changes.

2. *Production Test* The production test is used to make a better product. Therefore, the design of a production test emphasizes a "go–no-go" criteria. Errors often are expressed as having 3-σ limits. Small anomalies are generally ignored. The value of the production test is the value of the manufacturing change times the probability of finding the change.

3. *Acceptance Test* The acceptance test is used to support marketing activities and satisfy customers. Note that the results of the acceptance test do not in any way improve or change the antenna performance; this was previously accomplished in the production tests. Therefore, the design of the acceptance test should maximize the success rate of the test. The value of the acceptance test is the value of the customer times the probability of having a successful demonstration.

Once the reason for performing the test has been established, the required measurements and a preliminary uncertainty budget should be determined. The near-field test plan needs to be designed. Parameters such as scan widths, sample spacings, and scan speeds need to be established (see Chapter 3). The preliminary error budget should be compared with the test requirements to check test feasibility. The potential need for special probe antennas, fixtures, or microwave absorber may be discovered at this point. Operating frequencies may indicate the need for special RF hardware.

The preliminary uncertainty budget is established by listing all possible error sources and then estimating the measurement uncertainty. The measurement uncertainty can be estimated from previous experience, computer simulation, and analytical study. Dominant errors should be examined, if necessary, for ways to minimize the effects. The generation of measurement uncertainty budgets is covered in more detail in Chapter 9.

Once the test design has been completed, any special fixtures need to be built and any special purpose RF equipment should be procured. During this time interval, test logistics should be organized. The following list describes what normally is provided by the user and what is provided by the near-field test facility. The user provides this equipment:

1. Test plan,
2. Antenna under test,
3. Probe antennas,
4. *Standard gain antenna* (SGA), if required,
5. Mounting adapters for AUT and SGA,
6. Waveguide *et cetera* for an interface to the interferometer,
7. Special signal sources, receivers, and so on,
8. *S*-parameter test set for network analyzer, if required,

9. Security plan and equipment,
10. Data storage media.

The near-field test facility provides this equipment:

1. Near-field scanner,
2. Network analyzer or RF interferometer system,
3. Data acquisition computer system,
4. Data transformation computer system,
5. Optical or mechanical alignment equipment,
6. Personnel lifts and ladders, for large systems,
7. Office space.

The next step is to move the antenna into the facility. The highest efficiency can be achieved by performing as many steps in parallel as is possible. Some steps that can be performed in parallel are antenna alignment, RF hook-up, VSWR measurements, and SGA near-field error analysis measurement.

Several philosophies exist relating to antenna alignment issues. Most users tend to precisely align the antenna normal to the near-field scan plane. A precise knowledge of the antenna's mechanical orientation relative to the near-field scanner is generally required only when the electrical boresight orientation relative to a mechanical reference needs to be known. A precise alignment is not required for gain, AR, or sidelobe measurement, or for correct far-field transformation.

If a precise alignment or boresight measurement is required, it can be achieved by fulfilling these requirements:

1. Determine what hardware defines the antenna's mechanical reference; typically, reference surfaces, tooling balls, and autocollimation mirrors. The reference surfaces and tooling balls generally provide a better reference than the autocollimation mirrors. The autocollimation mirrors are very accurate but tend to measure local surface deformations rather than follow the antenna surface. The reference surfaces and tooling balls provide the highest accuracy when widely spaced.
2. Measure the scan plane orientation relative to the antenna. This can be accomplished by touch probes, theodolites, jig transits, photogrammetric methods, laser ranging hardware, or other instruments as appropriate.
3. Once the relative orientation between the antenna and scan plane has been determined, the antenna orientation can be corrected in one of three ways. The antenna can be physically aligned relative to the scanner. The near-field scan plane can be synthetically rotated (if the scanner has a z-axis) to correctly orient the scan plane relative to the antenna (see Chapter 7 and Appendix A for more details). The misalignment can be derotated in the processed data.

The most common alignment method is mounting the AUT on a two or three axis positioner that can be pointed precisely. This technique is expensive and provides only moderate accuracy. The positioner may creep with time.

A better technique is to add a z-axis to the near-field scanner and synthetically rotate the scan plane. This technique can provide a much higher accuracy at a lower cost than the first technique. The method allows the scan plane to be rapidly rotated into precise alignment with off-axis beams. It has been used extensively in the plane polar near-field testing of multibeam spacecraft antennas. In this case, the sampling density can be substantially reduced by aligning the antenna boresight with the rotated scan plane.

A third technique is to perform the rotation mathematically in the computer. This is a low-cost technique that provides very high accuracy and generally is recommended for most applications. The disadvantages include the potential for mixing up the sign of the tilt correction and additional mathematical complexities.

Once the antenna has been aligned, the near-field range checkout and final error budget should be determined. A representative test sequence follows. Ideally, the tests listed should be performed for both the AUT and SGA at all frequencies of interest. Common problems include forgetting the SGA tests and not systematically performing all of the required tests at the different test frequencies. Tests to determine near-field measurement uncertainty include

1. Interferometer stability test,
2. Reference cable stability test,
3. Interferometer linearity test,
4. RF leakage test,
5. Multipath test,
6. Scan plane truncation test,
7. Scan plane error test,
8. Antenna alignment test.

The design and analysis of these tests is further described in Chapter 9. Other tests may be required to support certain test plans. For example, a mechanical AUT mount-stability test using tiltmeters may be required for electrical boresight determinations. By this time, the user should have determined the sampling parameters (e.g., scan type, size, density). Some near-field programs include expert systems to assist in this determination. After the antenna has been aligned, the RF systems has been checked, and the measurement uncertainties have been determined, it is time to perform the actual near-field measurements.

After the measurements have been completed, a final report usually is needed. The final report normally would contain sections on the test description, test summary, detailed test results, resolution of any anomalies, and the measurement error budget.

8.2 AUTOMATED OPERATIONS

Many near-field measurement systems can be operated from command files. This allows an unattended system to acquire and process measurements 24 hours per day, which can substantially increase throughput over a manually operated system.

8.3 DOCUMENTATION AND USER TRAINING

The near-field measurement system should include the following documentation:

1. Near-field system operating manual,
2. Near-field system validation report,
3. Maintenance log,
4. Equipment manuals for vendor-supplied equipment,
5. Computer software manuals.

Near-field measurement systems are sophisticated robotic-microwave systems. As such, a good training program is essential. The training for a near-field measurement system normally includes the following courses, with some variations depending on the hardware options:

1. Near-field operations (technician level),
2. Near-field maintenance (technician level),
3. Near-field test design (engineering level),
4. Coordinate measurements (technician level).

REFERENCES

1. Jones, D., "Shape and Coordinate Measurements," TRW near-field class notes, TRW internal publication, 1987. Discusses test philosophy, inverse theory, shape measurement systems, photogrammetry, and kinematic mounts as applied to near-field measurement systems.

Chapter 9
ANTENNA TEST RANGE ERROR ANALYSIS

The amount of uncertainty in an antenna performance measurement must be determined if the measurements are to be of any value. This chapter explains how to derive an uncertainty estimate for a near-field measurement system. The uncertainty estimate is only a lower bound on the measurement accuracy unless all significant error sources have been correctly identified and bounded. Near-field measurement uncertainty is a function of many potential error sources. In the near-field measurement system, common sources of error include microwave interferometer stability, noise, and linearity; phase reference cable stability; scanner mechanical accuracy; and transform software nonlinearities and errors. In the test design, errors often emanate from the choice of test type; gravity-induced distortions of the AUT; sampling density and aliasing; the choice of transform method; probe selection, pattern accuracy, and alignment tolerances; antenna alignment tolerances; multipath leakage and reflections; and absorber placement. Errors due to test-specific hardware can include SGA to AUT gain differential, SGA gain uncertainty, attenuator calibration uncertainty, switch loss uncertainty, or switch VSWR.

To determine the accuracy of a specific antenna measurement,

1. Establish the required measurement accuracy,
2. Determine basic near-field measurement system accuracy,
3. Design the measurement test configuration,
4. Estimate the application-specific errors,
5. Run required tests to validate the test's accuracy.

9.1 NEAR-FIELD MEASUREMENT ASSUMPTIONS

Antenna performance measurements are of little value if their accuracy cannot be specified. The determination of the derived far-field antenna measurement accuracy from measurements made in a near-field test facility requires a detailed understanding of how various error sources propagate throughout the system. The planar near-field measurement technique is exact if certain conditions hold true. These conditions are slightly adapted from [1]:

1. The electromagnetic field outside the scan area is zero,
2. The scanner positioning is infinitely accurate,
3. The RF interferometer is perfectly linear and free of noise,
4. No multipath propagation occurs,
5. Computational errors in deriving the far field are nil,
6. The only coupling between the test and probe antennas is by free-space propagation (i.e., no evanescent coupling).

As real-world near-field measurement facilities violate all of these conditions to some extent, an error analysis is required. The analysis of the errors in the near-field measurement process is based on the following fundamental concepts, parts of which, again, are adapted from [1]:

1. The measurement uncertainties are a combined function of the antenna measurement system errors, the test geometry, and certain antenna properties. As such, an error budget will be specific to a given measurement system, geometry, and antenna.
2. The far-field antenna pattern can be considered to be the coherent sum of the actual antenna pattern and a series of far-field noise patterns corresponding to various error sources. The error patterns are produced from unbiased and uncorrelated white-noise phasors (Chapter 2; [2]). We will use a series of self-comparison tests to extract the various far-field noise patterns. We will determine the total magnitude of the measurement uncertainty by using a Pythagorean sum, root sum of the squares (rss), of the individual noise pattern voltages. This is equivalent to summing the noise powers corresponding to the error sources. The assumption here is that the individual uncertainty terms are uncorrelated and the system is linear with respect to voltage. This is a direct consequence of the central limit theorem. If error terms are correlated, they must instead be summed coherently. In certain cases, the identified noise patterns can be coherently subtracted to improve the quality of the measurement. For example, mutual coupling between the AUT and probe antennas can be largely suppressed by coherently processing a pair of planar scans separated by $\lambda/4$.
3. Measurement uncertainties can be experimentally identified through the use of overdetermined or redundant measurements. We define a series of self-comparison tests that perturb the system but should not change the final results. For example, a pair of measurements separated in time or with a different geometry (separation, translation, rotation) should provide identical results. The measurement uncertainty is a function of the extent that the overdetermined test results do not agree.

4. Analysis of near-field measurement uncertainty is greatly simplified if the uncertainty measurements are first transformed to the far field. Nearly identical techniques can be used to determine uncertainty in both near- and far-field measurements. Random and systematic near-field errors create different noise characteristics in the derived far field. Because of operation of the transform, correlated systematic errors may cause significantly more error than random errors and are more difficult to quantify. Therefore, the analysis is more easily performed on the transformed far-field results.

5. Gain, axial ratio, and other measurements have a common subset of error terms. This subset is the uncertainty in the measured far-field antenna pattern. Errors in the derived far-field pattern, such as the directive gain, sidelobe accuracy, and axial ratio, can be determined largely from a knowledge of the signal-to-noise ratios throughout the derived far-field pattern. The SNR for a given pattern varies primarily with the sidelobe level and to a smaller degree as a function of the angle from boresight if probe correction is used. We will first determine the pattern uncertainty and later combine it with other terms to determine the other test uncertainties. In the case of a comparison gain uncertainty budget, complete far-field pattern error determinations are required for both the AUT and the SGA.

6. If all significant error sources are identified and correctly modeled, the measurement error budget will correctly define the measurement accuracy. Otherwise, the error budget is only a lower limit on the measurement accuracy. Unknown or unmodeled terms will increase measurement error. An important part of an error budget is the identification of all important sources of error.

A variety of near-field measurement error sources should be considered. The more important error sources are preceded by an asterisk. Sources of random noise include antenna and receiver thermal noise, receiver $1/f$ noise, ADC quantization noise, *source amplitude stability and source frequency stability, and electromagnetic interference. Sources of coherent noise include *RF and *IF leakage, *multipath noise, and *scanner positioning errors. Sources of intermodulation distortion (nonlinearities) include transform and *receiver nonlinearity, *scanner positioning errors, and *scan plane truncation. Among unmodeled spatial filters, errors may be due to *probe pattern uncertainty, probe alignment errors, receiver IF bandwidth effects, and *aliasing.

9.1.1 Random Noise in the Microwave Interferometer

The microwave interferometer has a dynamic range that is established at one end by receiver saturation and nonlinearities and at the other end by the receiver thermal, $1/f$, and quantization noise. Dynamic range can be defined in a variety of ways. In this book, the receiver dynamic range is defined as the difference between the saturation and the 0 dB SNR points. The SNR is measured at the receiver output. The dynamic range generally is considerably higher if the SNR is measured at the output of the near- to far-field transformation. The increased dynamic range is due to the improved SNR created by the process gain of the far-field transformation. This concept is described later in more detail.

The transformed far-field voltage pattern for an antenna measured in a near-field range is the linear sum of the actual far-field antenna pattern, a far-field transformation of the receiver noise, and other error terms. This is a direct consequence of the principle of superposition for linear systems. The far-field transformed receiver noise appears as an additive noise to the antenna pattern. If the antenna is removed from the system, as in a leakage test, only the receiver noise (and leakage, if any) would remain. Ignoring other error sources, the far-field transform of the receiver noise is equivalent to the sidelobe noise level of the system. Note that the sidelobe noise level is a function of many terms including probe antenna selection, transmit power, receiver thermal noise, and number of points transformed to the far field.

Receiver saturation at high power levels and random noise at low power levels establishes the dynamic range of the microwave receiver. Noise in a near-field measurement system can be measured or calculated. We first will estimate the system noise from a representative near-field measurement system by using the link model shown in Figure 9.1. For this example, the AUT has a gain of 40 dB. The probe antenna has a gain of 6 dB. The insertion loss between the two uniform antennas is the area ratio mismatch between the apertures or the difference in antenna gains if expressed in dB (also see Table 9.1):

$$\text{Insertion loss} = |\text{gain } 1 - \text{gain } 2| = |40 - 6| = 34 \text{ dB} \qquad (9.1)$$

Additional losses can result if the system is operated in a pulsed mode with a pulse length shorter than the receiver integration time. The effective power loss is equal to the relative duty cycle. For example, a 10% duty cycle results in a 20 dB decrease in signal-to-noise ratio.

The receiver SNR is the receiver input power divided by the equivalent receiver noise power. For a HP-8510B/8511 network analyzer in single average mode at 5.6 GHz, the equivalent noise power is approximately −98 dBm. The SNR for this example is

$$\text{SNR} = -37 \text{ dBm} - (-98 \text{ dBm}) = 61 \text{ dB} \qquad (9.2)$$

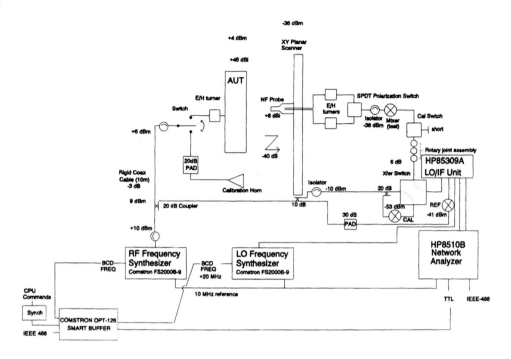

Figure 9.1 A representative link budget for a large near-field measurement system operating at 5.6 GHz.

Table 9.1

Device	Gain	Power Level	Comments
Source power		−10 dBm	
Amplifier output	+23 dB	+33 dBm	
Isolator output	−1 dB	+32 dBm	
AUT cable output	−10 dB	+22 dBm	1 dB/m
AUT to probe	−34 dB	−12 dBm	12 dB–40 dB
Probe cable output	−25 dB	−37 dBm	1 dB/m
Receiver input		−37 dBm	

9.1.2   Receiver Noise

In most receivers, random noise is due to one of four sources:

1. Mixer noise,
2. Thermal noise,

3. $1/f$ noise,
4. A/D converter (ADC) quantization.

Systematic (correlated) receiver noise is due to

1. dc drift,
2. Leakage,
3. Quadrature gain-phase unbalance,
4. Mixer compression,
5. Log converter errors (certain older designs),
6. Coherent interference (i.e., 60 Hz ground loop).

The thermal noise power of a matched termination is

$$P_n = kTB \qquad (9.3)$$

where

k = Boltzman's constant ($1.38\ e^{-23}$ J/K),
T = absolute noise temperature (K),
B = IF noise bandwidth.

Typical values:

P_n = -122 dBm,
T = 300 K,
B = 100 kHz.

The input equivalent noise temperature for a phase measurement receiver or vector network analyzer is the sum of the antenna, transmission line, and receiver noise temperatures. Significant additional losses (typically 20 dB) may be present in network analyzers configured for full S-parameter measurements because of the additional components in series with the receiver input. The interferometer noise level is a function of the receiver IF bandwidth, preamplifier noise, mixer losses, cable losses, and the antenna thermal environment. The input equivalent noise temperature, T, for a receiver is given by

$$T = a(T_a) + T_o(1 - a) + T_i + \sum_{M=2}^{n} \frac{T_n}{G(n - 1)} \qquad (9.4)$$

where

T = system noise temperature (3000 K),
a = transmission coefficient (0.5)

T_a = antenna noise temperature (300 K),
T_o = transmission line temperature (300 K),
T_i = input stage noise temperature (2600 K [10 dB NF]),
T_n = noise of nth stage (10,000 K),
G_n = gain of nth stage (20 dB).

Typical S-band values are shown in parentheses.

The antenna noise temperature is equal to that of the test facility environment, because all surfaces that can be viewed by the antenna are at the temperature of the facility. The facility temperature is assumed to be 290 K. Because the transmission line is also at 290 K, the transmission coefficient, a, need not be computed.

The largest noise contribution generally is at the receiver input stage, from a combination of thermal and other excess noise sources. The noise figure depends heavily on the receiver front-end design and can vary from less than 1 dB to more than 30 dB. The receivers used in near-field measurements are relatively noisy because they often use harmonic mixing and generally do not have a preamplifier.

Another source of receiver noise is $1/f$ or "flicker noise." The flicker noise power spectral density varies inversely with frequency. True homodyne receivers that use a zero frequency IF are quite susceptible to this noise source. The use of these receivers generally is not recommended. In general, $1/f$ noise is not significant when the first IF is above 10–100 kHz.

Quantization noise can be introduced into the receiver when the continuously variable analog IF signal is sampled and quantized into discrete values by an ADC. In a properly designed system, the analog IF signal should be integrated for the duration of the ADC sample period, resulting in a matched filter response. As an example, a 12-bit binary twos complement representation of the raw IF signal will result in a dynamic range, R, of

$$R = 20 \log 2^{n-1} = 66.2 \text{ dB} \quad (n = 12) \tag{9.5}$$

The previously described PMI receiver (Chapter 4) coherently processes 100 voltage samples at a 100 kHz rate to establish a 1 ms integration time. The process gain is the square root of 100, corresponding to an SNR enhancement of 20 dB.

9.1.3 Process Gain

The dynamic range requirements for most near-field measurements usually are not hard to meet. Smaller dynamic ranges and lower SNR values than would initially seem necessary are quite suitable for highly accurate near-field measurements. Significant amounts of random receiver noise are removed by the process gain of the far-field transformation. On the other hand, careful attention must be paid to correlated and deterministic noise sources.

Process gain is a term used to describe the increase in SNR when a series of independent, noisy, real measurements are combined additively. In the voltage domain, the real signal components add as a linear sum whereas the noise components add as a Pythagorean (rss) sum [2]. The noise components actually are phasors with real (I) and imaginary (Q) components. A series of noise phasors is summed by using the rules of vector arithmetic. The difference results in a square root of n improvement in SNR for n measurements. We are assuming that the noise is uncorrelated (white) and unbiased. The noise may have any arbitrary probability distribution as a consequence of the central-limit theorem (see Appendix B).

The situation is similar for noisy complex (I/Q) measurements as commonly found in near-field measurements. The actual measurements are the vector sum of a perfect measurement phasor and a series of uncorrelated, unbiased noise phasors (see Chapter 2). For example, assume we have 100 measurements of a 1 V signal corrupted with white noise with a standard deviation of 1 V. The average voltage is 1 V. The sum of a series of 100 uncorrelated, unbiased noise phasors is a new phasor with a standard deviation of 0.1 V ($1/\sqrt{100}$). This summation results in a 20 dB SNR improvement ($20 \log \sqrt{100}$).

The coherent signal power adds linearly in the voltage domain. The random signal power adds linearly in the power domain or in a square root manner in the voltage domain. The increase in SNR for n coherent voltage measurements corrupted by random noise is proportional to $\sqrt{n}$.

The far-field transform process can significantly improve both the receiver SNR and dynamic range because of the transform integration or averaging. The receiver output is simply the phase front RF measurement down-converted by the test frequency; that is, to dc. The signal has not been demodulated at the receiver output even though it may be in an amplitude-phase form. This is because the amplitude-phase representation is simply a conversion of the Cartesian I/Q signal in a polar coordinate system. The actual demodulation process will occur at the far-field transform output when the I/Q signal amplitude (AM) or phase (PM) component is extracted and displayed separately. The equivalent receiver IF bandwidth for a near-field measurement system is equal to the physical receiver IF bandwidth divided by the number of points processed in the near- to far-field transform. Equivalently, the physical receiver integration time multiplied by the number of measurements transformed is the integration time of the whole system.

The near- to far-field transformation coherently sums all measurements into each output point. Because of this, the transformation increases the SNR by 20 $\log \sqrt{n}$ dB, where n = the number of measurement points. For example, if 1000 measurements were taken of a uniform aperture antenna at a 0 dB SNR, the derived far-field pattern would have a rms noise level of -30 dB. The dynamic range of the system is increased by the same amount.

In the earlier link budget example (Figure 9.1), the dynamic range at the receiver output was 61 dB. With a 1000 point transform, the dynamic range at the transform output is extended by 30 to −91 dB. Equivalently, the sensitivity can be expressed as an equivalent processed sidelobe noise level −91 dB below the main beam.

Amplitude or phase nonlinearities in the receiver result in the generation of spatial frequency harmonic and intermodulation distortion products. Because, in the near field, the main-beam and sidelobe power are combined, receiver linearity is quite important. For example, a −40 dB sidelobe noise level requires that the spatial intermodulation products between various spatial frequency components on the boresight axis be more than −40 dB. Alternately, a probe with an axial null (see Chapter 3) can be used to minimize spatial intermodulation distortion.

9.2 FAR-FIELD PATTERN UNCERTAINTY

The accuracy of antenna parameter measurements such as gain, axial ratio, beamwidth, and sidelobe levels are dependent upon the quality of the basic far-field pattern. The first step, therefore, is to determine the uncertainties in the far-field pattern of the AUT. In the case of a gain comparison measurement, a pattern error budget is also required for the standard gain antenna. The uncertainty in the far-field pattern is a function of many error sources. A representative pattern error budget is shown in Table 9.2.

Table 9.2
Far-Field Pattern Errors

Error Term	Antenna under Test	
	Uncertainty (dB)	*Boresight SNR (dB)*
Random noise	0.010	59
Linearity	0.020	53
RF leakage	0.003	70
Multipath	0.060	43
Mutual coupling	0.180	34
Scan plane truncation	0.050	45
x-y positioning errors	0.010	59
z positioning errors	0.020	53
TOTAL (rss)	0.198	33

The theoretical evaluation of near-field measurement accuracy is difficult, particularly because a given near-field error source may cause massively different far-field effects, depending on its signal correlation properties. Using worst case theoretical values can result in unrealistically large error budgets. Fortunately, a relatively simple experimental approach based on self-comparison tests can provide an accurate determination of the uncertainties. To perform the required tests,

1. Determine the system random noise and leakage levels by measuring scan-to-scan repeatability, the system linearity, the transmitter leakage, and the receiver leakage.
2. Determine mutual coupling and multipath levels by repeating a series of scans at $\lambda/8$ wavelength Z intervals and another series of scans with small frequency offsets or geometry changes.
3. Determine scanner-induced systematic noise by measuring the phase reference cable stability, performing the scan plane truncation test, and probing for positioning errors.

9.3   RF STABILITY TEST

The amplitude and phase stability over time of the near-field measurement system needs to be determined. Factors that can influence the amplitude stability include

1. Source power stability,
2. Random cable flexure problems,
3. Loose connections,
4. Receiver drift.

Factors that can influence the phase stability include

1. Source frequency changes,
2. Random cable flexure problems,
3. Loose connections,
4. Thermal expansion and gradients,
5. Scanner positioning errors,
6. Receiver drift.

The aggregate effect of these error sources can be measured by a self-comparison test, which is run by repeating a series of near-field measurements (typically six) separated in time and comparing the far-field patterns. The variation in peak far-field power is an excellent measure of the system stability. Typical derived far-field beam peak stability values are in the vicinity of 0.005–0.02 dB. Common test errors include not waiting for the system to thermally stabilize and testing at improper receiver RF input levels.

If excessive instability is found, further tests may be required to localize the problem. The AUT, scanner, and moving cables can be eliminated from the test by tying the source directly to the receiver. The amplitude and phase can be plotted as a function of time as a diagnostic tool. If the amplitude and phase measurements are transformed to the far field, a pattern corresponding to a uniformly illuminated constant phase antenna would result. Repeat this several times and look at the variation. If the variation is now acceptable, the problem was in the AUT, scanner, or moving cables. A cable problem can be isolated by watching the receiver output as the cable is manually flexed.

9.4 SYSTEM LINEARITY TEST

A series of amplitude and phase linearity tests are required to determine the linearity of the near-field measurement system. Linearity tests verify that the system-wide gain and phase measurements are linear. These tests are performed by recording the receiver or, better, the transform output as a calibrated attenuator and phase shifter is used to introduce known gain and phase values into the measurements.

The interferometer and processing systems must be linear or spatial harmonic and spatial intermodulation distortion will occur. Nonlinearity in a near-field measurement system results in the production of spatial sum and difference frequencies that create spurious sidelobes. The principles here are very similar to conventional temporal domain harmonic and intermodulation distortions, except that these distortions are in the spatial frequency domain.

Certain receiver errors, such as lack of quadrature balance, can be detected by observing the change of amplitude as the phase shifter is varied. This effect is called *PM-to-AM conversion*. Likewise, the phase meter output can be monitored as the attenuator is varied. This effect is called *AM-to-PM conversion,* and it usually results from an internal receiver leakage or dc imbalance in the quadrature detector.

Significant nonlinearity is rare in modern receivers; however, older receivers may have more serious linearity problems. With the exception of errors caused by RF leakage, linearity errors are virtually always caused by the receiver or transform. Receiver linearity errors include

1. Compression in a mixer or amplifier (amplitude only),
2. Nonlinearity in a log generator (amplitude only),
3. I/Q Detector quadrature unbalance (PM-to-AM conversion),
4. Compression in a mixer or amplifier (AM-to-PM conversion),
5. dc offset at quadrature mixer output (AM-to-PM conversion),
6. RF signal leakage (AM-to-PM-to-AM conversion),
7. IF signal leakage (AM-to-PM-to-AM conversion).

Saturation or compression in a mixer or amplifier occurs when the receiver input power is too high. Compression usually occurs when the signal level approaches or exceeds the LO level. Compression can be eliminated by installing a suitable attenuator in series with the receiver input.

Certain older receivers use an analog logarithmic generator to calculate the decibel function. If the logarithmic generator is nonlinear, the receiver output will be nonlinear.

Most receivers use a quadrature detector to extract an I/Q signal. If the relative gains and phase (circularity) of this detector are not correctly balanced, PM-to-AM conversion will occur. This will cause the antenna pattern, gain, and AR to vary cyclically with Z separation.

Leakage within the receiver adds a constant amplitude phasor to the quadrature detector output, causing spurious energy on the boresight axis. Leakage affects low signal levels most. It is seen most easily in a leakage test, as described later. Common leakage sources within a receiver can include

1. Incorrect LO isolation in remote mixer configurations,
2. Inadequate IF or LO signal shielding,
3. dc imbalance at the quadrature detector output.

Users of near-field measurement systems often assume that the far-field transformation is linear to the extent that it could not introduce significant errors, which sometimes is an incorrect conclusion. Significant nonlinearities may be introduced by the far-field transformation program whenever a non-band-limited interpolation routine is used, which can result in aliased sidelobe energy. The practical effects of aliasing are to cause excessive sidelobe noise when the receiver SNR is low or to degrade complex sidelobe structures. This trap is particularly subtle. Examples of where interpolation methods are used in the transformation process include the following:

1. Receiver drift is often suppressed by interpolating between tie scans or plane polar center points. Sidelobe degradation definitely has been identified with the receiver drift suppression in certain antenna tests.
2. Certain formulations of the near- to far-field transformation algorithm use linear or polynomial interpolation methods. These interpolation methods are not band-limited. This error source has been suspected in certain antenna tests.
3. A non-band-limited interpolation of the derived far field can cause sidelobe degradation. This error source has been suspected in certain antenna tests.
4. Non-band-limited interpolation of the probe antenna pattern, particularly if complex, can introduce sidelobe errors.
5. Plot routines can corrupt complex sidelobe structures. As an example, plot a high frequency sine wave on a CRT terminal. The sine wave will appear to vary in amplitude. The amplitude variations are caused by the vector (linear) interpolation used to draw the plot. A band-limited reconstruction would draw the sine wave correctly.

Several types of tests are required to characterize the influence of receiver and transform nonlinearities on the far-field pattern. Amplitude nonlinearity is measured by a self-comparison test. Repeat the antenna measurement with a 10 dB attenuator in series with the AUT or probe antenna. Compare the far-field patterns at the two different attenuation settings. Because of the attenuation uncertainty of the attenuator, we need to look at the normalized pattern differences off the main beam. For example, select various pairs of corresponding points -10 dB from the beam peak. Determine the rms dB difference between these points. Divide the value by 3.24 to compensate for a 10 dB noise build-up. This value corresponds to an intermodulation product induced noise.

In a second form of this test, the far-field pattern is measured with different phase shifter settings. For more information, see PM-to-AM and AM-to-PM conversion above.

9.5   LEAKAGE TEST

Microwave leakage in the RF subsystem can seriously corrupt the antenna measurements. Stray leakage appears to the measurement system as additional ghost antenna elements. Because of this, leakage produces spurious sidelobes resulting in the corruption of derived far-field data. This error source can be quite insidious if not detected and suppressed. Fortunately leaks are relatively easy to both measure and control. Leakage is measured by performing three antenna measurements and transforming the results to the far field. Three separate measurements are required: a normal far-field pattern (scan 1), a far-field pattern with the probe antenna cable terminating into a load (scan 2), and a far-field pattern with the AUT cable terminating into a load (scan 3).

The load should be as close to the probe antenna or AUT as possible. All connections should be taped with copper foil. The three scans are transformed to the far field. The pattern amplitudes need to be normalized to the AUT or SGA gain (scan 1). Leakage pattern amplitudes are then in terms of sidelobe levels. After normalizing scans 2 and 3 to scan 1, the far-field plots show the equivalent sidelobe noise levels due to leakage and receiver noise (see Table 9.3). Figures 9.2 and 9.3 show examples of leakage plots. The peak contour level is 60 dB below the AUT boresight gain level.

After making the scans, compare the difference in peak far-field levels between the normal and the higher level terminated pattern. The difference in these values is the leakage noise level. Typically this ratio should be greater than 60 dB. If not, connections may need to be taped with copper tape.

Some leakage plots show a spike on the boresight axis. A spike on the boresight axis in a far-field pattern derived from planar near-field measurements indi-

Table 9.3
Example Leakage Test Summary

	Transmitter Terminated		Receiver Terminated	
	Level (dB)	Error (dB)	Level (dB)	Error (dB)
Leakage	−58.0	0.01	−52.4	0.02
dc imbalance	−43.0	0.05	−37.4	0.10

Notes:
1. Leakage levels are relative to the beam peak.
2. Error is the leakage effect on the beam peak.

cates a leak internal to the receiver or a dc unbalance. This type of leak forms the equivalent of a low-level axial plane wave integrated in the far-field transformation. Certain remote mixer receiver configurations are particularly prone to leakage if isolation amplifiers are not correctly installed in the mixer LO line.

If the leak is consistent, it can be coherently suppressed by subtracting the leakage signal from the measurement signal. This subtraction can be done either before or after the transformation. For those far-field transformations that are highly nonlinear in the presence of noise, the coherent subtraction should be done before transformation.

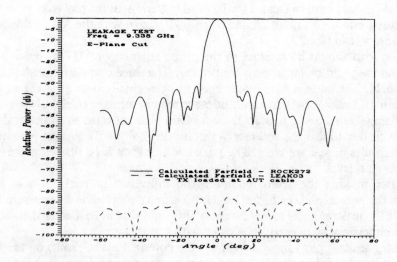

Figure 9.2 Example of a transmitter leak shown as an overlay on the antenna pattern.

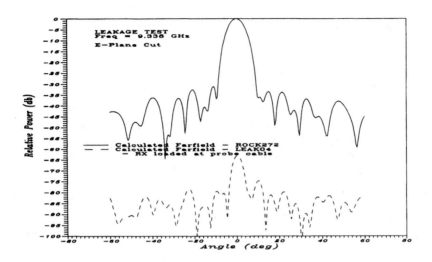

Figure 9.3 Example of receiver leakage shown as an overlay on the antenna pattern.

9.6   REFERENCE CABLE STABILITY TEST

The far-field pattern is particularly sensitive to systematic gain and phase errors in the phase reference cable. The reference cable stability test validates that the movement and flexing of the phase reference cable does not significantly affect the accuracy of the antenna measurements. Phase errors induced by cable stretching are directly equivalent to scanner positioning errors along the Z axis. The following points should be considered prior to running the test:

1. Care should be used to ensure that all connections are tight. A loose connection shows up as a spike or phase step in the unprocessed measurements.
2. The cables and related microwave components are sensitive to handling. The handling affects the temperature of the components. After handling semirigid coaxial cable, approximately 15 min is required to reach thermal equilibrium. Small microwave components such as multipliers generally require several hours to reach thermal equilibrium.
3. The use of subharmonic reference signals (i.e., for harmonic mixers or frequency multipliers) in the reference cable does not reduce the cable phase stability requirements (see Chapter 4).

One type of self-comparison test consists of a pair of scans with different reference cable geometries. For example, one pattern is recorded with the reference cable exiting along the bottom of the scanner mechanism and a second pattern with the cable supported from above. Identical far-field results should be obtained. The difference is an estimate of the pattern uncertainty caused by the cable flexure.

If the cable flexure self-comparison test results are poor, further diagnostic work can be performed by adding a second high-quality cable between the AUT and the probe. Perform a scan while recording the amplitude and phase. The scan dimensions are the same as those used during the actual antenna test. Cable faults often can be localized by this method.

Network analyzers such as the HP-8510B can be configured to make range gated S_{11} measurements. Using this capability, it is possible to directly measure cable phase flexure by installing a short or open circuit at the probe location. The network analyzer measures the range-gated phase angle of the reflection, which should remain at a constant time delay.

Real-time reference cable stability measurements and compensation are possible. For further information, refer to Chapter 4.

The determination of boresight pointing can be affected by a systematic phase slope induced by cable stretching. The magnitude of the error can be computed as the arctangent of the ratio of the cable induced phase tilt to the antenna aperture width.

9.7 MULTIPATH AND MUTUAL COUPLING TESTS

Multipath and mutual coupling tests detect and quantify the effects of spurious energy reflected from within various parts of the antenna test facility. Multipath reflections within the antenna test facility cause distortions of the far-field pattern, gain measurement errors, and electrical boresight uncertainties. Multipath errors can be minimized by absorber installation, range gating, probe selection, isolators, and in near-field measurements staggering or tilting the scan plane.

Tests for multipath and mutual coupling errors determine the amount of error introduced by energy traveling by a path other than the normal direct one. Although mutual coupling errors actually are a form of multipath errors, certain properties suggest that the two forms should be differentiated. In this book, *mutual coupling* is defined as undesired multiple propagation paths between objects in relative motion, such as between the probe antenna and AUT. Multipath is defined as multiple propagation paths between stationary objects, such as between the AUT and the floor. Figure 9.4 shows a typical multipath signal environment for a Cassegrain antenna in a horizontal planar near-field facility.

The tests for multipath and mutual coupling are slightly different. Although not obvious, both involve the SAR technique of separating multipath energy by doppler processing (see Chapter 2). The tests involve changing the path lengths and observing the change to the far-field pattern. In the mutual coupling test, the path length is changed by moving the probe antenna along the Z axis. In the multipath

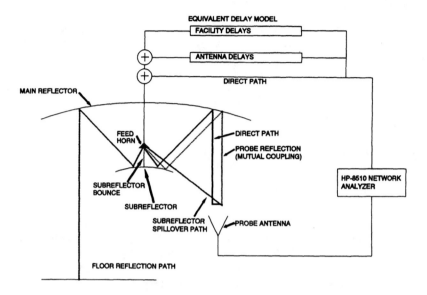

Figure 9.4 Multipath signal environment.

test, the path length (in wavelengths) is changed by a retuning of the RF frequency
or by physically changing the geometry.

Multipath error can be identified by changing the path length and observing
either the receiver or far-field transform output. The path length (measured in
wavelengths) is varied by retuning the test frequency slightly (typically 2–10 MHz).
A receiver or network analyzer that has swept frequency capability can be used to
measure path-length spectrum.

The required frequency span and number of frequency steps can be determined from basic radar concepts. The path length resolution (R_r) is a direct function of the frequency span (F_s):

$$R_r = c/F_s \tag{9.6}$$

where

  c = propagation velocity.

Typical values:

  $R_r = 0.3 \text{ m} = 11.8 \text{ in.},$
  $F_s = 1 \text{ GHz},$
  c = velocity of light (in vacuum) = 299792458 m/s.

The number of frequency steps, n, determines the alias-free path length (R_a). The division by two is to convert the total unaliased path length into the allowable pathlength differential:

$$R_a = nR_r/2 \qquad (9.7)$$

Typical values

R_a = 2366 in. = 197 ft.,
R_r = 11.8 in.,
n = 401 Δf = 2.49 MHz.

Most receivers currently are not fast enough to measure a large number of frequencies at each measurement point. Several measurement points are evaluated in detail and then a series of pattern measurements is repeated at slightly varying frequencies. Both data sets are then analyzed as will be explained.

Figure 9.5 shows a representative multipath response of a horn antenna in a near-field measurement system. The large peak at marker 1 is the desired direct path. The energy decay following the direct path is due to a combination of mutual coupling between the horn antenna and probe antenna at a -40 dB level and other facility reflections.

As another example, the Cassegrain antenna configuration shown in Figure 9.3 will be analyzed. The path lengths and relative levels are identified with an HP-8510B network analyzer operating in the time domain mode. The network analyzer is connected to the AUT and probe antennas and is configured for an S_{12} or S_{21} test.

The first step in the analysis of the multipath measurements is to establish whether the reflection involves the test facility or is purely internal to the antenna. Only reflections involving the facility will cause measurement uncertainty. Reflections internal to the antenna result in real cyclic antenna gain variations as a function of frequency and must not be disturbed.

Figures 9.6 through 9.9 show the path-length (time-domain) response for a Cassegrain antenna with different radial probe positions. Differences in the plots provide information relating to the multipath mechanisms.

The difference between Figures 9.6 and 9.7 is the inclusion of absorber on the floor. The lack of absorber is clearly visible in Figure 9.6. A series of peaks with decreasing amplitude following the direct path peak are caused by multiple reflections between the antenna feed and subreflector.

Subreflector spillover and diffraction effects are visible when the microwave probe antenna is positioned at certain locations. Spillover (see Figure 9.4) results in a path length that is less than the primary path length. Spillover is evident at marker 3 in Figure 9.8 and Figure 9.9. The spillover signal level is very sensitive to

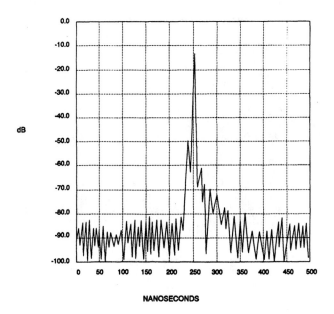

Figure 9.5 Near-field multipath (time domain) response of a standard gain horn.

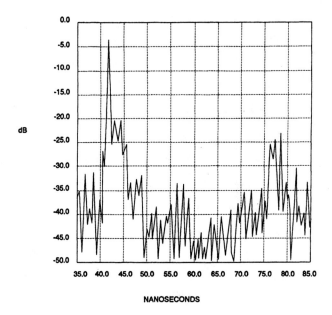

Figure 9.6 Probe at 50% radius, no absorber on floor.

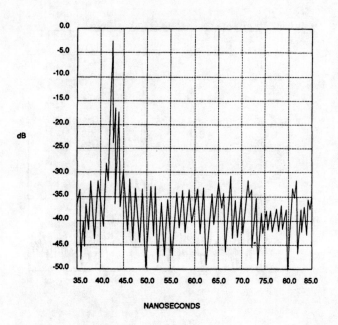

Figure 9.7 Probe at 50% radius, VHP 8 NRL absorber.

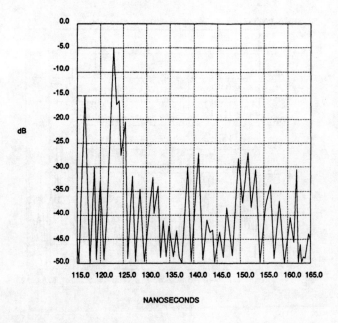

Figure 9.8 Probe at 30% radius, VHP 8 NRL absorber.

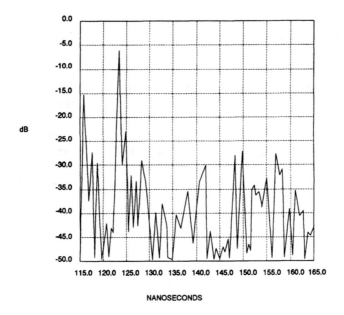

Figure 9.9 Probe moved radially inward by 10 in., VHP 8 NRL absorber.

position. The spillover signal component varied over a 40 dB range for the example antenna.

The probe antenna was moved radially inward by 10 in. in Figure 9.9 relative to Figure 9.8. The markers remained at a constant delay in both figures. The spillover time delay decreased as the probe antenna was moved radially inward.

The subreflector-feed multipath is internal to the antenna and must not be suppressed. This multipath mechanism forms part of the true antenna response. The −18 dB level used in the preceding example is responsible for a cyclic 2 dB peak-to-peak antenna gain variation as a function of frequency.

The spillover multipath is due to the antenna design and should not be suppressed. Such spillover is caused by excessive edge illumination of the subreflector and further modified by subreflector diffraction. It appears at a negative distance relative to the direct path. The spillover signal component is handled correctly by the far-field transformation if the Nyquist (sampling) theorem is correctly followed. The spillover signal level usually changes rapidly with probe position and polarization.

The primary spillover multipath signal can be identified as a signal with a negative path length. Multiple spillover bounces can be identified by measuring the path length at several different probe X/Y positions. The spillover path length will increase as a function of the probe-subreflector geometry when the probe is moved radially outward from the scan plane center (see Figures 9.8 and Figure 9.9 for an example). The multiple spillover bounces can corrupt the near-field measurements, because they may involve parts of the test facility. These reflections, however, tend to be suppressed by the transformation process, as they occur at localized areas and at large angular offsets relative to the main beam.

Table 9.4 shows the multipath distances and levels for various signal components at a single measurement point. After transformation to the far field, the multipath effects on various sidelobe levels can be determined. This is shown in Table 9.5. Multipath signals from the near-field scanner and floor will corrupt antenna measurements. The multipath environment varies significantly from measurement point to point. Because of this it is necessary to measure the total multipath effect in an entire near-field scan. A series of 10 to 20 scans at closely spaced frequencies is required.

Table 9.4
Multipath Mechanisms of Interest

Multipath Mechanism	Path Length (ft.)	Signal Level (dB)	Gain Variation (peak)
Subreflector spillover	−7	−12	AUT internal
Direct path	0	0	0.00 dB
Subreflector-feed 1×	2	−18	AUT internal
Subreflector-feed 2×	4	−27	AUT internal
Subreflector-feed 3×	6	−38	AUT internal
Spillover-floor	25	−25	insignificant
Near-field scanner	30	−34	0.18 dB
Floor bounce	33	−44	0.06 dB
TOTAL (rss)			0.25 dB

Table 9.5
Multipath Effects on Sidelobe Levels

Sidelobe Level (dB)	Randomness (dB rms)	Sidelobe to Noise Ratio (dB)
—	0.003	70
—	0.008	60
—	0.028	50
—	0.087	40
—	0.282	30
0	0.502	25
−5	0.915	20
−10	1.70	15
−15	3.3	10
−20	7.2	5
−25	—	0

Cyclic gain variations usually are the result of multipath effects. Slowly changing gain variations are due to small path-length differences such as feed-subreflector interaction. Rapidly changing gain variations are due to interaction between the antenna and facility. The gain variation as a function of frequency and path length are a Fourier transform pair. For a gain fluctuation with a frequency period, F, the path length differential, R, is

$$R = c/F \tag{9.8}$$

where

c = propagation velocity.

Typical values

$R = 9.99$ m $= 32.7$ ft.,
$F = 30$ MHz,
c = velocity of light (in vacuum) $= 299792458$ m/s.

An analysis of Figure 9.10 shows a low-frequency component with a period of 100 MHz and a high-frequency component with a period of 10 MHz. The low frequency component has an amplitude of 2 dB peak-to-peak and corresponds to a feed-subreflector interaction. The high frequency component has an amplitude of 0.5 dB peak-to-peak and corresponds to a reflection from the near-field scanner. The spillover-floor reflection does not appear in this plot because the spillover region is small, defocused, and pointed away from the boresight direction.

As receivers become faster, this process can be greatly simplified by imaging the antenna at different differential path-length delays. Suitable fast-receiver designs and time-delay imaging are discussed in Chapter 4.

A separate test can be made for mutual coupling between the test and probe antennas. Perform a self-comparison test by making a series of measurements with the spacing between the AUT and probe being increased in $\lambda/8$ wavelength increments along the z-axis. Any variations in the patterns are the sum of three components:

1. Mutual coupling between AUT and probe antenna,
2. Receiver PM-to-AM conversion or quadrature unbalance,
3. Random system noise.

Compare the far-field patterns. The variation in peak far-field power is a measure of the mutual coupling.

Multipath uncertainty can be minimized through the use of the following techniques:

1. *Installation of high quality absorber*—Particular attention should be paid to the absorber on the probe, probe carriage, and probe support rail.

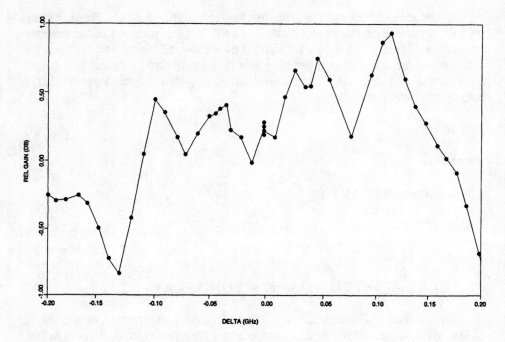

Figure 9.10 Measured gain as a function of frequency.

2. *Match antenna terminations*—The receiver mixer is often a significant reflection source. A high-quality termination match can reduce the mutual coupling by many decibels. Installation of attenuators or isolators at the AUT and probe ports ensures that any mismatch will not result in reradiated power. An even better antenna-to-load match can be obtained for CW tests by using a stub tuner.

3. *Low RCS probe antenna*—The probe antenna can be a significant reflector. The reflection level can be minimized by using a well matched, low-RCS design.

4. *Pulse range gating*—Pulse gating methods can be used to suppress multipath, but this method is only suitable for broadband antennas, as previously discussed in Chapter 4.

5. *Swept-frequency pulse compression range gating*—Pulse compression methods can be used to suppress multipath in a manner similar to pulse gating, but this method is only suitable for broadband antennas, as previously discussed in Chapter 4.

6. *Multiplanar scanning*—An unusual CW SAR technique called staggered *Z*, volumetric, or multiplanar scanning can be used to substantially reduce axial mutual coupling (typically 25 dB) between the near-field scanner and the antenna under test. This technique is described in Chapter 4 and [3].

For most near-field measurement systems, a well-matched, low-RCS probe is recommended to be used in conjunction with a high-quality pyramidal absorber. Staggered Z scanning can be used to improve the measurement quality further at some expense of time.

9.8 SCAN PLANE TRUNCATION

The near-field scanner should sample all significant near-field energy from both the AUT and SGA antennas. To the extent that all significant energy is not sampled, the derived far-field measurements will be in error. A truncation of the scan plane results in two effects:

1. The integrated power is lower. This causes an apparent gain reduction proportional to the ratio of the missing power to the total power. The directivity will tend to increase due to the truncation of off-axis energy.
2. The actual AUT aperture has been replaced at least partially by the uniformly illuminated synthetic aperture of the near-field scanner. The effect of scan plane truncation is to convolve in the scanner synthetic aperture. This introduces spurious sidelobe energy into the AUT pattern in the form of Gibbs's ripple and increases the apparent beamwidth. For plane polar scans, this energy can be approximated by the far-field diffraction pattern of a uniformly illuminated circular aperture, often called an *Airy pattern.*

One test involves acquiring a pair of measurement data sets corresponding to different scan dimensions and comparing the far-field patterns. Any difference is due to the scan plane truncation and random noise.

An alternate test developed by NIST is accomplished by transforming only the outer ring of near-field data. The energy output from this processing corresponds to the energy lost due to truncation.

9.9 PROBE POSITIONING ERRORS

The effect of probe positioning errors is to distort the element positions in the synthesized aperture. As such, the effects of these errors can be determined by standard phased array antenna analysis techniques.

The derived far-field measurements are insensitive to translational misalignments between the AUT and near-field scanner. This is a direct consequence of the spatial invariance of the Fourier transform. Angular tilts of a scan surface simply result in the equivalent tilts in the derived far-field pattern. This is true for planar, cylindrical, and spherical scans.

High-frequency random errors are equivalent to a rough aperture surface shape. This problem was studied by Ruze and is discussed further in Appendix B.

The primary effect of high-frequency errors is to increase the measured AUT side-lobe levels and decrease the AUT measured gain.

Other distortions such as shear, scale factor, warps, tacos, and low-frequency random errors are more difficult to analyze. Because these error sources are systematic, the distortions are analyzed most easily on a case-by-case basis by using simulation techniques. As an example, a taco distortion can be simulated by adding the phase error caused by the taco distortion to a data file containing actual RF measurements for a given antenna. Systematic errors affect low-level sidelobes, beamwidth measurements, focusing measurements, and autotrack patterns.

The far-field pattern is relatively insensitive to x and y positioning errors when measuring large aperture antennas on a planar near-field range. This is because the amplitude and phase change slowly with x and y position errors.

The measurement of the mechanical errors in a near-field scanner can be quite involved. For large systems, a series of tests is performed at installation and at yearly intervals. The system also should be rechecked after any significant earthquake. The results of the tests are used in computer models to either correct the errors or predict induced measurement uncertainties. The following is a representative sequence of tests:

1. Static mechanical performance, including a coordinate system test; a measurement system scale factor test; an x, y, z-axis orthogonality test; an x, y, z-plane error test; a probe attitude error test; a static positioning test.
2. Optical skeleton performance (if present), a sensor noise test, a stray light test, a sensor linearity test, a roll alignment test, a z-height test, an orthogonality test, a phase correction test.
3. Dynamic performance, including timing error tests (i.e., equivalent servo timing error test, for servo systems only, optical sensor lag and receiver lag tests); dynamic servo error tests, for servo systems only (i.e., instantaneous servo error and servo error spectrum tests); servo tuning stability tests for servo systems only (i.e., tests for velocity constant stability and linearity).
4. RF polarity test (increasing phase with decreasing separation).

In many cases, the test procedure just outlined can be greatly simplified. Many systems do not have optical sensors, so test group 2 can be eliminated.

A simple self-comparison test can provide a global go-nogo test for group 3 (dynamic performance) measurements. The test consists of comparing a far-field pattern acquired during continuous motion with a pattern acquired with the probe stationary at each measurement point.

9.10 FAR-FIELD PATTERN MEASUREMENT UNCERTAINTY

The evaluation of the previously described tests, in terms of equivalent sidelobe noise levels, provides a background for analyzing the test results in the far-field domain. For example, a transformation of a series of near-field scans results in a peak variation of 0.05 dB on boresight. The variation is caused by random noise. The pattern consists of the sum of an uncorrupted measurement and noise. The equivalent sidelobe noise level is −45 dB. Separate error budgets are required for the AUT and SGA antennas when gain comparison measurements are made.

Table 9.6 and equations (9.9) and (9.10) are based on the concept of summing a noise vector with a signal vector. For example, assume that a 25 dB sidelobe level needs to be measured with an accuracy of 0.5 dB. The sidelobe measurements are the sum of the actual sidelobe levels and a random noise term caused by the receiver (principle of superposition).

The rms level of sidelobe noise should be low enough to not distort to −25 dB sidelobe level by more than 0.5 dB rms. The 0.5 dB variation corresponds to a rms voltage ratio variation of 1.06 to 1. The noise component equals 0.06 of the 1.06 (i.e., signal = 1, noise = .06). This level is −24.4 dB relative to −25 dB sidelobe level and corresponds to a −49.4 dB sidelobe noise level. A pair of representative pattern uncertainty budgets for a test and reference antenna are shown in Tables 9.7 and 9.8.

Table 9.6
RMS Gain and Phase Error Due to Random Noise

Signal-to-Noise Ratio (dB)	RMS Gain Error (+dB)	RMS Gain Error (−dB)	RMS Phase Error (°)
90	0.000	−0.000	0.002
80	0.001	−0.001	0.006
70	0.003	−0.003	0.018
60	0.009	−0.009	0.057
50	0.027	−0.028	0.181
40	0.086	−0.087	0.573
30	0.270	−0.279	1.81
25	0.475	−0.503	3.22
20	0.828	−0.915	5.73
15	1.42	−1.70	10.2
10	2.39	−3.30	18.0
5	3.88	−7.18	31.4
0	6.02	∞	53.1
−5	8.88	∞	83.3
−10	12.39	∞	115.4

Note:

$$\text{Gain error (dB)} = 10 \log\{1 - 1/10^{[SNR(dB)/20]}\} \tag{9.9}$$

$$\text{Phase error (°)} = 2 \arctan\{2/10^{[SNR(dB)/20]}\} \tag{9.10}$$

Table 9.7
Far-Field Pattern Errors in Antenna under Test (dB)

Error Term	Uncertainty	Boresight SNR
Random noise	±0.010	59
Linearity	±0.020	53
RF leakage	±0.003	70
Multipath	±0.060	43
Mutual coupling	±0.180	34
Scan plane truncation	±0.050	45
x/y positioning errors	±0.010	59
z positioning errors	±0.020	53
TOTAL (rss)	±0.198	33

Table 9.8
Far-Field Pattern Errors in Standard Gain Antenna (dB)

Error Term	Uncertainty	Boresight SNR
Random noise	±0.060	43
Linearity	±0.003	69
RF leakage	±0.040	47
Multipath	±0.070	42
Mutual coupling	±0.050	45
Scan plane truncation	±0.010	59
x/y positioning errors	±0.010	59
z positioning errors	±0.010	59
TOTAL (rss)	±0.133	38

9.11 GAIN MEASUREMENT UNCERTAINTY

Gain can be measured in a variety of ways. In this example, we use the antenna comparison method, in which the gain of the unknown antenna is determined by comparing it to the gain of a known antenna. As prerequisites, we need pattern measurement uncertainty budgets for both the AUT and the gain reference antenna. The method of determining these uncertainty budgets was described previously.

Usually, the largest term in the gain uncertainty budget is the reference antenna gain uncertainty. When Naval Research Laboratory (NRL) curves are used, the standard gain horn uncertainty is approximately ±0.3 dB. Calibrations by NIST or by using the three antenna method can result in gain standard uncertainties less than ±0.1 dB.

PM-to-AM conversion in the receiver can reduce the gain measurement accuracy. PM-to-AM conversion occurs in older receivers when the quadrature detector is unbalanced. The effect of this error is to change the signal level as a function of the received phase angle. This error source can be measured by repeating a series of relative gain measurements with an adjustable phase shifter installed in series with the antenna. There should be no change in relative gain as the phase shifter is adjusted to different values.

High-gain antennas in a planar near-field range and low-gain antennas in a spherical near- or far-field range tend to present a constant phase value to the receiver. There is a one-to-one relationship between PM-to-AM error and induced gain error. Conversely, low-gain antennas in the planar near-field or high-gain antennas in a spherical near- or far-field range tend to have large phase variations and are less sensitive to PM-to-AM conversion induced gain errors.

Mismatch errors are caused by impedance deviations. The impedance mismatches cause reflections. The amount of mismatch (VSWR) can be measured by a *vector network analyzer* (VNA), as shown in Table 9.9. Because VSWR measurements do not include phase information, the VSWR mismatch will cause an uncertainty in loss. Mismatch errors, in principle, can be largely eliminated by using a modern VNA with an *S*-parameter test set, although the correction process often significantly reduces the network analyzer throughput. The VNA can reduce the mismatch error by measuring the mismatch characteristics in complex form. Range gating may be required when long cables are used.

Table 9.9
Comparison Gain Error Budget Example

	VSWR	Mismatch Loss (dB)	Mismatch Uncertainty (dB)
AUT	1.70	0.32	0.14
AUT network	1.13		
SGA	1.09	0.17	0.07
SGA network	1.47		
TOTAL (rss)			±0.16

The calculated uncertainty (see Table 9.10) is a lower limit on the gain measurement uncertainty. If other unidentified error sources are present, as is probable, the measurements will contain more error than indicated.

Table 9.10
Uncertainty

Error Term	Value (dB)	Source
SGA gain uncertainty	±0.30	NRL data
Cable loss calibration	±0.05	measurement
AUT network mismatch uncertainty	±0.14	Table 9.9
SGA network mismatch uncertainty	±0.07	Table 9.9
Network gain uncertainty	±0.05	calculation
AUT relative gain uncertainty	±0.20	Table 9.7
SGA relative gain uncertainty	±0.13	Table 9.8
AUT PM to AM conversion	±0.05	measurement
SGA PM to AM conversion	±0.01	measurement
Linearity error	±0.05	receiver specification
TOTAL	±0.42	

9.12 BORESIGHT MEASUREMENT UNCERTAINTY

The measurement of the direction in which an antenna is electrically pointed often needs to be related to a mechanical reference frame. Boresight measurement uncertainties fall into the following categories:

1. Mechanical reference, such as orientation of the antenna or measurement system relative to a reference coordinate system, or scanner mechanical errors.
2. Electrical reference, such as errors induced by systematic phase errors, uncertainty in determining the RF beam center, or multipath distortions.
3. Facility induced, such as gravitational distortions of the AUT.

The mechanical reference of the AUT must be established. Common references used include tooling balls, flat or shaped parabolic reference surfaces, and mirrors and optical cubes.

Tooling balls and reference surface orientations are generally sensed with a coordinate measurement probe on the near-field scanner or a jig transit. Mirrors and optical cube alignments are performed by autocollimation and other optical tooling methods. Orientation measurements of the AUT generally are limited by the accuracy of the AUT reference. For example, measuring the positions of three AUT reference tooling balls to an accuracy of 0.001 inch over a separation of 2 feet will result in a typical uncertainty of 10 arcseconds.

Often more than three tooling balls are used to provide redundancy, a measure of uncertainty, and a general check of antenna integrity. In another case, a parabolic dish antenna, the reference surface was determined by a least squares fit. In both cases, the measurements are overdetermined. This is a self-comparison test. The deviation of the individual measurements from the mean value is the measurement residual. The residual provides a good estimate of the measurement uncertainty. Least squares methods additionally provide a covariance matrix with the diagonal elements containing the mean squared estimation error.

Optical references can be measured very accurately (better than 1 arcsec) by autocollimation or by sighting optical targets. One problem is that the AUT-mounted mirror often is not stable relative to the AUT. The scanner reference frame (for a planar scanner) is readily measured with a jig transit. The accuracy of a jig transit is typically 0.001 inch and 1 arcsecond. This translates to a scan plane orientation accuracy of 1 arcsecond for a 20×20 feet scanner and 10 arcseconds for a 2×2 feet scanner, assuming no errors in the scanner mechanism.

Unknown scan plane tilts can be present due to mechanical deformations or systematic phase errors. These errors can be identified by repeating measurements at different roll orientations if no secondary gravitational effects are present, which generally is true when the scan plane is horizontal.

RF multipath errors can shift the location of the beam centroid. A self-comparison test can be performed in which the beam peak position shift is monitored as the multipath geometry is changed.

Gravitational distortions of the AUT can be a very significant error source in certain applications (spacecraft antennas). Often, the magnitude of this uncertainty is determined analytically. Alternately, by repeating a series of measurements with the antenna and test system at different orientations a measurement uncertainty can be estimated. In planar near-field range scanners with a vertical scan plane, a series of scans are repeated with the AUT at different roll angles. The differences are generally due to gravitational distortions.

A representative boresight uncertainty budget is shown in Table 9.11.

9.13 MINIMIZATION OF MEASUREMENT ERRORS

Measurement errors often can be reduced by modifying the test setup. Representative measurement error suppression techniques are listed in Table 9.12.

9.14 ACCURACY OF HOLOGRAPHIC MEASUREMENTS

Focused holographic back projections can be used to provide a detailed look at the aperture plane of a phased array antenna. The output of the holographic transform is a set of complex numbers that describes the electromagnetic field intensity in a region of interest.

Errors in the measurement process result in a degradation of the holographic image. This error analysis will be limited to holographic back projections along the z-axis derived from near-field measurements. Holographic transformations of rotated and far-field measurements require a slightly different error analysis, pri-

Table 9.11
Boresight Measurement Error Budget

Error Term	Value (arcsec)	Source
Scanner-to-gravity (g) alignment	±10.0	residual
AUT-to-gravity alignment	±120.0	residual
AUT mounting structure stability	±6.0	measurement
Reference cable errors	±20.0	self-compare
Multipath	±10.0	self-compare
RF beam peak location	±6.0	self-compare
1 g correction uncertainty	±30.0	analysis
TOTAL (rss)	±125.9	

Note:
Angle equivalences:

$$1° = \quad 60 \text{ arcminutes}$$
$$= \quad 3600 \text{ arcseconds}$$
$$= \quad 174.5329 \text{ milliradians (mr)}$$
$$= 17453.29 \text{ microradians } (\mu r)$$

Table 9.12
Control of Measurement Errors

Error Source	Control Technique
Linearity	attenuator
	good receiver and transform
PM-to-AM conversion	phase shifter
	tilt of scan plane
Leakage	copper tape on all joints
	improvement of isolators in remote mixers
	vector cancellation
Multipath	range gate
	rotation of antenna
	microwave absorber
Mutual coupling	better absorber placement
	coherent cancellation (staggered Z)
	increased AUT-to-probe separation
	range gate
	tilt scan plane
Cable phase errors	S_{11} measurement and cancellation
Mismatch errors	pads, isolators at AUT, probe
	vector network analyzer calibration
Scan plane truncation	increased scan area
	analytical correction
Transform nonlinearity	increased output sample density

marily due to the increase in processing gain. Evanescent energy is not measured or processed. The errors present in the near-field holographic measurement process include

1. Loss of axial (z-axis) resolution,
2. Loss of lateral (x,y-axis) resolution,
3. Loss of image contrast due to spurious sidelobes induced by truncation. This is similar to the *integrated sidelobe return* (ISR) problem in SAR radars.

The following errors are caused by errors in the near-field measurements and the holographic transformation process. Near field pattern measurement errors may be due to receiver SNR or linearity, phase reference cable stability, interferometer leakage, multipath and mutual coupling errors, scanner positioning errors, or probe compensation. Holographic transform errors may be due to focusing distance or aliasing.

The near-field measurement errors have been previously discussed. The axial resolution of the correctly focused holographic transform is established by looking at the phase noise properties of the near-field measurements in the near-field domain and assuming no process gain (because near-field measurement and holographic image points are heavily coupled). A representative longitudinal hologram resolution for a small X-band phased array antenna is shown in Table 9.13.

Table 9.13
Longitudinal Hologram Resolution

Error Term	Signal-to-Noise Ratio (dB)	Wavelength (λ)
Receiver SNR	75.0	0.0000
Receiver phase linearity		0.0000
Phase reference cable stability	29.1	0.0056
RF leakage	63.0	0.0001
Multipath and mutual coupling	38.2	0.0020
Scanner z plane accuracy	31.9	0.0040
Aliasing		0.0000
TOTAL (rss)	26.8	0.0072

In Table 9.13, the receiver SNR is approximately 75 dB. The equivalent phase noise is

$$\arctan(1/10^{(75/20)}) = 0.01° = 0.000028\lambda \tag{9.11}$$

A typical HP-8510B network analyzer will not introduce significant linearity errors. The phase reference cable stability is 2° rms at 9.338 GHz, which is equivalent to

0.0056λ or 0.0071-inch rms error. Near-field RF leakage is 63 dB down relative to the phase front energy, which translates to a phase error of 0.04° or 0.0001λ. Multipaths and mutual coupling can cause significant near-field phase errors. The uncorrected near-field measurements had a signal-to-multipath ratio of approximately 22 dB, which corresponds to a rms phase noise of 4.5° or 0.013λ. The use of the volumetric scan technique [3] provides a ratio of approximately 38.2 dB, which corresponds to a phase noise of 0.7° or 0.002λ. The scanner position error along the z axis was measured with a Taylor Hobson alignment telescope and a K&E plane generator. Peak z error is 0.005 in., which corresponds to 0.004λ.

The near-field phase front was sampled according to the Nyquist sampling theorem. No significant aliasing errors should be present as based on the following concepts:

1. The near-field is sampled at less than 0.5λ intervals. Energy is band-limited to 1 cycle/λ by free-space propagation. There is no significant evanescent energy that would violate the sampling theorem as shown by the consistency of the far-field pattern with distance.
2. Multipath energy may appear at any spatial frequency, which would become aliased. The aliased multipath energy is significantly below the unaliased multipath energy, which is used in the uncertainty budget.

The lateral resolution is driven primarily by the higher spatial frequencies. The lateral resolution (r) of the correctly focused holographic transformation ($\pm 60°$ far field at 9.338 GHz) is approximately

$$r = \lambda/\sin(60) = 1.264/0.866 = 1.45 \text{ in.} \tag{9.12}$$

Measurement uncertainties can decrease this resolution. The loss of image contrast due to ISR is minimal. Phased array antennas have fairly uniform aperture illumination, which, in general, are not prone to ISR effects.

REFERENCES

1. Yaghjian, A.D., "Upper Bound Errors in Far-field Antenna Parameters Determined from Planar Near-field Measurements, Part 1 (Analysis)," Technical Note 667, National Bureau of Standards, Washington, DC, 1975. This widely circulated report describes upper-bound errors for near-field measurements. The results are often excessively pessimistic.
2. Goldman, S., *Frequency Analysis, Modulation and Noise,* McGraw-Hill, New York, 1948. Contains an excellent, although mathematical, discussion of noise theory.
3. Hindman, G., and D. Slater, "Error Suppression Techniques for Nearfield Measurements," Antenna Measurement Techniques Assoc. Symp., Monterey, CA, 1989. Describes a simple, effective multipath suppression technique using a volumetric scanning and processing technique.

Appendix A
NEAR-FIELD TEST FACILITY COORDINATE SYSTEM

A variety of coordinate systems are used in the near-field measurement process. Some representative coordinate systems used by the example near-field measurement systems follow. All coordinate systems are right-hand Cartesian. The three most important coordinate systems used in the near-field measurement process are the scanner coordinate system, the antenna coordinate system, and the scan coordinate system.

The axes, along which the servos move independently, define the scanner coordinate system. Different near-field range systems use different gantry coordinate systems. The gantry coordinate system for horizontal scanners usually is defined as follows:

1. The z-axis is aligned with the local gravity vector. The $+z$ faces down. The positive yaw rotates clockwise around the z vector when looking along the $+z$-axis.
2. The x-axis (north) is perpendicular to the z-axis. The $+x$ is aligned with the facility north. A positive roll rotates clockwise around the x-axis when looking along the $+x$-axis.
3. The y-axis (east) completes the right-handed coordinate system. The positive pitch corresponds to a clockwise rotation when looking along the $+y$-axis.

The gantry coordinate system for the free-floating CMM-based scanners is defined as follows:

1. The z-axis is normal to the granite table beneath the gantry. The granite table is free floating on a vibration isolation system. The positive z faces toward the granite table. The positive yaw rotates clockwise around the z vector when looking along the $+z$-axis.
2. The x-axis (north) is perpendicular to the z-axis. The $+x$ is aligned with the facility north. The positive roll rotates clockwise around the x-axis when looking along the $+x$-axis.

3. The *y*-axis (east) completes the right-hand coordinate system. The positive pitch corresponds to a clockwise rotation when looking along the $+y$-axis.

The gantry coordinate system for representative vertical scanner is defined as follows:

1. The *x*-axis (north) is normal to the gravity vector, and $+x$ is aligned with the facility north. The positive pitch rotates clockwise around the *x*-axis when looking along the $+x$-axis.
2. The *y*-axis aligned with the gravity vector. The $+y$ faces up. The positive yaw rotates clockwise around the *y* vector when looking along the $+y$-axis.
3. The *z*-axis (west) completes the right-hand coordinate system. The $+z$-axis faces toward the antenna under test. The positive roll rotates clockwise when looking along the $-z$-axis.

During operation the scanner commands are transformed from the scan coordinate system into the gantry reference frame through the use of a 4×4 homogeneous transformation matrix. The transform matrix allows an unlimited concatenation of translation, rotation, scale and shear operations. The scan coordinate is augmented into four vectors and transformed by a matrix multiplication into the gantry reference frame. Dividing by the scale factor, *W* results in the transformed coordinate. An example of a simple homogeneous transformation between two coordinate reference frames is:

$$
\begin{bmatrix} W_x' \\ W_y' \\ W_z' \\ W \end{bmatrix} = \begin{bmatrix} a & b & c & x_o \\ d & e & f & y_o \\ g & h & i & z_o \\ 0 & 0 & 0 & 1 \end{bmatrix} \begin{bmatrix} x \\ y \\ z \\ 1 \end{bmatrix}
$$

where
a through *i* form a direction cosine matrix [1], with elements equal to

$a = \cos(\text{yaw}) \cos(\text{pitch}),$

$b = \sin(\text{roll}) \cos(\text{yaw}) \sin(\text{pitch}) - \cos(\text{roll}) \sin(\text{yaw}),$

$c = \sin(\text{roll}) \sin(\text{yaw}) + \cos(\text{roll}) \cos(\text{yaw}) \sin(\text{pitch}),$

$d = \sin(\text{yaw}) \cos(\text{pitch}),$

$e = \cos(\text{roll}) \cos(\text{yaw}) + \sin(\text{roll}) \sin(\text{yaw}) \sin(\text{pitch}),$

$f = \cos(\text{roll}) \sin(\text{yaw}) \sin(\text{pitch}) - \sin(\text{roll}) \cos(\text{yaw}),$

$g = -\sin(\text{pitch}),$

$$h = \sin(\text{roll}) \cos(\text{pitch}),$$
$$i = \cos(\text{roll}) \cos(\text{pitch}),$$

and

$$x_o = x\text{-axis origin},$$
$$y_o = y\text{-axis origin},$$
$$z_o = z\text{-axis origin}.$$

The scan plane orientation and probe phase center position relative to the AUT is established by a second coordinate transformation. This allows the scan plane position and orientation to be conveniently expressed in terms of a set of beam azimuth and elevation angles. The scan plane rotation origin typically is at the antenna phase center. For computational efficiency, the scan plane-to-AUT and AUT-to-gantry coordinate transformations are concatenated, by using the previously described homogeneous transformation method.

REFERENCE

1.   Wertz, J., *Spacecraft Attitude Determination and Control,* D. Reidel Publishing, Boston, 1978. Discusses coordinate systems, transformations, Euler angles, direction cosine matrixes, and related material in detail.

Appendix B
NEAR-FIELD MEASUREMENT TERMINOLOGY

This appendix contains definitions of terms often used in near-field measurement.

Alias An aliased signal has spurious frequency components due to a violation of the sampling theorem. This effect can be seen visually in old movie westerns, where the wagon wheels sometimes appear to rotate backwards. The most common aliasing problem in near-field measurements is taking too few data points. The resulting antenna measurements have spurious sidelobes in a manner similar to grating lobes in phased array antennas. See *sampling theorem* for more details.

Analytic signal An analytic signal is one in which the real and imaginary signal components are related by the Hilbert transform. Equivalently, an analytic signal can have only positive or negative frequency components. The analytic signal, also known as a *preenvelope signal,* is used in the HTR microwave receiver to derive phase information. For further information refer to Appendix D.

Angular spectrum The antenna gain or received power as a function of the azimuth and elevation angles from boresight is the angular spectrum. A plot of the amplitude of the angular spectrum is often called an *antenna pattern.* The angular spectrum is related to the spatial frequency (K space) spectrum by the arcsine function:

$$F(\Theta) = \text{arcsine} \, [\, f(s)] \tag{B.1}$$

Antenna A structure or transducer that transforms between guided and free space waves.

Axial ratio The polarization purity of a circularly polarized antenna can be specified in terms of the axial ratio of the polarization ellipse. The axial ratio (r) can be defined in terms of the right-hand and left-hand circularly polarized (RHCP and LHCP, respectively) electric field magnitudes:

$$r(\text{dB}) = 20 \log \left| \frac{E_r + E_l}{E_r - E_l} \right| \qquad (\text{B.2})$$

where

E_r = RHCP E field,
E_l = LHCP E field.

Basis function A basis function, also known as a kernel, is the function with which data is multiplied by in a transform:

Transform	Basis function
Fourier transform	exponential (imaginary)
Laplace transform	exponential (real, imaginary)
Hankel transform	Bessel function
Sine transform	sine function
Cosine transform	cosine function
Hadamard transform	Walsh function
Slant transform	saw-toothed wave
Two-dimensional Fourier transform	plane wave
Spherical	spherical wave functions

Beamwidth Beamwidth is a measure of the width of the main antenna lobe. Several different types of beamwidth definitions exist: *half power full width,* 3 dB beamwidth (HPFW), *half power beamwidth,* same as HPFW (HPBW), *beamwidth between first nulls* (BWFN), and *tenth-power beamwidth* (TPBW).

Central limit theorem The central limit theorem states that the sum of a series of uncorrelated noise sources with arbitrary probability density functions will approach a Gaussian distribution at the limit.

Circular polarization A special case of elliptical polarization in which the amplitude is constant and the direction rotates synchronously with the radio frequency. The axial ratio is equal to 1. Circular polarization has either a right-hand or a left-hand orientation.

Collimator Collimator is a term often used in optics to describe a system that produces a planar phase front. The collimator normally consists of a source that emits a spherical phase front followed by a collimating element, such as a lens or parabolic mirror. The collimating element converts the spherical phase front into a planar phase front. The RF equivalent is a compact or a near-field range.

An antenna tested with a planar phase front, by definition, is being tested in the far field. The collimator will produce the planar phase front. A compact range uses a parabolic reflector to produce a planar phase front. The near-field range is a multibeam, synthetic aperture version of a compact range. The near-field range uses a phased array instead of a parabolic reflector.

Complex gain The complex gain is the complex ratio of the output of a system relative to its input. The microwave interferometer used in the near-field measurement system provides a measure of the complex gain (i.e., amplitude and phase response) of the AUT-probe antenna combination.

Complex numbers A number having both a real and an imaginary component is a complex number. The imaginary part is multiplied by the square root of -1, commonly represented by the letter i. In near-field measurements, complex numbers are used in the vector or phasor representation of the electric field intensity. The real part (often called the *in-phase* or simply *I component*) represents the projection of the vector onto the x-axis. The imaginary part (often called the *quadrature* or simply *Q component*) represents the projection of the vector onto the y-axis. Complex addition:

$$(a + bi) + (c + di) = (a + c) + (b + d)i \tag{B.3}$$

Complex multiplication:

$$(a + bi)(c + di) = (ac - bd) + (ad + bc)i \tag{B.4}$$

Also see *Euler's identity.*

Convolution Two antennas (probe antenna and AUT) are used simultaneously in the near field measurement process. The phase-front measurement corresponds to the composite response of both antennas. The composite response at a position x, y is the convolution between the two antennas:

$$E(x, y) = E_a(x, y) * E_p(x, y) \tag{B.5}$$

where

$$
\begin{aligned}
E(x, y) &= \text{measured complex gain,} \\
E_p(x, y) &= \text{probe complex gain,} \\
E_a(x, y) &= \text{AUT complex gain,} \\
* &= \text{convolution operator.}
\end{aligned}
$$

There are various equivalent definitions of the convolution operator. One definition suitable for the near-field measurement process is based on the Fourier transform. The convolution between a pair of antennas is the product of the two-dimensional Fourier transforms of the two antenna phase fronts. The convolution, therefore, can be defined simply as the product of the probe and AUT angular spectrums.

A true measure of the AUT angular spectrum is obtained by deconvolving the probe response from the near-field measurements. The deconvolution is the inverse of a convolution, performed by dividing the AUT angular spectrum by the probe angular spectrum. This operation is often called a *probe correction*.

Other examples of convolution operations in the near-field measurement process include spatial filters and receiver IF bandwidth restrictions.

Correlation Correlation is a measure of the similarity between a pair of functions. The correlation between two functions is determined by integrating the product of the two functions as a function of the independent variable. The concept of correlation is used in the near- to far-field transformation process and in the HTR receiver. The near- to far-field transformation can be considered a correlation measurement between the measured phase front and a series of reference planewave phase fronts. The concept of correlation is closely related to the Fourier transform and the convolution integral.

Cross polarization The component of the electric field normal to the desired polarization.

Diffraction When a wavefront is partially obstructed, diffraction is the process that causes the waves to spread in all directions. It is a direct consequence of Huygen's principle.

Directive gain The directive gain is 4π times the ratio of the power radiated per unit solid angle (steradian) in a given direction to the total power radiated by the antenna. Losses within the antenna are unspecified.

Directivity Directivity is the maximum value of the directive gain. Directivity is similar to gain but assumes a lossless antenna. All input power is assumed to be radiated.

Doppler Doppler frequency shifts arise as a consequence of the Lorentz transformation in special relativity. The doppler shifted receive frequency (f_r) for a receiver moving at a speed, v, and at an angle θ relative to a transmitter is

$$f_r = \Gamma f_t [1 - (v/c) \cos\theta] \tag{B.6}$$

where

$$\Gamma = [1 - (v/c)^2]^{-1/2},$$
$$c = \text{velocity of light.}$$

Because of the low near-field scan velocities relative to the speed of light, the Lorentz contraction term (Γ) can be ignored. For reasons that will become apparent later, θ will be redefined with a 90° offset. The term θ equals 90° when the transmitter is approaching, $-90°$ when the transmitter is receding, and 0° when the transmitter is moving at right angles to the receiver. Solving for the frequency change (f_d) due to the doppler shift and replacing the cosine with a sine results in a very simple equation:

$$f_d = f_t \, v/c \, \sin\theta \tag{B.7}$$

or, equivalently,

$$f_d = (v/\lambda) \, \sin\theta \tag{B.8}$$

where

$$\lambda = c/f_t.$$

Doppler beam sharpening Energy arriving at a moving antenna produces a doppler shift. If the energy arrives from a source in front of an antenna, the resulting doppler shift will increase the received frequency slightly. Conversely, energy that arrives from the rear will be downshifted in frequency. If the receiver has a sufficiently narrow IF filter, the energy arriving from a specific direction can be filtered out. This is equivalent to increasing the directivity of the antenna. In the near-field application, the directivity of the probe antenna can be modified by the IF bandwidth of the receiver.

E field The electric field is a component of the energy emitted by an antenna. Electric field intensity is measured in V per m. The electric field is what typically is measured by the near-field probe antenna.

E plane The E (electric) plane is parallel to the propagating electric field vector.

Electromagnetic fields An electromagnetic field has both electric (**E**) and magnetic (**H**) field components. The vector cross-product between the **E** and **H** fields results in the Poynting vector (**S**), which is aligned with the direction of propagation:

$$\mathbf{S} = \mathbf{E} \times \mathbf{H} \tag{B.9}$$

Outside of the reactive (evanescent) near-field region, the **E** and **H** fields are related by the characteristic impedance of free space (377 Ω). The units on the *E* and *H* fields are V/m and A/m, respectively. The Poynting vector describes power density of the electromagnetic field in units of W/m^2.

The near-field range scanner generally measures either the E or H field of the AUT. The other field can be derived from the measured field after the transformation of the measured field into a derived planewave spectrum.

Efficiency The ratio of power radiated by an antenna to the power accepted is efficiency. Efficiency is equal to the ratio of gain to directivity.

Euler's identity Euler's identity establishes the relationship between complex exponential and sine functions. Euler's identity defines a unit length vector rotated to an angle of θ:

$$e^{i\theta} = \cos\theta + i \sin\theta \qquad \text{(B.10)}$$

Evanescent region The evanescent or reactive near-field region is an area very near a conductive surface. Energy in this region is nonpropagating and capacitively or inductively coupled to the probe antenna.

The high spatial frequencies are produced by the very rapid changes in phase near the antenna structure. As an example, assume that an antenna has two elements driven 180° out of phase that are separated by 0.1λ. A probe sampling very near the two elements would measure 180° phase shift in a distance of 0.1λ. This effect falls off very rapidly with distance.

The evanescent region extends from any conductive surface to a distance of a few wavelengths away from that surface and decays very rapidly with distance. The evanescent energy is superimposed onto the propagating energy and coupled to the near-field probe capacitively or inductively, not by free space propagation. The E and H fields are not orthogonal and not related by the impedance of free space (377 Ω) in the evanescent region. Near-field measurements generally are taken outside of the evanescent region. Otherwise, higher sampling densities and separate E and H field measurements are required.

Evanescent energy can be detected in near-field measurements as energy with a spatial frequency greater than 1 cycle per wavelength, although certain types of multipath signals have a similar signature. Energy coupled by an evanescent mechanism will decay very rapidly with an increased probe stand-off. The evanescent energy normally has completely decayed beyond a few wavelengths from an antenna. For this reason, near-field measurements usually are taken at a distance greater than 1 to 3λ from any part of the antenna.

Far field A distance from the antenna in which the angular energy distribution is independent of distance, also known as the *Fraunhofer region*.

Flicker noise Random noise with a power spectral density that varies inversely with frequency. Flicker noise, also called $1/f$ *noise,* typically is important at audio and lower frequencies. The cause of $1/f$ noise is not well understood. Certain microwave receivers use low intermediate frequencies, which are susceptible to the effects of flicker noise. As an example, the flicker noise becomes dominant at an IF lower than 100 kHz when millimeter-wave gallium arsenide (GaAs) mixers are used.

Fourier transform See Appendix D.

Fraunhofer Region Generally the same as *far-field region*.

Fresnel region Generally the same as *near-field region*.

Gain Gain is the ratio of power radiated in a specified direction to that which would be radiated by a lossless isotropic (omnidirectional) antenna with the same input power.

H field The magnetic field is a component of the energy emitted by an antenna. The magnetic field intensity is measured in A/m and can be measured by a loop antenna.

H plane The *H* (magnetic) plane is parallel to the propagating magnetic field vector.

Hankel transform The Hankel transform, in essence, is a two-dimensional Fourier transform of a purely radially symmetric object.

Hilbert transform The Hilbert transform is a mathematical method of simulating a broadband 90° phase shifter. The Hilbert transform is used for certain phase measurement receivers. For further information see Appendix D.

Huygen's principle Huygen's principle states that every element of a phase front can be considered the source of a secondary wavelet. The position of the phase front at a later time is the complex sum of all such wavelets.

This concept can be used to transform a phase front to a different distance from the antenna. For example, a near-field phase front could be transformed to a far-field position.

Huygen's-Fresnel principle The Huygen's-Fresnel principle is an extension to Huygen's principle. The extension, which is quite involved, is required to explain unidirectional propagation.

Insertion loss Insertion loss is a measure of the loss of a network. In near-field measurements, insertion loss usually refers to the loss of the AUT-probe path. The minimum AUT-probe insertion loss is approximately equal to the difference between the AUT and probe gains.

Interferometer Interference occurs when propagating wavefronts travel through more than one path from a source to a detector. Interference works the same for RF, light, sound, ocean waves, *et cetera*. As the relative path lengths change, the intensity of the signal at the detector fluctuates in a periodic manner. The pair of propagating wavefronts can be combined at the detector either by addition or multiplication. Most microwave interferometers use the multiplicative technique. The multiplicative technique increases the mutual coherence (fringe visibility) relative to the additive interferometer for unequal amplitude wavefronts because the additive design produces a spurious dc component. The vector network analyzer or receiving system used in near-field measurements is a form of the multiplicative interferometer.

The microwave interferometer (often implemented as a network analyzer) measures the interference between a pair of microwave signals that have traveled through two separate paths, only one of which has traveled through the AUT (see Figure B.1). This results in a measure of the complex gain (amplitude and phase response) of the AUT-probe antenna transmission path relative to a reference path.

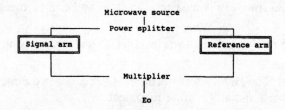

Figure B.1 Microwave Interferometer.

Isotropic Radiating equally in all directions.

Isotropic antenna A theoretical antenna, not physically obtainable, that radiates uniformly in all directions and has a directive gain of 1.

Johnson noise Same as *thermal noise.*

K *space* A domain with the dimensions of spatial frequency. The output of a two-dimensional Fourier transform of a phase front is in K space. The K space can be mapped into an angle space by using an arcsine function.

Kalman filter A Kalman filter is used to estimate parameters from noisy measurements. Some near-field measurement ranges use Kalman filtering techniques to adaptively tune the servo control system in real time. The Kalman filter has application in real-time microwave holographic metrology applications.

The basic Kalman filter can be described by six equations, according to the following two assumptions.

1. The state of the system in the future $X(k)$ is defined by a system model, which is dependent on the previous state of the system and unbiased white noise $W(k)$ with a covariance $Q(k - 1)$. The noise term, $Q(k)$, called *plant noise,* corresponds to unmodeled terms. The previous state is propagated into the future by a state space model of the system dynamics in the form of the state transition matrix $\Phi(k)$:

$$X(k) = \Phi(k - 1)\,X(k - 1) + W(k - 1) \tag{B.11}$$

2. A measurement of the state $z(k)$ is the sum of the actual state $X(k)$ transformed into the measurement coordinate system by a geometry matrix $H(k)$ and summed with uncorrelated, zero mean, measurement sensor noise $v(k)$ with a covariance $R(k)$:

$$z(k) = H(k) X(k) + v(k) \tag{B.12}$$

The six equations that describe a Kalman filter are as follows.

1. The state vector estimate is extrapolated into the future. For a linear system, this is accomplished by a matrix vector product between the transition matrix $\Phi(k)$ and the state vector $X(k)$:

$$X(k) = \Phi(k - 1) X(k - 1) \tag{B.13}$$

2. The error covariance matrix $P(k)$ is extrapolated into the future. $Q(k)$ is the covariance of the plant noise corresponding to modeling errors in the filter:

$$P(k)-) = \Phi(k - 1) P(k - 1+) \Phi(k - 1)T + Q(k - 1) \tag{B.14}$$

3. The error in the estimation process, called the *innovations sequence* $v(k)$, is computed by subtracting the state estimate $X(k)$ transformed into measurement coordinates by the matrix $H(k)$ from the actual measurement $z(k)$. In a properly designed Kalman filter, the innovations sequence should be uncorrelated and unbiased:

$$v(k) = z(k) - H(k) X(k-) \tag{B.15}$$

4. The state estimate is refined by adding the estimation error $v(k)$ weighted by the Kalman gain matrix $K(k)$ to the current state vector $X(k)$:

$$X(k+) = x(k-) + K(k) v(k) \tag{B.16}$$

5. The error covariance matrix is updated to provide a new estimate of the uncertainty in the estimate of the state vector. The covariance values will decrease as the measurement noise decreases or as the plant noise increases:

$$P(k+) = [I - K(k) H(k)] P(k-) \tag{B.17}$$

6. The Kalman gains are computed as the ratios between the statistical measures of the uncertainty in the state estimate $P(k)$ and the uncertainty in the mea-

surement $R(k)$. The matrix $\mathbf{H}(k)$ transforms the covariance matrix into the measurement coordinate system:

$$K(k) = \mathbf{P}(k-)\,\mathbf{H}(k)^T\,\{H_k\,P_k^{-1}(-)\,H_k^T + R(k)\}^{-1} \tag{B.18}$$

Note that in this version of the Kalman filter, the error covariance matrix and Kalman gain matrix are not a function of the actual measurements.

Linear polarization The polarization of an electric field whose amplitude changes at the radio frequency and whose direction remains fixed.

Linearity The concept of linearity is of fundamental importance to near-field measurements. Linearity is a measure of the ratio of change in the output to change in the input of a system. Nonlinearities in real-world near-field measurements result in errors, including distortions in the far-field angular spectrum and gain measurement errors. See also *principle of superposition.*

Matched filter A filter that maximizes the signal-to-noise ratio in the presence of additive white Gaussian noise. A matched filter can be implemented by performing a convolution between a signal and the time-reversed complex conjugate of the desired signal component. Matched filter concepts can be used to explain the near-to far-field transformation process and certain operations within the HTR receiver.

In the near- to far-field transformation process, the phase-front is convolved with the complex conjugate of a spatially reversed plane wave. This operation is equivalent to the Fourier transform of the phase front.

Mismatch uncertainty Mismatch uncertainty is a gain uncertainty caused by a lack of knowledge of the phase angle of multiple reflections between a source and load. Vector network analyzers, such as the HP-8510B, can suppress this error source.

Multipath energy Multipath energy is energy that travels from the transmitter by some path other than the primary one. In near-field measurements, the primary path is a line-of-sight path between the probe and AUT. Multipath energy results from microwave reflections off of antenna parts, scanners, facility walls, and so on. Multipath energy also can result from microwave leakage at connections. Multipath effects are analyzed most easily by considering each individual path and then using the principle of superposition to derive the composite response.

Multipath effects degrade the quality of the near-field measurements. Degradations include increased sidelobe noise, spurious peaks, and poor measurement repeatability.

The presence of multipath effects can be determined by swept frequency or swept distance techniques. Swept frequency measurements can be processed by radar techniques to show complex gain as a function of path length. Any energy at other than the desired direct path length energy is multipath energy.

Multipath effects can be controlled by absorber, range gating, probe design, special scan patterns, and computer-based spatial filtering techniques. Changing a probe antenna from a transmitter to a receiver will not affect multipath levels. This is a direct consequence of the reciprocity theorem.

Mutual coupling energy Mutual coupling energy is multipath energy traveling between the probe antenna and the AUT. Mutual coupling energy normally is detected by observing the variation in gain when a series of near-field scans are made at different distances from the AUT. Note that this test does not measure multipath energy between the AUT and other parts of the facility.

Near field A region near an antenna in which the direction of energy travel is not discernible without further processing. The near-field region exists from a few wavelengths of an antenna to a somewhat arbitrary distance where phase errors across the aperture are less than 22.5° ($\lambda/16$). This distance is equal to $2D^2$ wavelengths.

Network analyzer A vector network analyzer is composed of a source and an amplitude-phase measuring receiver. The vector network analyzer measures the complex gain through a path that includes the probe and test antennas. The network analyzer is equivalent to a microwave interferometer. Also see *interferometer*.

Noise bandwidth An equivalent rectangular pass band that passes the same amount of noise power as the actual system under consideration, approximately equal to the 3 dB bandwidth.

Noise temperature The equivalent temperature of a matched passive resistive source delivering the same power as the actual source. It is used as a measure of receiver sensitivity. See also *thermal noise*.

Nyquist criteria See *sampling theorem*.

1/f noise See *flicker noise*.

Orthomode transducer The orthomode transducer is used to excite two polarizations within an antenna. It often is used so that two polarizations can be measured simultaneously.

Parseval's theorem Parseval's theorem states that an arbitrary signal and its Fourier transform will have identical energies. This is true because the Fourier transform converts the information between two domains without removing or modifying any components of the signal.

Parseval's theorem is useful in near-field theory to explain the range invariance of the near- to far-field transform. If the antenna is sampled at two different ranges and all significant energy is measured, then both measurements must have the same total power. Using Parseval's theorem and realizing that both patterns must have the same angular spectra, both far-field patterns must be identical.

Phase Phase is the degree to which the individual cycles of a wave or signal coincide with those of a reference at the same frequency. Phase can be measured in degrees, radians, or cycles:

$$360° = 2\pi \text{ rad} = 1 \text{ cycle} = 1\lambda \qquad (B.19)$$

Phased array A phased array is an array of antennas with the outputs coherently combined in a beam-forming network. A beam-forming network consists of a series of phase shifters and a summer. The beam former can be implemented either as hardware or computer software.

The near-field test range system can be considered to be a form of a phased array antenna. The array elements are formed synthetically by moving a single antenna element (probe antenna) to all points required to produce the phased array. The data reduction computer does the beam forming by a two-dimensional Fourier transform. A large number of beams are formed simultaneously by the transform operation. The Fourier transform is equivalent to a series of phase shifter and summer operations.

Phase center The phase center of an antenna is the apparent point from which all energy is emanating. When an antenna is pivoted about the phase center there is no change in the far-field phase. The phase center position can be a function of frequency, as in a log-periodic antenna. Other antennas have aberrations of the phase center that change the phase center position with aspect angle.

Phase front A phase front is defined as a surface of equal phase. A phase front with a surface of equal phase that is flat is called a *plane wave*. The tangential component of the field (i.e., the field in the direction of propagation) is always zero in free space.

Phasor The electric field at a given point and time can be described by a two-dimensional vector called a *phasor*. The phasor has a complex value:

$$\mathbf{A} = I + Q\mathrm{i} \tag{B.20}$$

where

I = in-phase component,
Q = quadrature component,
i = square root of -1.

The length of the phasor is equal to the magnitude of the electric field intensity:

$$\text{Length} = \sqrt{I^2 + Q^2} \tag{B.21}$$

The angular orientation of the phasor is equal to the phase angle of the electric field intensity relative to a reference phase angle:

$$\text{Angle} = \arctan(Q/I) \tag{B.22}$$

Plane-polar scan The same as a *starburst scan*.

Plane wave A phase front with a surface of equal phase that is flat.

Plane-wave spectrum The plane-wave spectrum is a spectrum defined in terms of plane waves. Equivalently, an audio spectrum is defined in terms of audio sine waves.

Polarization The polarization of a monochromatic source is a function of two terms:

1. The rotation angle of the peak *E* field component around the Poynting vector (direction of propagation),
2. The relative phase between the vertical (*V*) and horizontal (*H*) components of the *E* field.

A field is linearly polarized if the *V* and *H* components are at the same phase. The relative values of the *V* and *H* components determine the orientation of the linear polarization. If only the *V* component of the *E* field is present, then the field is vertically, linearly polarized. If only the *H* component is present, then the field is horizontally polarized. Table B.1 compare types of polarization.

Table B.1
Examples of Polarization

Polarization	V	H	V to H Phase (°)	Axial Ratio (dB)
V linear	1	0	—	∞
H linear	0	1	—	∞
45° linear	0.707	0.707	0	∞
Circular	0.707	0.707	90	0
Elliptical	0.707	0.707	60	4.8
Elliptical	0.866	0.500	90	4.8

The field is circularly polarized if the *V* and *H* components are of equal value and shifted by 90° in phase, which results in the *E* field orientation rotating at 360° per cycle. If the field is rotating to the right when viewing in the direction of propagation, then the field is right-hand circular polarized, or RHCP. For example, a cylindrical helix antenna fed from the base that rotates in the same direction as a screw is RHCP. The opposite polarization is left-hand circular polarization, or LHCP.

Any conditions other than those ending in linear or circular polarization result in elliptical polarization. The degrees and types of polarization can be described in a variety of ways. The transfer of energy from free space into an antenna is affected by the polarization match of the incoming energy to the antenna. The degree of polarization match will determine whether most, some, or none of the incident energy will be received. Normally, the goal is to maximize the polarization match, however, in some cases cross-polarization techniques are used to reject jammers and interference sources. Table B.2 shows the polarization requirements for maximum and minimum power coupling between two antennas.

The polarization purity of a circularly polarized antenna often is specified in terms of the axial ratio of the polarization ellipse. The axial ratio (r) of a wavefront traveling in a given direction can be defined in terms of the RHCP and LHCP electric field magnitudes:

$$r(\text{dB}) = 20 \log \left| \frac{E_r + E_l}{E_r - E_l} \right| \tag{B.23}$$

where

E_r = RHCP E field,
E_l = LHCP E field.

The axial ratio is always equal to or greater than 0 dB. An ideal circularly polarized antenna will have an axial ratio of 1 or 0 dB. A typical spacecraft CP antenna will have an axial ratio in the vicinity of 1 dB. An ideal linearly polarized antenna will have an axial ratio of infinity. Elliptically polarized antennas have intermediate values.

Closely related to the axial ratio is the *circular polarization ratio* (CPR). The CPR defined in terms of the RHCP and LHCP voltages is

$$p(\text{dB}) = 20 \log (E_r/E_l) \tag{B.24}$$

The CPR is equal to 0 dB for a linearly polarized antenna and $\pm\infty$ for circularly polarized antennas. The conversions between axial ratio and CPR are

$$p = \frac{r+1}{r-1}$$
$$r = \frac{p+1}{p-1} \tag{B.25}$$

An electric field vector defined in terms of vertical and horizontal components can be converted into the RHCP and LHCP equivalent by forming the sum and difference with a 90° phase shift:

$$\mathbf{E}_r = \mathbf{E}_v - i\,\mathbf{E}_h$$
$$\mathbf{E}_l = \mathbf{E}_v + i\,\mathbf{E}_h \tag{B.26}$$

Table B.2
Power Coupling between Antennas

	Maximum Power Transfer	*Minimum Power Transfer*
Ellipse axes	aligned	orthogonal
Axial ratio	matched	matched
Field rotation	same	opposite

This operation is equivalent to the physical construction of a CP antenna by combining the output from two orthogonal, linearly polarized antennas in a 90° hybrid.

Principal planes The principal planes are two orthogonal planes that intersect along the direction of maximum gain. One of the principal planes usually is aligned along the vertical axis or *E* plane.

Principle of superposition The principle of superposition states that, if a system is linear, the response of that system to the sum of *n* components is equal to the sum of the responses of the *n* individual field components. For example, the output of an electrical filter driven by a square wave is equal to the sum of the filter outputs to an equivalent Fourier series of sine waves.

In near-field antenna measurements, the principle of superposition may be used to show that a real antenna can be described equivalently as a set of ideal antennas transmitting plane waves, which results in the concept of a plane-wave spectrum.

Process gain Process gain is an improvement in the signal-to-noise ratio due to certain signal processing operations. Process gain occurs at several points in the near-field measurement process, as shown in Table B.3.

In general, the effect of process gain is to reduce SNR requirements. The improvement in SNR is equal to the square root of the number of samples in the process. For example, if 512 frequencies are used in a pulse compression, the SNR improvement will be a factor 22.6 or 27.1 dB.

The far-field transform has a large amount of process gain, resulting in suppression of random noise. Patterns can be successfully produced from near-field

Table B.3
Process Gain

Process	*Typical SNR Improvement*
1. Near- to far-field conversion	30 dB (1000 measurements)
2. Swept frequency pulse compression	29 dB (801 measurements)
3. Receiving correlator (HTR receiver)	20 dB (100 measurements)

measurements with the receiver operating at an SNR below 1 and with what appears to be random phase information.

For example, assume a pattern has 16,384 points and the receiver is operating at unity signal to noise ratio. The receiver is operating in a linear range so that the principle of superposition holds. The receiver output is the sum of the random thermal noise and the coherent measured phase front. The receiver amplitude and phase measurements are converted from polar form into a complex I/Q form and then transformed into an angular spectrum by a Fourier integral. Each output point is a summation of all input points. The Fourier integral results in the summation of all 16,384 points. The integration process is equivalent to reducing the receiver IF bandwidth by a factor of 16,384. The power improvement in SNR is 16,384. The voltage improvement in SNR, called *process gain,* is equal to the square root of 16,384, or 128. This is equivalent to a noise reduction of 42 dB, indicating that the far-field pattern will have a sidelobe noise level of -42 dB relative to the beam peak when the receiver SNR is 0 dB.

Pulse compression Pulse compression is a concept developed in radar, in which swept frequency measurements can be converted into an equivalent pulse. Pulse compression techniques can be used in the near-field measurement process to measure and control multipath effects.

A conventional radar operates by transmitting a pulse and measuring the time interval to reflection. If the radar transmitter were connected to the AUT and the radar receiver were connected to the probe antenna, a plot of signal level *versus* range would appear. This plot would provide a direct measure of multipath interference.

Another form of radar operates by passing the radar pulse through a dispersive all-pass filter. The filter, known as a *pulse expansion filter,* modifies the pulse shape by passing different frequency components of the pulse with different time delays. As a result, the pulse is smeared in time. If the filter delay is a linear function of frequency, the pulse will be smeared into a frequency sweep or chirp. An inverse filter located in the receiver then compresses the frequency sweep back into a pulse. This concept is called *pulse compression.*

Several near-field receivers (HP-8510B, Wiltron 360, and HTR) are capable of using pulse compression software. The software operates by sweeping the frequency source over a bandwidth and reading the receiver. The swept frequency receiver measurements are compressed into an equivalent pulse response by Fourier transform techniques. The pulse response can be analyzed to determine the location of reflections or gated to eliminate the reflections.

Radiation pattern A diagram of the directive gain as a function of the direction. The antenna is located at the origin of a spherical coordinate system.

Raster scan The raster scan is one possible trajectory that the near-field probe can follow while measuring the phase front. The raster scan results in a two-dimensional *XY* matrix in the computer, which easily is processed into the far-field measurements by a two-dimensional Fourier transform. Because of the simplicity in the processing, the raster scan is very popular in many facilities.

Reactive near-field region Same as *evanescent region.*

Reciprocity theorem The reciprocity theorem states that, if an electromotive force is applied to the terminals of antenna A and the current is measured at the terminals of another, antenna B, then an equal current (in both amplitude and phase) can be obtained at the terminals of antenna A, when the same electromotive force is applied to the terminals of antenna B. The reciprocity theorem is valid when the antenna contains no ferrite components (such as isolators or circulators) or amplifiers or other active components, and the propagation path external to the antennas is reciprocal. Faraday rotation, for example, will cause a space-to-ground link to be somewhat nonreciprocal. The free space propagation path within any near-field range environment, for all practical purposes, is entirely reciprocal. Two important consequences of the reciprocity theorem must be kept in mind: transmitting and receiving patterns for a reciprocal antenna are identical, and multipath effects are identical in a near-field test setup irrespective of whether the probe transmits or receives.

Ruze Equation The gain of an antenna is directly affected by the surface quality of the reflector. An approximation developed by Ruze for random surface errors provides reasonable results for surface roughness less than 0.2 λ. The gain loss due to a rms surface deviation error, *e*, is

$$\text{Gain loss (dB)} = 10 \log \{\exp [-(4\pi e/\lambda)^2]\} \qquad \text{(B.27)}$$

where

$$\lambda = \text{RF wavelength.}$$

Sampling theorem The sampling theorem as applied to near-field measurements states that a spatially band-limited signal of finite energy that has no spatial frequency components higher than *W* cycles/λ is completely described by specifying the values of the signal at distance intervals of less than *W*/2.

A corollary to the sampling theorem states that a spatially band-limited signal of finite energy that has no spatial frequency components higher than *W* cycles/λ is completely described by specifying the values of the signal at distance intervals of less than 180° of phase change for the highest spatial frequency present.

A signal is correctly sampled if the phase of the highest spatial frequency present changes by less than 180° between two adjacent samples. In the starburst scan, two adjacent samples are two points along a ray or two points at equal radius on two adjacent rays.

Important consequences of the sampling theorem are as follows:

1. If no multipath or evanescent energy is present, there is little reason to sample the phase front more densely than at ½λ plus 1 sample intervals.
2. If the phase front is further band-limited by a spatial filter, the sampling density often can be reduced by an order of magnitude. Examples of spatial filters in the near-field environment include a scalar horn probe antenna, the AUT, or the IF bandwidth restriction within the receiver.
3. If the sampling theorem is violated, energy will appear at spurious angles in the far field. This phenomenon is called *aliasing*.
4. Oversampling (taking samples more densely than required by the sampling theorem) generally is not advisable because more time and computer disk storage are required. Also more system drift is probable. The only advantages in oversampling are an increase in the SNR and suppression of certain multipath and evanescent signal components. Typical sample spacings range between 0.5–5λ.

Self-comparison tests Self-comparison tests utilize overdetermined measurements that perturb the system in a temporally and spatially invariant manner. For example, a pair of near-field measurements separated in time or by geometry (e.g., separation, translation, rotation) should provide identical far-field results. These tests are a primary method of determining measurement uncertainties.

Serrodyne A technique in which the phase of a signal is modulated in a sawtooth fashion is called *serrodyne*. Serrodyning originally was accomplished by sweeping the helix voltage in a traveling wave tube. A frequency offset is generated when the phase is swept at a constant rate from 0 to 360°. The frequency offset is equal to the derivative of the phase angle with respect to time. The serrodyne technique is used in some near-field phase measurement receivers to develop an IF offset frequency. In this case, the serrodyne function is accomplished by a digital phase shifter or quadraphase-shift keying (QPSK) modulator.

Spatial filter A spatial filter modifies the spatial frequency spectrum in the near-field region. Most spatial filters are produced unintentionally; however, spatial filters may be intentionally introduced into the system to improve performance. An example of an intentionally introduced spatial filter is a high-gain probe antenna used to reduce the sampling density.

All spatial filters, whether intentional or not, affect the measured far-field response. Ignoring the effects of spatial filtering can result in antenna boresight shifts, beamwidth errors, and off-axis gain errors. The far-field effects of the spatial filters can be suppressed if required by a deconvolution operation. The most common deconvolution operation is the so-called probe correction, in which the spatial filter effect of the probe antenna is deconvolved from the measured response. This results in the true AUT response.

Examples of spatial filters present in the near-field environment include the following:

Scalar horn (low pass),

Dish antenna (low pass),

Receiver IF filter (low pass, doppler beam sharpening),

Free-space propagation (low pass as compared to evanescent propagation),

Multibeam antenna (band-pass, if steered off-axis),

Phased array (band-pass, if steered off-axis),

Autotrack dish (band-pass),

Autotrack feed (high-pass),

Nulling antenna (band-reject),

Probe antenna (low-pass, high-pass, band-pass, band-reject, and others; for most applications probe is low pass),

Near- to far-field transform (band-pass, n simultaneous filters),

Computer generated (low-pass, high-pass, band-pass, band-reject, and others).

Note that low-pass filters become bandpass filters if tilted.

Spatial frequency Spatial frequency is a frequency measured in units of distance (cycles/distance) as compared to temporal frequency, which is measured in units of time (cycles/second). For example, the lines on a TV monitor may repeat at 0.1-inch intervals and would have a spatial frequency of 10 cycles per inch. Spatial frequency may be measured in a variety of units:

$$1 \text{ cycle/wavelength} = 2\pi \text{ rad}/\lambda$$
$$= 360°/\lambda$$
$$= c/f \text{ cycles/m}$$

where

c = propagation velocity (m/s),
f = frequency (Hz).

Spatial frequency is a direct measure of beam tilt:

Beam tilt (degree) = arcsine (spatial frequency)

Note that spatial frequency is measured in cycles/λ.

Starburst scan The starburst scan, also called a *plane-polar scan,* is one possible trajectory the near-field probe can follow while measuring the phase front. The starburst trajectory is a radially symmetric pattern with a set of rays emanating from a common center point. The starburst scan is very efficient for radially symmetric antennas. See also *raster scan.*

Synthetic aperture A synthetic aperture is formed by moving a small antenna throughout an area that "synthetically" defines a large antenna. The output of the small antenna is coherently integrated to form a beam equivalent to that produced by an equivalent real aperture. This technique is also called *aperture synthesis.* The near-field measurement systems fundamentally use this technique. The probe antenna is moved in a raster or starburst pattern over an area defined by the scan plane.

Thermal noise Thermal noise results from the random motion of a body of particles as a consequence of its finite temperature. The amount of power that can be removed from a body at a temperature T is equal to

Noise power = kTB

where

k = Boltzmann's constant = $1.38\ e^{-23}$ J/K,
T = absolute temperature (K),
B = bandwidth of the transmission path (Hz).

The thermal noise power at the input of a near-field receiver is established by the temperature and bandwidth terms. A temperature of approximately 290 K is established by the antenna radiation temperature. The antenna radiation temperature is established by the view of the high bay surroundings from the antenna. The effective receiver bandwidth is a function of both the actual receiver IF bandwidth and the additional IF processing performed in the far-field transform.

Time-bandwidth product The time-bandwidth product is a measure of the dispersion of a pulse as used in pulse compression radar. The value is equal to the product of the pulse bandwidth and the time period over which it is transmitted. For example, if a frequency sweep 1 GHz wide were transmitted over a time period of 1 μs, the time bandwidth product would be 1000. Also see *pulse compression.*

Wavenumber A measure of frequency in terms of rad per m. The wavenumber is equal to $2\pi/\lambda$.

Window function A window function is used to minimize diffracted energy or energy produced by truncating a function. Equivalent terms include *apodizing* and *tapering*. For example, low sidelobe antennas are produced by tapering the aperture illumination at the aperture edge. In a similar manner, the measurements made by a near-field measurement system can be tapered to allow viewing of multipath energy within an anechoic chamber. The synthetic aperture normally is not tapered when conventional near-field antenna measurements are made, as the desired windowing normally is supplied by the AUT. Windowing can be of some value if the scanner is slightly undersized.

Windows also are used in pulse compression (network analyzer time-domain) processing to reduce range sidelobes. Commonly used windows include uniform (no window), Hann or hanning, and Hamming windows. The Kaiser-Bessel window is recommended particularly for near-field and pulse compression applications.

Appendix C
COMMON MISCONCEPTIONS ABOUT NEAR-FIELD MEASUREMENTS

Testing antennas in the near field sometimes leads to unexpected results. Some of the more common unexpected surprises and pitfalls are discussed in this appendix.

C.1 HIGHER RF POWER IS OFTEN REQUIRED WHEN TESTING LARGE ANTENNAS

Higher gain antennas under test typically (but not always) have a *higher* insertion loss. This is because the power density in the aperture of a high-gain antenna is lower, as the energy is dispersed over a larger area. The insertion loss in the near-field region is approximately equal to the relative aperture mismatch loss. Much of the effect of the insertion loss, however, is counteracted by the process gain in the far-field transformation. The insertion loss based on area ratios (valid for uniformly illuminated apertures) is equal to the absolute value of the difference (in dB) between the probe and test antennas.

C.2 INSERTION LOSS IS NOT AFFECTED BY THE DIRECTION OF RF TRAVEL

The insertion loss for reciprocal antennas is not affected by changing the probe antenna from a receiving to transmitting configuration. This is a direct consequence of the reciprocity theorem.

C.3 MULTIPATH ERRORS ARE NOT AFFECTED BY DIRECTION OF RF TRAVEL

Multipath levels and errors are not affected in any manner by changing the probe antenna from a receiving to a transmitting configuration. This is a direct consequence of the reciprocity theorem.

C.4 HIGH-GAIN PROBES OFTEN PROVIDE SIGNIFICANT ADVANTAGES OVER THE COMMONLY USED OPEN-ENDED WAVEGUIDE PROBE

A common misconception is that only physically small, low-gain probes should be used, minimizing all disturbances to the electromagnetic field. A large-aperture, high-gain probe often can provide significant advantages by operating as a spatial filter to mimimize multipath errors, reduce sampling densities, and reduce insertion loss. The disturbances to the electromagnetic field are similar to those produced by a low-gain probe because fewer data points are taken with the high-gain probe antenna. The high-gain probe often cannot be used for other reasons. For example, it is not the probe of choice if wide-angle sidelobe measurements are required.

C.5 THE GAIN OF THE PROBE ANTENNA NEED NOT BE LESS THAN THE AUT

The far-field response derived from the phase front measurement is a measure of the convolution of the probe and AUT response. If the response of one antenna is available, the response of the other antenna can be obtained by deconvolution. As in most deconvolutions, noise can build. For high-quality processing, the probe gain should be high over the range of far-field angles required in the output data.

C.6 THE PLANAR NEAR- TO FAR-FIELD TRANSFORMATION IS A MISNOMER; IT DOES NOT TRANSFORM THE NEAR FIELD TO THE FAR FIELD

The "near- to far-field transformation" is a misnomer because the transformation actually converts a phase front into an equivalent angular energy distribution at the phase front location. The correct term would be a *phase front to angular spectrum transformation*. The phase front at any distance from the AUT, including far-field distances and the angular spectrum, are a Fourier transform pair.

The term *near- to far-field transformation* came about because the antenna normally, but not always, is probed in the near-field region. The angular spectrum is equivalent to the far-field radiation pattern.

An example of the invariance of the far-field transformation to distance is demonstrated in *very long baseline inferometry* (VLBI) and *very large array* (VLA) radioastronomy, where the far-field transformation is used to form images of distant radio sources external to our galaxy. In this configuration, the extragalactic radio sources clearly are in the far field of the radio telescope. In one VLA radio telescope, 27 large 85 ft antennas are connected to phase measurement receivers to form an even larger aperture with a dimension of many miles. This concept, called *aperture synthesis,* is produced through the use of the "far-field" transform. The phase front, as sampled by the 27 antennas, is transformed into an angular spectrum to form the image of the radio star.

C.7 THE PLANAR FAR-FIELD TRANSFORMATION IS AMPLITUDE INVARIANT TO THE PROBE-AUT SEPARATION DISTANCE

The distance between the probe antenna and AUT does not affect the far-field amplitude pattern or measured gain. The phase front of the antenna can be measured at any distance, including in the far field. The only requirement is that all significant emissions from the AUT are sampled at a suitable density. The amplitude invariance with distance is due to the conservation of the total energy because all energy emitted by the antenna is sampled by the near-field probe. An application of Parseval's theorem indicates that the total power is conserved in the near- to far-field transformation.

C.8 PROBE CORRECTION IS NOT REQUIRED FOR ON-AXIS GAIN COMPARISON MEASUREMENTS

The probe correction affects gain only at off-axis angles. Most antenna gain measurements are made on boresight, requiring no probe correction. Multibeam antenna gain measurements usually require probe correction. Probe correction, however, is required for directivity measurements.

C.9 GOOD NEAR-FIELD DATA CAN BE TAKEN WITH A LOW RECEIVER SNR

The far-field transformation has a large amount of process gain resulting in the suppression of random noise. Patterns can be produced successfully from near-field measurements with the receiver operating at an SNR below unity and with what appears to be random phase information.

For example, assume a measurement set of a uniform aperture has 16,384 points, and the receiver is operating at a unity SNR. The receiver is operating in a linear range so that the principle of superposition holds. The receiver output is the sum of the random thermal noise and the coherent phase front. The receiver amplitude and phase measurements are converted from polar form into a complex I/Q form and then transformed into an angular spectrum by a Fourier integral. The Fourier integral results in the summation of all 16,384 points. The integration process is equivalent to reducing the receiver IF bandwidth. The improvement in SNR, called *process gain,* is equal to the square root of 16,384, or 128. This is equivalent to a noise reduction of 42 dB, indicating that the far-field pattern will have a sidelobe noise level of -42 dB relative to the beam peak when the receiver SNR is 0 dB.

C.10 THE ANTENNA PATTERN, BEAM POINTING, AND GAIN ARE NOT AFFECTED BY THE *X, Y,* OR *Z* POSITION OF THE SCAN PLANE, CYLINDER, OR SPHERE

As long as all significant energy is measured and no aliasing occurs, this is true. It is a direct consequence of the spatial invariance of the Fourier transform.

C.11 SOME FAR-FIELD TRANSFORMATION PROGRAMS HAVE SIGNIFICANT NONLINEARITIES

The transformed far-field measurements are corrupted by nonlinearities anywhere in the processing chain. The primary nonlinearities usually are the receiver or transformation program. The nonlinearities in the transformation process generally are not obvious.

An example of nonlinearity occurs when the angular spectrum is interpolated incorrectly. The angular spectrum is band limited, and if the interpolation is not band limited, aliasing will occur. This effect would distort sidelobes and complex autotrack patterns.

C.12 THE PHASE REFERENCE CABLE WILL NOT PROVIDE BETTER PHASE STABILITY WHEN USED AT A SUBHARMONIC

A common misconception is that lower phase stability is needed when the phase reference cable carries a subharmonic of the test frequency. Subharmonic levels often are used to drive varactor frequency multipliers and harmonic mixers. For example, assume a test frequency of 10 GHz with a subharmonic frequency of 1 GHz passing through the cable. If the cable stretches 0.01 inch, the phase will change by approximately 3° at 10 GHz and 0.3° at 1 GHz. A 10✕ frequency multiplier, whether external or part of a harmonic mixer, will change the 0.3° phase shift to 3°.

C.13   GENERALLY, ONLY ONE FLEXIBLE PHASE-STABLE CABLE IS NEEDED TO CONNECT THE PROBE ANTENNA TO THE OTHER RF COMPONENTS

When the probe transmits, only one cable is required. When the probe receives, usually the LO and IF signals need to be carried to and from the probe. Usually, the IF is relatively low; therefore, time delay variations in the IF signal line will not have a significant effect. If the signal IF is a significant portion of the RF test frequency, the IF signal line also will need to become phase stable. The LO line always needs to be phase stable.

Appendix D
FOURIER AND RELATED TRANSFORMS

D.1 FOURIER TRANSFORM

The Fourier transform is the foundation of the near-field measurement technique. The Fourier transform is defined as

$$A(f) = \int A(t) \, e^{-i2\pi f t} \, dt \qquad \qquad (D.1)$$

where

$A(t)$ = complex amplitude corresponding to time t,
  i = square root of -1,
  f = frequency,
  t = time

Table D.1 lists Fourier transform pairs.

The following list discusses properties of the Fourier transform (with particular relevance to near-field measurements):

1. The Fourier transform of the sum of two functions $G_1(x)$ and $G_2(x)$ is equal to the sum of the Fourier transforms of those functions. This is known as the *property of linearity* or *superposition*. The proof is based on the linearity of the Fourier integrals.
2. The area under a function $G(x)$ is equal to $G(f = 0)$, which simply says that the average value of the time series is equal to the dc component of the frequency spectrum. In near-field measurements, the axial gain can be determined by adding up all complex phase-front measurements and dividing by the number of measurements.
3. If a given function is shifted in time or space, only phase changes will occur. Each Fourier component is delayed in phase by an amount proportional to

---

Table D.1
Fourier Transform Pairs

$G(t)$	$G(f)$	Application
1	$d(f)$	
$\cos(xt)$	$d(x+f) + d(x-f)$	
$\sin(xt)$	$d(x+f) - d(x-f)$	
$e^{**i}(xt)$	$d(x+f)$	
$e^{-\pi x^{**2}}$	$e^{-\pi x^{**2}}$	
$-1/\pi t$	$-i\,\text{sgn}(f)$	Hilbert transform
Time	frequency	waveform analysis
Distance	frequency	pulse compression
Phase front	spatial frequency	far-field transform
Visibility	brightness function	radioastronomy
Phase shift	receiver errors	receiver calibration

its frequency. This concept, known as the *shift theorem,* is the fundamental concept behind the focusing and back-projection concepts used in microwave holography and SAR radar.

4. The convolution of two functions in the time domain is equivalent to the product of the Fourier transforms of the two functions. This property is used in near-field probe correction.

5. The integral of the total power of the function $G(x)$ is equal to the integral of the total power of $G(f)$. This property, also known as *Parseval's theorem,* is used to show the far-field amplitude invariance to Z distance.

6. The inverse Fourier transform of the Fourier transform of a signal will result in the original signal. The Fourier transform neither adds nor deletes information.

7. The Fourier transform of a real-time function with no imaginary component will be a Hermitian function. The Hermitian function must have an even real part and an odd imaginary part. $G(f)$ is equal to the complex conjugate of $G(-f)$. The Fourier transform is pure real. Likewise, the Fourier transform of an imaginary time function is anti-Hermitian. The anti-Hermitian function has an odd real part and an even imaginary part. The Fourier transform is pure imaginary. The proof is accomplished by defining $G(x)$ as the sum of the even and odd functions. The Fourier transform is factored into a sum of a sine and cosine transform. The even function is orthogonal to the sine transform; likewise, the odd function is orthogonal to the cosine transform. As a result, if a function is even then the transform must be even. This property is used in the development of the Hilbert transform and certain near-field phase measurement receivers.

A two-dimensional antenna aperture field distribution $f(x, y)$ has a two-dimensional Fourier transform $F(u, v)$ defined as follows:

$$F(u, v) = \iint f(x, y)\, e^{-i2\pi(ux+vy)}\, dx\, dy \qquad (D.2)$$
$$f(x, y) = \iint F(u, v)\, e^{i2\pi(ux+vy)}\, du\, dv$$

where

$x = x$ position (λ)
$y = y$ position (λ)
$u = $ horizontal spatial frequency (rad/λ),
$v = $ vertical spatial frequency (rad/λ).

Near-field measurements are taken at discrete points. For this reason, a discrete version of the Fourier transform is used. The *discrete Fourier transform* (DFT) was described in Chapter 2.

A significant computational efficiency can be achieved by an algorithm developed by Cooley and Tukey. This algorithm, called the *fast Fourier transform* (FFT), increased the computational speed by several orders of magnitude. The FFT takes advantage of certain redundancies in the DFT by factoring its rotations into powers of 2.

D.2 HILBERT TRANSFORM

The Hilbert transform can be used to derive a quadrature signal component from a real causal signal. The Hilbert transform is equivalent to a broadband 90° phase shifter. It can be implemented numerically in the digital computer.

The Hilbert transform is used by the HTR near-field receiver to derive the quadrature signal during swept frequency measurements, during certain receiver calibration operations, and when a quadrature signal is not available from hardware. The quadrature (Q) channel can be derived from the I channel by applying a broadband 90° phase shifter to the output of the I channel mixer if negative frequency components are not present.

The Hilbert transform relationship between the real and imaginary parts of a signal is valid if the signal is causal or, equivalently, if no negative frequencies are present.

There are several definitions of the Hilbert transform, all of which are equivalent:

$$H(x) = \frac{1}{\pi} \int \frac{G(x')}{x' - x}\, dx' \qquad (D.4)$$

Equivalently, this integral for $H(x)$ can be expressed as a convolution between $G(x)$ and $-1/\pi x$:

$$H(x) = \frac{-1}{\pi x} * G(x) \tag{D.5}$$

A convolution between the two functions is equivalent to the product of the Fourier transforms of $G(x)$ and $-1/\pi x$. The Fourier transform of $-1/\pi x$ is $-i$ $\text{sgn}(f)$, where i is the square root of -1 and $\text{sgn}(f)$ is the signum function defined as:

$$\begin{aligned} \text{sgn}(f) &= 1, \quad f > 0 \\ &= 0, \quad f = 0 \\ &= -1, \quad f < 0 \end{aligned} \tag{D.6}$$

The Hilbert transform of $G(f)$, therefore, is defined by $H(f)$, where f is the frequency and i is the square root of -1:

$$H(f) = -i\, \text{sgn}(f)\, G(f) \tag{D.7}$$

The orthogonal real (I) and imaginary (Q) components of the signal can be summed, resulting in an analytic or preenvelope signal. An analytic or preenvelope signal is defined as a complex valued function with a Hilbert transform relationship between the real and imaginary components. Because the real part of the analytic signal is an even function and the imaginary part of the signal is an odd function, all negative frequencies are cancelled, resulting in

$$G(f) + i\, H(f) = \begin{cases} 2G(f), & f > 0 \\ G(0), & f = 0 \\ 0, & f < 0 \end{cases} \tag{D.7}$$

The analytic signal is a rotating phasor that, when converted to polar form, provides the instantaneous amplitude and phase of the received signal.

Table D.2 lists Hilbert transform pairs.

The following list discusses the properties of the Hilbert transform:

1. A signal, $G(x)$, and its Hilbert transform, $H(x)$, have the same energy density spectrum. Equivalently, if the signal $G(x)$ is bandlimited, then $H(x)$ is also bandlimited. This can be proved by noting that the absolute value of the signum function is equal to 1 for all nonzero values.

Table D.2
Hilbert Transform Pairs

$G(x)$	$H(x)$
$\cos x$	$-\sin x$
$\sin x$	$\cos x$
$(\sin x)/x$	$[(\cos x) - 1]/x$
$\delta(x)$	$-1/\pi x$
$\ln(x)$	phase(x)

2. The Hilbert transform of the Hilbert transform of $G(x)$ is $-G(x)$. This corresponds to a 180° phase shift.
3. A signal, $G(x)$, and its Hilbert transform, $H(x)$, are orthogonal. This can be proved by noting that $G(f)$ is an even function and $H(f)$ is an odd function of frequency.
4. The Hilbert transform of the sum of $G_1(x)$ and $G_2(x)$ is equal to the sums of the Hilbert transforms of $H_1(x)$ and $H_2(x)$.

Appendix E
NEAR- TO FAR-FIELD TRANSFORMATION PROGRAM

```
*********************************************************************************
C *                                                                           *
C *          Convert a phase front into an angular spectrum                   *
C *                                                                           *
C
*********************************************************************************
C
C     This program transforms a near-field phase front into an
C equivalent angular spectrum. The program is compatible with
C both raster and plane polar data formats. The transformation
C is accomplished by a direct, factored integration of the
C electromagnetic field.
C
C Program input:
C
C        LUN 1 - File header followed by data records
C
C                     V amplitude(dB), phase(deg)
C                     H amplitude(dB), phase(deg)
C                     X,Y,Z probe position (inches)
C
C Program output:
C
C        LUN 7 - File header followed by V amplitude (dB)
C        LUN 8 - File header followed by H amplitude (dB)
C        LUN 9 - File header followed by RHCP amplitude (dB)
C        LUN 10 - File header followed by LHCP amplitude (dB)
C
```

```
        PROGRAM FAR
        COMPLEX AV,AH                           ! V,H complex
                                                  amplitude

        COMPLEX AVBW,AHBW,BW,CW(1000)           ! Weighting terms
        COMPLEX CV(10000),    CH(10000)         ! V,H angular spectrum
        REAL*4 KX(100),       KY(100)           ! Spatial frequency
                                                  table

        REAL*4 LAMDA                            ! Wavelength
        PI = 3.14159265
        RAD=57.2957795                          ! Degrees / radian
C
C ***** Read near field data file header
        READ (1,*)FREQ,MODE,DTH,NPTS            ! Frequency
                                                ! 0=raster, 1=
                                                  starburst
                                                ! Delta, # of points
        LAMBDA = 30 / FREQ / 2.54               ! Wavelength
C
C ***** Establish the output far field angle limits
        STHETA = −4.5                           ! Elevation start angle
          SPHI = −4.5                           ! Azimuth start angle
        DTHETA = 0.1                            ! Elevation increment
          DPHI = 0.1                            ! Azimuth increment
        NTHETA = 91                             ! # of elevations points
          NPHI = 91                             ! # of azimuth points
C
        WRITE(  7,50) NTHETA,NPHI, STHETA,SPHI, DTHETA, DPHI
        WRITE(  8,50) NTHETA,NPHI, STHETA,SPHI, DTHETA,DPHI
        WRITE(  9,50) NTHETA,NPHI, STHETA,SPHI, DTHETA,DPHI
        WRITE(10,50) NTHETA,NPHI, STHETA,SPHI, DTHETA,DPHI
50      FORMAT(2I5,4F11.4)
C
C ***** Build the azimuth & elevation spatial frequency vectors
        AL = 2*PI / LAMDA                       ! Wavenumber
                                                  conversion
        OUTPTS = NTHETA * NPHI                  ! # of far field points
        DO J = 1,NPHI                           ! Azimuth vector
        THETAX = SPHI+(J−1)*DPHI
        KX(J) = SIN(THETAX/RAD)
        END DO
C
        DO J = 1,NTHETA                         ! Elevation vector
        THETAY = STHETA+(J-1)*DTHETA
```

```
        KY(J) = AL * SIN(THETAY/RAD)
        END DO
C
        DO J = 1,OUTPTS                        ! Erase output vectors
        CV(J) = 0.
        CH(J) = 0.
        END DO
C
C ***** Transform the phase front into an angular spectrum
        DO J = 1,NPTS                          ! Process all points
        READ(1,*) AMPV,PV,AMPH,PH,X            ! Read jth record
        AV = 10.**(AMPV/20.)                   ! V to IQ format
       1 *CMPLX(COSD(PV),SIND(PV))
        AH = 10.**(AMPH/20.)                   ! H to IQ format
       1 *CMPLX(COSD(PH),SIND(PH))
C
C ***** Starburst radial weighting
        IF(MODE.EQ.1) THEN                     ! Starburst ?
        RWEIGHT=SQRT(X(1)**2+X(2)**2)          ! Measurement radius
        AR = 2.*PI*RWEIGHT*DTH                 ! Area of DTH width
                                               !  ring
        IF(J.EQ.1) AR = .25*PI*DTH**2          ! Center point
        AV = AV * AR                           ! Apply radial weight
        AH = AH * AR
        END IF
C
        DO L = 1,NTHETA                        ! Elevation weight
                                               !  vector
        C = KY(L)*X(2)
        CW(L) = CMPLX (COS(C),SIN(C))          ! 1st correlation weight
        END DO
C
        M = 1                                  ! Output point number
        DO K = 1,NPHI                          ! Azimuth weight
                                               !  vector
        B = AL * (KX(K)*X(1) + X(3))
        BW = CMPLX (COS(B),SIN(B))             ! 2nd correlation weight
        AVBW = AV * BW                         ! Premultiply amplitude
        AHBW = AH * BW
C
        DO L = 1,NTHETA                        ! Inner loop
        CV(M) = AVBW*CW(L)+CV(M)               ! Integrate V far field
        CH(M) = AHBW*CW(L)+CH(M)               ! Integrate H far field
```

```
        M = M+1
        END DO
        END DO
        END DO
C
C ***** Convert I/Q format to dB for V,H,RHCP and LHCP
        DO K = 1,OUTPTS
        WRITE (  7,*) 20.*LOG10 (CABS(CV(K)                )) ! V
        WRITE (  8,*) 20.*LOG10 (CABS(CH(K)                )) ! H
        WRITE (  9,*) 20.*LOG10 (CABS(CV(K) +(0,-1)*CH(K))) ! RHCP
        WRITE (10,*) 20.*LOG10 (CABS(CV(K) +(0, 1)*CH(K))) ! LHCP
        END DO
        END
```

LIST OF ACRONYMS

Acronym	Definition
ac	Alternating current
ACTS	Advanced communications technology satellite
AGC	Automatic gain control
AM	Amplitude modulation
AR	Axial ratio
ASL	Antenna Systems Laboratory
AUT	Antenna under test, article under test
AWF	Aplanatic wave function
BITE	Built-in test equipment
BRH	Bureau of Radiological Health
BWFN	Beamwidth between first nulls
CCD	Charge coupled device (video camera)
CMM	Coordinate measurement machine
CMOS	Complementary symmetry metal oxide semiconductor
CNC	Computerized numerical control
CP	Circularly polarized
CPC	Continuous path control
CPR	Circular polarization ratio
CPU	Central processor unit
CRT	Cathode ray tube (computer video display terminal)
CW	Continuous wave
DAC	Digital-to-analog converter
DBF	Digital beam former
dc	Direct current
DFT	Discrete Fourier transform
DMA	Direct memory access
DOF	Degrees of freedom

DSN	Deep space network
DSP	Digital signal processor
DUT	Device under test
ELINT	Electronic intelligence
EMI	Electromagnetic interference
EMP	Exponentially mapped past
EPROM	Electrically programmable read-only memory
EW	East-west (x) axis
EW	Electronic warfare
FDFT	Factored discrete Fourier transform
FFT	Fast Fourier transform
FMCW	Frequency modulated continuous wave
FO	Fiber optic
GaAlAs	Gallium aluminum arsenide
GaAs	Gallium arsenide
GDOP	Geometric dilution of precision
GPIB	General-purpose interface buss
GPS	Global positioning system
HeNe	Helium neon (laser)
HP-8510B	Vector network analyzer model
HPBW	Half-power beamwidth
HPFW	Half-power full-width
HTR	Hilbert transform-based receiver
I	In-phase channel
IF	Intermediate frequency
IFFT	Inverse fast Fourier transform
InGaAsP	Indium gallium arsenide phosphide
IQ	In-phase and quadrature channels
IRU	Inertial reference unit
ISAR	Inverse synthetic aperture radar
JPL	Jet Propulsion Laboratory
KSA	K-band single access (TDRSS satellite antenna)
LAPIS	Large area precision inspection machine
LEP	Large electron positron collider
LHCP	Left-hand circular polarization
$LiNbO_3$	Lithium niobate (electro-optical modulator)
LO	Local oscillator
LP	Log-periodic (antenna)
LRP	Laser ranging probe
LVDT	Linear variable differential transformer
MA	Multiple access (TDRSS satellite antenna)
MDA	Motor drive amplifier

MHM	Microwave holographic metrology
MMFO	Multimode fiber optic
MRA	Model reference adaptive
MTI	Moving target indicator
MTTR	Motor tachometer torsional resonance
NASA	National Aeronautics and Space Administration
Nd:YAG	Neodymium yttrium aluminum garnet (laser)
NEP	Noise equivalent power
NFTF	Near-field test facility
NFTR	Near-field test range
NIST	National Institute of Standards
NRAO	National Radio Astronomy Observatory
NS	North-South (y) axis
NSI	Nearfield Systems, Inc.
NTTF	Network Test and Training Facility (NASA)
OC	Open collector
OEWG	Open-ended waveguide (probe antenna)
OMT	Orthomode transducer
OSC	Optical Science Center
PEP	Positron-electron project
PID	Proportional, integral, derivative
PIN	Positive-intrinsic-negative (semiconductor)
PM	Phase modulation
PMI	Phase modulated interferometer
PNS	Portable near-field system
PTFE	Polytetrafluoroethylene
Q	Quadrature receiver channel
QIF	Quadrature intermediate frequency
QIFM	Quadrature intermediate frequency mixer
QPSK	Quadraphase-shift keying
RCS	Radar cross section
RF	Radio frequency
RHCP	Right-hand circular polarization
RMS	Root mean square
RTSP	Real-time signal processor
RSS	Root sum square
RS-232	A computer communication standard
SA	Single-access (TDRSS antenna)
SAR	Synthetic aperture radar
SGA	Standard gain antenna
SGH	Standard gain horn
SGL	Space-ground link

SIM	System integrity monitor
SMFO	Single-mode fiber optic
SNR	Signal-to-noise ratio
SPASYN	Space Synchro
SSB	Single-sideband
STDN	Space Tracking and Data Network
STP	Standard temperature and pressure
TBD	To be determined
TDRS	Tracking and data relay satellite
TDRSS	Tracking and data relay satellite system
TEM	Transverse electromagnetic propagation mode
TIR	Total indicated runout
TT&C	Telemetry, tracking, and command
TTL	Transistor transistor logic
TWT	Traveling wave tube
UDT	United detector technology (vendor)
V	Vertical (z) axis
VAX	Computer manufactured by Digital Equipment Corporation
VLA	Very large array (radio telescope)
VLBI	Very long baseline interferometry
VNA	Vector network analyzer
VSWR	Voltage standing wave ratio
WG	Waveguide

LIST OF SYMBOLS

Symbol	Definition	Units
c	Propagation velocity	(m/s)
D	Antenna width or diameter	(m)
$E(j)$	jth complex voltage	(V)
$E(n)$	Voltage at nth serrodyne harmonic	(V)
f	Frequency	(Hz)
f_d	Doppler frequency	(Hz or cycles/λ)
$H(f)$	Hilbert transform of f	
i	Square root of -1	dimensionless
I	In-phase signal	(V)
K	Wavenumber $= 2\pi/\lambda$	
K	Obliquity factor	dimensionless
K_1	Receiver gain unbalance	dimensionless
K_2	Receiver phase unbalance	(radians)
K_3	Receiver filter damping	dimensionless
K_x	Horizontal spatial frequency	(cycles/λ)
K_y	Vertical spatial frequency	(cycles/λ)
K_z	Depth spatial frequency	(cycles/λ)
n	Number of measurements	dimensionless
P	Probe antenna width	(m)
Q	Quadrature signal	(V)
$R(j)$	jth radial weighting term	m$_2$
u	Same as K_x	(cycles/λ)
v	Same as K_y	(cycles/λ)
$W(j)$	jth correlation weight	
$W_x(j)$	Horizontal weighting term	
$W_y(j)$	Vertical weighting term	
$W_z(j)$	Depth weighting term	
w	*See K_z*	(cycles/λ)

w	Transform gain	dimensionless
$x(j)$	X position for jth measurement	(m)
$y(j)$	Y position for jth measurement	(m)
$z(j)$	Z position for jth measurement	(m)
Z	Probe to antenna spacing	(m)
δ	Ring width in starburst transform	(m)
λ	Wavelength	(m)
π	Radius of a circle $= 3.14159265$	
ϕ	Angle (longitude)	(rad)
θ	Angle (latitude)	(rad)
Φ	Phase shifter command angle	(rad)

INDEX

CPSIA information can be obtained at www.ICGtesting.com
Printed in the USA
LVOW08*1056140314

377441LV00002B/12/P